# SOMETHING HUMAN

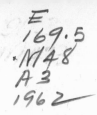

MOHAMED MEHDEVI

# Something Human

"Something human is dearer to me than
all else in the world," said the dwarf.
*Grimm's Fairy Tales*

ST MARTIN'S PRESS
NEW YORK

Some of the material in Part I, Chapter XIII,
and Part II, Chapters II–VII, originally
appeared in a different form in *The New
Yorker*; © 1956, 1957, The New Yorker Magazine, Inc.

First published in the United States of America 1962
Copyright © Mohamed Mehdevi 1961
All rights reserved
Library of Congress Catalog Card Number: 62-18726
Published in Great Britain by The Bodley Head, Ltd 1961
Manufactured in the United States of America

# NOTE

This book was begun in a New York hospital and completed, in stages, abroad. My story is autobiographical; yet it would be precipitous on the part of the reader to account for it in terms of my background or place of birth. The fact that a Persian tells this story is of no account. No incident, however odd, would be worth the telling here if it had no greater significance than its effect upon a single person. But sometimes the reaction of a single person can serve as a magnifying glass for prevailing conditions and the impact they have upon man and his times.

MOHAMED MEHDEVI

*'Il faut beaucoup de philosophie pour savoir observer une fois ce qu'on voit tous les jours.'*
J. J. ROUSSEAU

# PART I

I Long after the train pulled up from the labyrinth of Penn Station, I stayed on the coach platform looking through the window, waiting for the pageant of the American countryside to come into view. I expected it to be no less a marvel than New York City had been, though I knew nothing about it save the personal climax it had in store for me—my destination a thousand miles and twenty-four hours away, a college town somewhere in the mid-peninsula of Florida.

But the perfunctory industrial suburbs of New York—not particularly different from the suburbs of European cities I had known —extended on and on. Whenever a decline in the tracks left only the sky visible through the uppermost part of the window, I was sure the countryside would soon emerge. But when the rails rose again, I faced the same suburban residues.

I also expected the wide asphalt highway which ran alongside the rails to veer off out of sight, to narrow down or give way to some cruder, less perfect surface, and the traffic to peter out. But new cars for ever caught up with the train or were overtaken by it, an apparently endless belt. The cars failed to comply with the vague picture I had of such vehicles on country highways. Almost all had only a single occupant, the driver, eyes straight ahead. I wondered what brought all these cars out today. It was not Sunday. It might be a holiday; but then, the drivers ought to be out with their wives and children, or with lovers, their goal some outing or excursion.

Evidently I was wrong about them, as I'd been wrong about so many things in New York. I thought about the previous afternoon when, with Alex, a school-friend from Vienna, I had been crossing Park Avenue in the mid-forties. He hurried me across, but I couldn't help glancing back to make sure the cars were still coming as thickly as before. Numbers, whether applied to cars or anything else, usually had a comprehensible finiteness which I couldn't reconcile with the unending stream on the avenue. I hadn't yet conceived of the phenomenon of infinite accumulation, not realizing that any accumulation can reach a point which releases an impact and contains a meaning beyond its mere aggregate, a point after which it acquires a new dimension requiring a new yardstick.

America seemed to abound in these incomprehensible aggregates in which the sum of the parts was not equal to the whole, the whole was so overwhelming. Like skyscrapers, I thought, which are not just so many storeys added to each other. A five, ten, thirteen storey building was still just a building. The highest building I remembered from the continent had been just an edifice a little more imposing than the others. But beyond a certain number of storeys—I couldn't say where—the new element took over. At what floor—the fourteenth, the nineteenth, the fortieth—did a building become a skyscraper, something more than a number of floors just added and added?

Still, nothing I had seen during my week in New York, neither the traffic nor the skyscrapers nor the long-legged girls, could match in wonder the sheer fact that I, myself, had arrived in America; that of all the people in Vienna, Alex and I should have been the ones to come here.

Alex had come first, two years before. And if it hadn't been for his extravagant letters I would never have thought of coming myself.

When Alex left Vienna, the news of his venture made the rounds in a dozen versions. That he did go to America on a college scholarship was simply due to the fact that no one else had applied for it. None of us had ever thought of going to America; none wanted to go and none was likely to go later. Some might set out later perhaps for South America or Australia or South Africa. But emigrating to America was simply not done.

So the scholarship was Alex's. And even for him America would have remained the prodigious and slightly ridiculous country it was rumoured to be, had it not been for his father's ultimatum: either return to help run the estate after graduation or no more money. Alex threw up his hands and set about raising the passage money, mostly on credit.

Though Alex claimed, like a modern Caesar, that he would return a millionaire in a few years, the derogatory word 'emigrant' was never applied to him. It would have been rather tactless to do so. He was a baron of a good old family and not so poor as all that. Of course, it couldn't be maintained that he was just going for a visit or for pleasure. He couldn't afford that, and, anyway, no one ever went to America for pleasure. In the end Alex was spoken of vaguely as 'having left' for America.

The gossip about him would have gone stale, as all gossip does, if he hadn't kept it alive by bombarding us with extravagant letters in which he hailed America as a circus of fantastic proportions and goings-on, a spectacle not to be taken seriously but definitely not to be missed. Alex admitted that he hadn't seen any redskins yet, but he labelled the *homo Americanus* as no less outlandish. The people

8

over here, he wrote, were like peasants gone wild who had taken over the cities. They had taken European customs and made a holy parody of them; had even vulgarized the English language to a point which made it unfit for civilized parlance. Except for New York, America was a hopeless habitat with wooden houses, paper money and no manners. Instead of wine, a beverage practically unknown, they drank whisky chilled by so many pretty ice cubes that they were in danger of losing their taste buds along with their teeth. He liked their bathrooms best. They were palatial and beyond compare, nicely heated and ideal for reading. The nation's diet consisted of two pieces of bread incarcerating a lettuce leaf, which was washed down with bottled sugar water. If it weren't for the women —and Alex's paeans had no end on this subject—the country would be worse off than before Columbus discovered it. The husbands, of course, were lackeys.

If Alex's letters had been of the conventional kind, the idea of going to America might never have entered my mind. But a joke sometimes plays midwife to an impulse which otherwise might remain for ever in gestation. When one of Alex's letters ended up by challenging, cajoling, imploring me not to miss my chance, and enclosed a scholarship application, I couldn't help asking myself, 'Why not?' Why not follow up Alex and spend a year in America? I couldn't muster up a weighty enough counter-argument. My studies in Vienna and my career in the diplomatic service could wait for a year.

The college was in Florida, and Florida seemed to me some primitive version of the French Riviera, *das Land wo die Zitronen blühen*, where the lemons actually did bloom, as Alex assured me.

That same evening I filled out the application blank with the help of a dictionary and signed my 'respectful request' for a scholarship.

When a month later my scholarship was approved, I felt that fate had called my bluff. I couldn't back out, and anyway, the trip was just an intermission. In a year I would return to pick up life in Vienna where I left off. As for my family in Persia, I would have to explain the move to them somehow.

Because my father in Meshed—my home town on the Russian–Afghan border—wouldn't grasp so easily the idea of a scholarship, I wrote him that I had been invited as a guest to America. I would have to pay only for my crossing and incidentals; but since I was one of the very few Persians to set foot on American soil, my allowance must be generous enough to enable me to represent my country in proper style.

9

**II** I left the train platform and went inside the coach car to my seat. Facing me was a man half hidden behind a newspaper. I appraised him, as I did every American. His shoes were not as tidy and shiny as they should have been; wrinkles on the instep told me the fellow wasn't using shoe-trees. And the crease of his trousers wasn't pronounced enough to be proper.

My appraisal was interrupted when he lowered his newspaper to turn the page. He returned my glance as if to say, 'Well, what's the matter with you? When are you going to start on your paper?' His hat was pushed back from his forehead and his negligent lips revealed the chewed-up end of his cigar, a shade darker from spittle. I disapproved unreservedly of his appearance and manners. Yet I couldn't help but envy the way he lounged in his seat, evidently at ease and unconcerned with what anybody might think of him. In Europe and at home in Persia, people always seemed over-aware of each other's appraisal.

Pretending to take something out of my trench-coat pocket, I got up to glance over the other passengers in the coach. They all appeared to be reading or getting ready to doze. I missed the intangible excitements which I associated with people who travelled. There was only one passenger worth noting. She was facing my way, her legs crossed, reading a magazine and smoking a cigarette. A flower was stuck in the lapel of her pin-striped jacket. Her face attracted me, though her expression seemed strangely pat and without animation. Even when she drew on her cigarette her features hardly changed, except for two deep lines on either side of her mouth which grew more pronounced. I guessed her to be about thirty, and judging by her legs she must have a nice figure. After my week in New York I no longer hesitated to judge a woman's figure when she was seated. In Europe it had been different. There, no one could ever trust a woman, however attractive, as long as she was sitting. As often as not she shamed you with her hips when she rose to her feet.

The girl must have felt my scrutiny; she met my eyes. But courage left me and I looked down. Something about the whole set-up of the train was discouraging. In Europe, trains were the best of pimps. Any trip tricked so many flirts together, softened inhibitions, provoked possibilities. The seat next to the girl's was empty, and if my English weren't so rickety I might have a chance. But the way it was, my chances were hopeless. I sat down again.

Outside, the landscape hadn't changed. Another small city, no different from those already passed, took over the land before the previous one had quite let it go. I was getting bored and the cigar smoke was bothering me.

The man opposite me suddenly rose to his feet.

'Care to read the paper?' he addressed me.

10

His undisguised indifference permitted but one answer. 'No, thank you.'

'Going far?'

'Yes, I am *en route* to Florida.'

'Nice place, Florida. Lots of people moving down there. You on your way to college?'

In spite of my habitual reserve and my broken English, the excitement of talking to an American by myself for the first time got the better of me. I checked myself only when I caught myself repeating 'yess, yess,' precipitately. I poured out a full account of my coming to America, my scholarship, my week in New York.

In my excitement I must have failed to notice the girl walking by us on her way to the washroom; for, just as I was in the middle of a sentence, I saw her pass back to her seat. My garbled talk, aggravated by my awkward pronunciation, must have provoked her attention. I caught her glance and her inadvertent smile when she turned away.

My monologue faltered and died out. The man asked no more questions, and after what I thought was an adequate pause, I excused myself and walked down the aisle towards the girl's seat. I pretended not to notice her until the last moment.

'You laughed, yess? Over my English?' I challenged.

'Oh no. I didn't. I just . . . ,' she protested, surprised.

'But you laughed, yess?'

'Well, not exactly . . .'

'Ah! A little. A smile perhaps over my English?'

'No, no,' she protested again. 'Your English is all right.'

'But if good English nothing and bad English a smile from you, I keep bad English, yess?'

'Oh, no, it wouldn't be worth it.' She laughed at last.

I pressed my advantage. 'Oh yes. Very much worth, very much. Exception you promise smiling also when English good and better. You promise?'

She smiled now without embarrassment, and I went on with mock seriousness. 'You promise, yes? For if no, I shall not learn English.'

'All right. But you certainly do all right as it is.'

'Yes? And if you think good English better, you must learn me. . . .' That was terribly trite, I realized. Every foreigner everywhere rode on that line. I continued with barely a pause, though I would have thought anyone else a fool to talk the way I did. 'I shall satisfy you very much. . . .'

A touch of panic crossed her face. It didn't mount beyond the preparatory alarm, but I sensed that something drastic had gone wrong. Looking at her as ingenuously as I could, I hastened to add modestly, 'I can be very good student if I like teacher.'

11

There was a faint relief in her chuckle when she answered, 'I'm sure of that.'

'How do you say for smell, bad smell?' I asked her.

'What do you mean?'

'If. . . .' I inhaled deeply through my nose and then shook my head. 'When bad?'

'Just a bad smell, I suppose.'

'No, I want verb.'

She thought for a moment. 'Well, there isn't exactly a verb for it, if that's what you mean. We just say something smells bad or it has an odour.'

'But there must be verb. Must be one word,' I insisted.

She pursed her lips, and in mulling over the problem her face relaxed. Suddenly she appeared much older, as if her make-up were matched to the bright-eyed, attentive expression only. Then her eyes lit up and retrieved the smile which, for the first time, spread beyond her lips.

'Well, there is.' She looked furtively about and seemed to lean a little closer. 'It's stink. You say something stinks.'

'Stink,' I repeated experimentally. 'Very good. Like *stinken*. But not polite, yes?'

'No, you shouldn't use it.'

'Well, pardon me, but I like change seat. With your permission, that cigar. . . .' I nodded towards my former companion. 'That man with cigar stinks, yes?'

She smiled in agreement, her smile a little pronounced, though I couldn't tell whether this was meant for me or only appeared so because of her over-rouged lips. 'I don't like it myself,' she said.

'Thank you.' I straightened up, making ready to go. 'It stinks very much. Insupportable.'

'But don't tell him.'

'No, no. I bring coat here.'

She was a buyer going to Raleigh, North Carolina. I didn't know exactly what a buyer was, but since I never thought of women as having occupations, I didn't ask her to explain. The conception of buying vaguely connected itself in my mind with shopping; and even had I bothered with the paradox of anyone from New York travelling anywhere else for shopping I would have written it off as an American whim—like importing things from Europe when everything I had seen in New York seemed so much better. That she, or anyone with her looks, would travel on business never entered my mind.

I invited her to dinner in the dining car that evening. When she had to get off at Raleigh I cursed my luck. But I had her New York address. Though I wouldn't be able to afford to visit her during

12

the college year, I chalked up the event as an IOU from fate which I would try to collect on my return to the city.

The next morning, an hour before my train pulled into the Lakeville station, I looked up the conductor and tried to explain that I wished my luggage transferred to a first-class car. I felt that arriving by coach might reflect on my social standing. After all, though I was short of money I was not an immigrant. My father had a name that had to be reckoned with in our city of Meshed and my European upbringing demanded that I maintain a certain etiquette. The arrival of a foreign student from a country as far away as Persia seemed to me an event of sufficient moment to require formality.

The conductor, nice as he was, couldn't understand what I was after. There were no first-class chair cars, he insisted, only roomettes, and I mustn't waste my money now that we were so near Lakeville. He led me to the club car, which seemed more luxurious than any first-class compartment I remembered, and I couldn't understand why he wouldn't let me pay for the privilege of sitting there.

The elderly conductor, grey, tall and with that slight stoop which affects youngsters as a sign of kindliness and reliability rather than as an attribute of age, kept an eye on me until the train pulled in. He calmed my apprehensions with repeated assurances that somebody would be sure to meet me, since I had wired the time of my arrival from New York. At the station, the few porters were all busy, so, feeling rather guilty, I let the old conductor put my luggage off the train. I was afraid to be seen doing it myself. I stood on the platform waiting for someone from the college to approach me. In spite of the September heat, I kept my hat on. My topcoat was folded over my left arm, and in my right hand were my gloves and briefcase.

When the train began to move, I turned. The conductor was closing the door, and he waved at me, smiling. I suddenly remembered I had forgotten to tip him. With an awkward feeling of attempting to reward kindness with money, I rushed after the train and, fumbling with my wallet, took out a five-dollar bill. I held it out to the conductor, saying, 'Please, please.'

I watched the smiling, fatherly face recede with the departing train. I was still waving when I heard someone say, 'Are you the Persian student?'


III At my side stood a short, plump man with white hair. Except for his rainbow-coloured tie, he was dressed all in white, even to his belt and shoes. He told me his name and we shook hands. I supposed he was some sort of orderly or caretaker,

13

probably the college porter; I had distinctly heard the word 'porter' when he introduced himself. Because of an emergency of some sort, I concluded, he was the one who had been sent to meet me, and in an effort to make himself presentable he had overdone his toilette. (Or perhaps his outfit was some kind of uniform.) Though I was a little put out that my arrival did not rate a more formal reception, I had no choice but to accept the man as my guide and let him chauffeur me to the campus.

A final turn of the car brought us into an expanse crowded with hundreds of cars. We stopped and got out. Nothing in my experience had prepared me for what my companion now casually pointed out as the campus of Watson college—an enormous park with sun-dappled lawns and flowerbeds. Beyond lay tennis courts and the glittering surface of a lake. I followed my guide along a gravel path past one spacious building after another. Around us, passing students, boys and girls, called out to each other in greeting and banter. Their cheerful calls, mixed with laughter, floated past me like snatches of a strange but simple melody familiar to all but me.

We approached a group of cottages that in their setting and style reminded me of a postcard I had once received from Spain. We entered one of them. The lounge was dark, the blinds fully drawn. After the bright sunlight I could barely make out the outlines of furniture and, at the far end of the room, a fireplace flanked by two couches on which lounged three motionless figures. It sounded to me as if the room were full of people, each playing a different instrument at its loudest pitch.

The small, white figure at my side stood still, like a helpless warder in Bedlam. Then, he moved a step forward. I heard him say, 'Boys . . . boys. . . .' The rest was drowned by the shriek of a trumpet.

'Oh, hello Mr. Porter . . . how are you, Mr. Porter,' voices called back from the couches, but none of the three students stood up, though Mr. Porter had told me during the ride that he was the dormitory superintendent.

'Thank you, fine,' Mr. Porter replied, repeating 'fine, fine' as if to himself. I waited for him to say or do something more than just stand there and mutter fine, fine to himself.

'Boys . . . ,' Mr. Porter began again, but his voice was not up to the music. He was apparently hoping for the music to cease or subside. At last he stepped over to the nearest figure. 'Carey,' he said, 'better turn that off for a minute, will you? I want to say a few words to you boys.'

The student addressed as Carey got up and walked over to the record-player but another voice yelled, 'Hey, Carey, let it be. Just listen to this, Mr. Porter. Now, listen . . . wait . . . it's coming up now.'

'Phil . . . ,' Mr. Porter began.

14

'It'll just take a second. There. Now, listen.' A horn, floating on low drums, rose in solo, winding higher and higher to a whining pitch. The young man called Phil got to his feet, his hand across his stomach as if he were in pain, and the other hand pointing with index finger to the ceiling. Shaking his body in time to the music, he shuffled over to the record-player and snapped it off.

'Boys,' Mr. Porter was saying again in his exasperatingly slow way. I wondered what right he had to address the students as boys. 'Boys, I want you to meet our new student. He is from . . . Persia. Yes, from Persia. His name is . . . his name . . .' Just at the dead point of the second pause Mr. Porter retrieved himself with haste. 'His name is Mahmud. Yes, Mahmud,' he reassured his listeners as if this startling revelation must be accepted as commonplace from now on. 'Mahmud,' he repeated and relapsed into a pensive pause.

I didn't want to embarrass Mr. Porter by correcting Mahmud to Mohamed, and waited uncomfortably watching him as he stood, head inclined sideways looking downward as if contemplating the protrusion of his own stomach. 'Mehdivani, Mehdivani!' Mr. Porter suddenly exclaimed. 'Mahmud Mehdivani.'

After the expectancy created by Mr. Porter's delays, my name, though interestingly mispronounced, sounded awfully common and not worth the waiting.

Mr. Porter launched into an account of what a wonderful young man I was. '. . . studied at the University of Vienna, a fine gentleman, a very fine gentleman indeed.' I winced at each new compliment—the languages I spoke, the countries I had visited, the good athlete I was. There seemed no end to Mr. Porter's praise of me. I felt like a tourist being exhibited and explained to the natives. I was willing to bear with the ritual if Mr. Porter would only hurry up with it. But as he talked on, my impatience turned into indignation. What right did Mr. Porter have to presume his praise was wanted? How could he talk like that when we had just met? I was an absolute stranger to him. What words could he use, I wondered, if he actually wanted to introduce someone he knew, someone he really admired? His exaggerations were turning the introduction into a parody.

'I am sure you'll all agree with me that he's a very fine fellow,' Mr. Porter was saying. 'And we are all proud to have him with us. He is . . .' I was perspiring. I felt the twin shames of being far below what Mr. Porter made me out to be, and of being open to the suspicion of having coached him. I would have given anything to cut the man short, to warn the three listeners not to believe a single word, not even my mispronounced name. All I would ask for myself was a chance to show my mettle.

By the time Mr. Porter finished, I was ready to accept any reaction, even a roar of laughter, from the three students. Anything

15

would have been better, more just, than their generous silence which seemed to accept in good faith all Mr. Porter had claimed for me. The three young men stepped up to me and shook hands.
'Glad to meet you, Mahmud.'
'Nice to have you with us, Mahmud.'
'Welcome to Watson, Mahmud.'
Their frank, open faces, their simple words of welcome, their firm handshakes, were to me a pledge of loyalty and good faith. I felt a surge of gratitude. And as Carey led me upstairs to the room we were to share, I silently pledged him my trust and friendship.


IV From the first day, everybody at college seemed to go out of his way to make me feel at home. Carey stuck to me till I was thoroughly familiar with the campus, and introduced me to everyone as if he personally were vouching for me. Others did things for me that I would never have done for a newcomer. One student took care of my laundry; another carried off all my suits for dry cleaning. And still another sympathized so much with my worry about having to learn English quickly that he arranged three subscriptions to weekly magazines. It didn't occur to me that a commission was involved!

I had never imagined I could be accepted so readily. In our school in Vienna a new boy was held at arm's length the first month or two. Cutting across the campus to the beanery each morning, I couldn't keep up with the cheerful greetings that came my way. 'Hello, there . . .' 'Hiya, Mohamed . . .' 'How are you today?' 'How's everything, Mohamed?' I felt that everyone took a personal interest in how I was getting along. In my eagerness to return the greetings, I often stopped to give a full account of myself. But while I struggled for English words, another student would address me, or the first would interrupt without hearing me out, saying, 'That's fine. Glad to hear it. See you later,' and pass on.

Occasionally I would try to weigh on my own scale of values, try to translate into my own emotional vocabulary, the expressions of friendship so freely extended to me. I speculated about what I would have to feel for anyone to treat him in such intimate fashion as everyone treated me here. Compared to the open-handed generosity and kindness of Watson, my own instinctive reserve and fastidiousness seemed petty. In all my life I had never treated more than half a dozen people with the cordial informality which everybody held out to me here.

But rather than find fault with myself in the past and with the people who were so kind in my present, I found a middle way; I

16

was forced to re-evaluate myself. Apparently I cut a better figure than I realized. I must possess qualities I hadn't known about, qualities which had never been appreciated before in Vienna or in Persia, but which were recognized instantly here.

V   The day after my arrival Carey had given me a copy of the college handbook from which I was to select my courses. The glossy cover, thick paper, large print and the profusion of campus photographs were so attractive that I felt as if I were perusing the catalogue of some club. The friendly introduction, too, and the general information which made up the first half of the book, seemed composed to please me rather than to impose upon me conditions and rules.

But when I came to the second part of the handbook, which described and listed the actual courses, my heart sank. Some of the titles looked familiar enough, but the accompanying commentaries stupefied me. 'History 208, Culture of the Western world from the Greeks to the 20th century. . . .' 'Comparative philosophy 330, a comprehensive survey of the great thinkers and their works from Plato to John Dewey . . . This course surveys the great books which have decisively influenced human thought and shaped our civilization.' There seemed to be no limit to the scope of each course, each covering centuries and even millennia in a single term. I simply lacked the preliminary knowledge and training to cope with any of them. I couldn't help assuming that academic requirements here were geared to the same high standards which marked the material aspects of American life—standards which put all other countries to shame.

I read the pages over and over again, searching for a subject or two that might give me a chance. English 101, beginners—that was all. No one would object, probably, to my taking a course in French or German, though that was cheating a little. But one or two, or even three, courses weren't enough to let me pass as a full-time student, justifying my scholarship. I wouldn't last through the first term, much less survive the year. What I couldn't understand was how Alex had bluffed his way through.

I didn't have Alex's effrontery nor his talent for laughing things off. Worst of all was the thought of being accused of having made misleading claims in my scholarship application, which Alex had admittedly doctored. The best solution was to make a clean breast of it and confess to the President that I wasn't up to American standards. Perhaps he'd let me stay on as a guest student now that I was here.

But I couldn't summon up enough courage to face the President.

I let several days pass without doing anything. Then the calls came in from the Dean's office. They wanted to know what classes I was attending. I dodged them for another day and then, feeling trapped, I asked Carey to telephone to the President's office for an appointment for me. To my dismay, it was granted instantly. I could see him in an hour.

Crossing the campus to the President's office, spruced up in a dark suit and tie, I felt—amongst the sports shirts and slacks of the other students—like an overdressed peasant on Sunday. But what really worried me was another problem: how to conduct myself in front of an American college President. Formally, or informally as Alex had insisted I should? If Alex hadn't coached me, I would have approached such a man with the instinctive respect I granted a man of his age and standing. But Alex had shaken my self-confidence.

'For heaven's sake, don't be too formal. You'll only make an ass of yourself,' Alex had warned me in New York one night at dinner.

'For instance?' I had asked.

'Oh, you and your damned "for instances". For instance when you meet the Prexy—the President—don't go through all those contortions and rigmaroles of formality. Relax. Be casual.'

I wanted to know how to go about it, but it was impossible to pin Alex down or get him to be serious. Foreigners, particularly those of recent vintage, and their ways were his special pets. According to Alex, they turned into clowns at disembarkation by exhibiting the grotesque antics of European manners and by taking everything American too seriously.

'My God, don't be a hick,' Alex warned me. 'Forget all you know about etiquette. Might as well do an African tribal dance or play the whirling dervish as kiss hands or stand at attention over here. Who on God's earth do you want to be formal with, anyway? Sometimes, with women. Fine. That's still pardonable. Some of them fall for that sort of thing over here, though heaven knows why. They . . .'

I tried to nudge him back to the subject.

'With men,' he went on, 'just forget about etiquette. The sooner the better. As a matter of fact—*instanter*. Just try to hold a door open for one of these birds à la après-vous-Gaston, he'll think you're nuts or worse.'

I still wanted a specific example of permissible informality when meeting the college President. Alex threw up his hands and refused to utter another word on the subject until I paid for another drink.

18

VI I gave my name to the secretary at the President's office and she asked me to step right in, indicating an open door behind her. I stopped in the doorway. Across the room a tall, spare man was standing at the open window as if listening for whatever sounds the breeze might waft up to him from the campus. Beyond him, the tree-tops swayed peacefully in the afternoon sun. He seemed lost in contemplating the idyll outside.

'Hello. Come in,' he called out when he saw me.

The greeting, so unlike any I might have expected from a man of the President's position, caught me unprepared. Without coat, his tie held in place by one of those clips I had seen others wearing around the campus, he came towards me holding out his hand, a friendly smile on his lips. His welcome touched me like a benediction. I stepped forward to shake hands. Then, closing the door behind me, I waited respectfully for the next remark from my superior.

'Sit down, sit down,' he invited me, as if receiving a friend who had dropped in for a chat. 'Well, well. . . .' He kept on looking at me with a mixture of sage-like wisdom and a dash of conspiracy, as if sure of some problem ahead, but equally sure of solving it. 'Well, how do you like it here?' His thin lips seemed to hold his smile from spreading, as if sparing me the embarrassment of finding myself the cause of amusement. At the same time, his smile reassured me not to worry; everything would turn out all right in the end, it seemed to be confiding, although he couldn't say so right away without belittling his position as President and my problem as well. We mustn't make things too difficult for each other, he seemed to be saying.

'Sit down, sit down. Make yourself comfortable,' he encouraged me.

I stepped over to the proffered chair, but with no intention of sitting down as long as the President himself was standing. 'Thank you, sir,' I answered promptly. Perspiration was spreading all over me, and with my handkerchief I wiped my forehead.

'It's rather warm in here, isn't it?' the President said. 'Better take off your coat. It'll help a little.' He walked over and opened the door. 'There, that's better now, isn't it?'

'Very much better, thank you, sir.' Not sure of the precise connotation of my words, I censured myself for saying more than just 'thank you, sir'. Who was I to express concurrence? I fervently hoped he wouldn't ask me again to take off my coat, a move certain to add to my self-consciousness rather than to my comfort.

'Do sit down, please,' he urged again.

But how could I sit down when the President remained standing? I didn't move. Luckily, just then the President sat down behind his desk. Then, I took the chair he had indicated to me.

19

We looked at each other. Though the silence added disproportionately to my strain, I was as remote from opening the conversation as I was from lighting a cigarette. At last he spoke up.

'We have been expecting you. How was the trip? When did you arrive?'

Though I had prepared my excuse for arriving a week late, the imperative necessity of replying to two questions at once shattered my vocabulary. 'You must apologize, sir, for that I am late,' I blurted out. 'But I could not obtain reservations to come. The ships ... the ships ...' I couldn't repeat 'the ships' again and I couldn't remember the next word, 'booked-up', though I had found it in the dictionary and verified it with Carey. Silently, I implored the President to finish the sentence for me.

The startled expression on his face gave way to a smile as he said, 'I shan't apologize to you for your arriving a few days late, and you needn't apologize to me. It doesn't matter.'

'But the courses, sir ... I cannot ...'

'I wouldn't worry if I were you. You will catch up.'

'Yes, sir.' I wished he had not interrupted my confession. Now I had the added burden of explaining that what I had come to say was entirely unconnected with my late arrival. I must explain somehow that I wasn't qualified for any of the Watson courses. I was so preoccupied with finding enough English words and with how to pronounce them, that my efforts actually were a mere groping for *any* words that, by luck, might yield the meaning I wanted to get across. But the more I concentrated, the farther I seemed from expression, till, ultimately, as if stricken by blight or drought, all sprouts of the English language were scorched in my mind. Not a single word would rise to my rescue. It was no longer a matter of finding the right words, but of finding any English words at all.

'Take your time, don't hurry,' the President said after a long silence.

I was surprised that I understood him. Evidently my mind could register recognition of words, but it was paralysed when it came to forming some of my own and giving them sound and pressing them into service. This débâcle left me but one way out. To ask permission to speak in French or German.

'Do you speak English, sir?' I brought out at last.

This time there was no doubt about it. The President was definitely startled. Then, he chuckled and said with mock seriousness, 'Yes, I believe I understand English. I hope you are not doubting me.'

I was sure I had misunderstood. Of course the President understood English. Perhaps I was being made fun of in an obscure way? I felt trapped in an imbecile paradox.

20

'May I speak French or German, sir?' I tried again. 'My English very bad.'

'Well, neither my French nor German is better than your English, but go ahead. We'll get together somehow. Better try English, though. Sooner or later you'll have to get used to it.'

Rapidly I launched into my confession: the courses described in the handbook demanded far more background than I had. I couldn't possibly keep up; my scholastic qualifications were completely inadequate. But the President didn't seem to understand what I was saying. We were talking by each other, and he kept reassuring me that my English would get better in no time and that I would have no trouble keeping up with the other students. Whenever I stopped for breath there would be too many 'Oui, oui, naturellements' and 'Ja, ja, natürlichs' from him. And when he spoke, there was the inevitable 'Yess, yess' on my part.

In the end, I found myself shaking hands at the door again, not having explained myself at all, yet feeling somehow at peace and reassured.

'Come again, any time you feel like it,' the President said. 'And if there's anything we can do to help, we'll all be glad to do so.' His lively eyes seemed really to mean what he was saying.

'Thank you, sir.' And while shaking his hand I vowed that I must not disappoint this man.

VII It was just as well that the language barrier had prevented my confession. I picked out the courses that seemed to require least of me—speech, French, European History and a couple of courses which I had covered at the University of Vienna. But I needn't have worried. The dreaded classes turned out not to be so forbidding after all. The vast scope and high claims, as set up in the college handbook, turned out, when put to the test in the classroom, to be merely topics for discussion.

Thanks to my broken English, which at the beginning I took pains to exaggerate, I was temporarily excused from taking part in the discussions. To make up for this, I was to present a special paper at the end of the term. Soon, I felt quite sure of myself in the classrooms.

It was outside the classrooms—with the girls—that my background and experience let me down. The guilelessness of the girls at Watson, the friendly way they smiled at me and sought my company, were in sharp contrast to the reserve and wariness of the girls I had known in Europe. I couldn't help but conclude that I was much better looking than I realized.

Barely a week after my arrival Carey told me that Rita wanted

21

to meet me. I didn't even know who Rita was until I recognized her from Carey's description as one of the most glamorous girls at Watson. That same evening I met Rita with no more formality than Carey's introduction, spoken with the self-consciousness of an actor hired for a single line: 'Rita, this is Mohamed.'

She called me Mohamed at once, as if my name were an endearment, and entwined her fingers with mine as we crossed the campus. When we reached her car she stood with head tipped a bit sideways, her big eyes wide, as she held out the keys to me with a kind of simulated innocence, as if submitting to her fate. With her long blonde hair falling to one side of her dreamy doll-like face in imitation of an actress I had seen in the movies, she seemed an exquisite pierrette waiting to be called to perform its pantomime.

I might have risked kissing her right then and there if it hadn't been for other couples converging on the parking lot.

I took her dancing. It never occurred to me that she might insist on observing the rule that a girl must be back in her dormitory by eleven. But the evening ended as abruptly as it began. When she kissed me good-night, unmindful of the other couples around, I felt myself in some fairy tale, suspended on the midnight hour (though it was only eleven). Walking back across the silent campus in the warm night I was steeped in wonder at finding that such a beautiful girl had fallen in love with me so quickly. I fell to picturing our evenings together which would soon extend into nights.

But such nights never came, neither with Rita nor with any of the girls I dated after her. Yet it was hard not to hope, most of all on the evenings when the dining-room, with its large windows thrown open to the warm air of the ever-green campus, was charged with a heady and infectious excitement. The faces around me in the dining-room always had an air of well-being and anticipation. The formality of the hour—the boys in ties and coats, the girls groomed and neat—supported their romantic ambition to appear as men and women of the world. The couples already matched for the evening's movie or dance smiled intimately at each other across the white of the tables. And those still unspoken-for let their eyes roam in search of late-comers and luck.

Every evening I got caught up in the excitement, almost in spite of myself, though I soon learned that there was more glitter than substance to the occasion. I dated more girls in the first two months at Watson than I ever managed anywhere else in a year, and with less success.

I was hopeful, for instance, about Susan. A certain air of timidity and reserve about her led me to think she might be different from the others. But after ten evenings, I reached the same impasse with her as with the others.

22

Lingering over dessert one evening, I told myself over and over again that I ought to go on to the library and brush up on my English rather than waste my time and temper on yet another date. Rather than go through another evening of what was called necking, I decided I would be better off going to the movies alone, if I couldn't summon up enough drive to go to the library.

But in the gay and festive dining-room, so alive with easy talk and laughter, the prospect of spending the evening alone in the library loomed austere and forbidding, almost unnatural; and the library itself a place fit only for the patient, kindly, virginal librarian whose selfless air of cheerful dedication always reminded me of a nun in a modern cloister.

My resolve to study was already undermined. I had eaten too much again, glutted myself on sliced pineapple, ice cream and chocolate brownies. I was left with that not unpleasant satiation which shirks initiative and effort. Vaguely, I speculated on my chances of dating a girl after all, though the best of them were probably booked up by now. I looked indifferently around the room. I could always swallow my pride and join Susan. She was waiting for me, I was sure, as she always did; if not on the veranda, then probably somewhere near her car, as if knowing all along that I would give in and accept her compromise of just kissing and necking.

Or I might fall in with some of the boys for the evening, as I had done so gratefully during the first week. They had piled into cars and driven over to another town, which looked very much like Lakeville, to take in a movie; after it was over they lingered in front of illuminated show-windows or drove still farther on to a place which 'serves the best barbecue' or the 'best hamburger'. Or, changing plans at the last moment, they would make for a bar, where after a drink or two they would pretend to be gayer than they really were, as if preferring each other's company to any other adventure.

Driving home, they proclaimed their fellowship and good cheer to the world with loud, sentimental songs, insisting that I learn the words and join in. Too embarrassed to accept or reject this com-radeliness, I would pantomime their gay chorusing though I couldn't understand a word of it.

Back in the dormitory they greeted Mr. Porter as if he were an old, lost friend. They hung about in the hall, reluctant to count off the night for good, all the time announcing to each other how well the evening had come off. At last, climbing the stairs to their rooms, they would inject an extra dose of sincerity into their 'good-nights' and 'see you tomorrows'. Someone would start again one of the songs they had sung in the car. But the song, like the residue of the evening, trailed off, unwanted, left to die on its own weary note.

23

When I left the dining-room I caught sight of Susan on the veranda, standing at the edge of a group as if about to go on her way. The light on the veranda heightened the whiteness of her face which was framed by her dark hair braided into a knot at the back. There was a touch of pride, almost distinction in the way she carried herself. Her full figure gave her that womanly air which I sometimes missed in the slender, almost boyish build of the other girls. Some day she might even grow fat, I thought. But what a fool I had been to mistake the heftier, fleshier curves of her body for a ripening and maturing of sex. Still, she was attractive, terribly so, the way she stood there, and my fancy was teased by the knowledge that she was waiting for me. I almost went up to her, but at the last moment veered off and walked to my dormitory, where I picked up my dictionary, text-book and folder. Then, I set out across the campus to the library.

The librarian looked up and smiled at me as if I were late, as if she had been waiting especially for me; for me, who unlike others would never come in with a girl or just stay a short while or make light of her sanctuary by sprawling in a chair and glancing up at every newcomer and indulging in whispers; but who, like a disciple, stayed with her the whole afternoon or evening, earnest, studious and alone.

The librarian's stretched smile shifted into greeting. Her thin lips moulded a mute 'good evening'. I reciprocated the dumb show with a light bow, and walked off to a table near the window.

The library, though luxurious and large, was almost deserted. At the far end, a few couples, heads close together, seemed immersed in playing a game simulating studying. I knew they would leave shortly, in half an hour at the most. Then, a few solitary figures like myself would be left scattered about the vast room, each at a table intended for six. The sight of these solitary companions always made me uncomfortable. There seemed to be some defect about each of them, even if they didn't wear thick glasses and didn't appear too short, too fat or too tall. They looked as if they weren't wanted anywhere else and had nowhere to go. Whenever I met one of them at closing time I felt embarrassed, afraid to be taken as one of them.

I tried to keep my mind on the English text in front of me, feeling guilty whenever I made a guess at a word instead of looking up its precise meaning in the dictionary. But my concentration could not cope with the vague, distracting sounds wafted in through the open windows. A shout, faint laughter, the footfalls of couples, the slamming of a car door, then the start of the motor followed by humming treads—each sound beckoned my listless consciousness to follow in pursuit till, left too far behind, it returned to the book, weary and forlorn.

I could not rivet my attention on those English words which had

24

no meaning unless I looked them up. But by the time I was reading the definition, I had forgotten why I had looked the word up. I felt caught in a pose for which no one cared, except perhaps the librarian. A mounting regret, almost alarm, welled up in me because I knew nothing would happen, as nothing had happened on those other wasted evenings I had spent in the library. I was driven to the verge of confessing that dating a girl, any girl—even driving out with Susan again—was more desirable than this pretence of sitting in front of my dictionary. Even the miserable let-down I felt after each evening with Susan was preferable to sitting here. I shouldn't have passed her up tonight. I should have tried once more. Perhaps, she might have changed her mind.

We would have driven again, as we had done every night we had been out, to that gravelled side-lane which ended up in a tiny clearing, just wide enough to hold the car. Even before I turned off the ignition key, I would feel Susan's eyes resting on me, her features so soft and submissive that when I faced her I almost felt tardy with my embrace.

Each night I had tried to rush her with caresses. She confined me to her lips and breasts. I could not reconcile her abandon with her persistent evasion and refusal, nor understand why she catered to the sensual if she was so set against yielding to it. Sometimes when I could sense how wrought up she was, I felt the same contempt for her—wallowing as she was in substitutes for love-making —that I felt for certain boys at my boarding school in Vienna who indulged alone. Yet there were moments when I could not begrudge her a grain of compassion, almost admiration, for holding off what I had thought, at first, was inevitable. Her whipped-up senses were bound to betray her, sooner or later. Some night, temptation was bound to catch her off guard and carry her beyond self-control. It was just a matter of time. Another night or two, I thought.

But the débâcle was repeated night after night. When it was time to drive back, I would watch her while she buttoned up her blouse, straightened her skirt and braided her loose hair back into a knot. After finishing her make-up, she would look at me as if expecting a compliment for restoring so quickly and skilfully a proper appearance. Sometimes I thought I detected a touch of superiority in her smile, for having enjoyed herself at my expense. There was something smug about the way she offered me a cigarette and smoked her own, as if inviting the whole world to step up to the car and witness her bearing and aplomb, while barely suppressing her satisfaction at having toyed with the sensual without transgressing; of having indulged in forbidden throes and being restored to calm and propriety as easily as her make-up was.

Though I chafed at being in bondage to her sterile temptations, I lacked the will-power to break off with her for good. An evening alone in the library drove me back to compromise and Susan. But there came one night when I suddenly felt weary of her and what lay ahead. For the first time in my life I felt bored in a woman's company. I was caught in that dread of ennui which blights any indulgence done once too often. Suddenly the evening ahead with Susan loomed up as a burden, a routine that must be got over. And when we drove past the white moonlit façade of the library I wished I could jump out of the car and rush off into that quiet, book-lined room where I would be on my own with my dictionary and notebook, free to let my thoughts roam beyond the open window into the darkness, where my imagination could weave its own tales of youth and circumstance.

**VIII** Instead of crowded benches facing a platform, there was a large table ringed by chairs in our classrooms. None of the students ever seemed nervous or apprehensive, and the professor no more than a private tutor or paternal friend who gave a touch of dignity and official patent to the group, though without intruding his authority upon the easy flow of self-expression about him. I marvelled, at first, at the spontaneous questions and fluent answers of the students, accepting their fluent speech for fluent knowledge and their informality for the self-assurance of the competent. Soon, I learned to judge the show better.

Very soon I regretted that I hadn't dared take American History; except for a few odd facts I knew nothing about the United States or its history. I had been brought up to regard the Americas only in relation to Europe. Even the date of Columbus's discovery was primarily relevant in my mind to the subsequent Spanish ascendancy and Philip's financing of the Armada. I had heard of the Louisiana Purchase because it involved Napoleon, and of Alaska because it involved Russia, and of Lincoln by way of Maximilian of Mexico. The Civil War I remembered as no more than a skirmish, a local rebellion which couldn't be compared to a European Civil War like the Wars of the Roses. And the Monroe Doctrine I had been taught to interpret as being really due to the string-pulling of England and France, who wanted to keep new colonial powers out of South America.

Yet instead of reminding myself how little I knew about America, I was constantly surprised at how little the other students knew about Europe and the rest of the world.

After sailing without difficulty through the first term, I grew bolder in class. My European background seemed to furnish me with a halo of knowledge. Even the professor listened with special attention when I spoke. And I couldn't resist the temptation to show off with odd facts which the other students took as samples of a deeper knowledge, instead of the oddities they were: that the radical socialist party in France was less radical than the socialist party; that Hungary had been a kingdom without a king, and with an admiral for regent though the country was landlocked and possessed no navy; that theocracy still existed in the world, in Tibet; that a stateless person didn't or shouldn't legally exist. Sometimes I challenged the class with out-of-the-way questions to which I already knew the answers, just to create an opportunity for parading my knowledge. It wasn't long before I realized that I could say almost anything about Europe and the Middle East and get away with it, though sometimes I held my breath for fear that someone would call my bluff. Anyone could have stumped me by asking a single question about America. That they didn't, made me assume they didn't know any more about their own country than they did about the rest of the world.

I never felt quite comfortable though, after having my say or scoring a point. An element of friction, almost antagonism, seemed to trail my interference, as if by posing a question which required a fact as answer rather than an opinion or a discussion in which everyone's say was as good as the next person's, I were playing unfairly. The long silences which followed my remarks always prodded in me a sense of guilt for having thrown their game off the track. I felt everyone's eyes resting on me, expecting me to rectify the confusion I had created.

I might have accepted the classes in better grace—as a man might accept the church ritual of another faith—if there had been any ritual or traditional order in them, some proper relation between teacher and student. But the students lounged around the table like familiar guests in their favourite coffee-house. And if it hadn't been for the professor's age and place at the head of the table, it would have been difficult to single him out as the authority in charge. He seemed anxious to avoid setting himself apart. Instead of dominating the class, he encouraged the students to talk, as if through the mere process of talking, their casual and haphazard opinions might eventually crystallize into thought.

In spite of my repeated resolves to stay out of arguments, I couldn't manage to keep my mouth shut, least of all in the Comparative Government class. The condescending way in which everyone spoke of any form of government except the American exasperated me. Even other democracies were spoken of as misfits, at best poor imitations of the American example. Nobody had a good word for any other country; nor for Socialism, Fascism, Monarchy or Communism, not even for their theories or ideals.

Instead of formulating arguments, pro and con, the students simply reiterated their preferences in stock phrases, vigorously

27

expressed, for the 'best government yet devised by man'. When I mentioned that Americans didn't take very good care of their democracy, since barely half the people bothered to vote, half a dozen voices told me that didn't mean anything. People here didn't bother to vote because they liked the government the way it was. Every American, they assured me, would rush out to vote if he didn't like the way the country was run. Where else in the world could an ordinary man tell the President to go to hell? He'd be jailed or worse. I wouldn't concede all this, not even to myself, but this last claim always impressed me, more than any learned argument could have done. I felt it was really so.

But unlike most of my fellow students in Europe, who were violently drawn to one political party or another, the students here never seemed to bother with national politics outside the classroom discussions. I had never seen a political rally on the campus, and never caught anyone in a political argument. Except when they were arguing with me, politics just didn't seem to exist for them. No more than a few ever troubled to read the daily newspaper, but only the campus newspaper which contained no real news.

And yet whatever I said in the Comparative Government class seemed to rub the others up the wrong way. Any comment of mine, even a purely theoretical one, unless in praise of their institutions and their ways seemed to rouse a suspicion that I didn't like America. As often as not I argued on, not because I thought I was right, but because I resented their collective and righteous pressure. When the class discussed Fascism and the co-operate state, I felt suspected of Fascism each time I spoke up. It grew worse when, discussing Communism, I maintained that in theory every form of government, even Communism, claimed to represent the people and to work for the common good.

The day I said this, even Luke, the football star, who was also a scholarship student, stared at me from across the table as if he wanted to get his big hands on me. For a moment I wondered what reaction a convinced Communist or Fascist would get, though freedom of speech and discussion was Watson's biggest boast.

There were loud protests around the table. The professor leaned back, content, almost proud at such a sudden flare of participation among his flock. But the protests subsided into disgruntled silence. The students seemed to be waiting for the professor to guide the discussion back into its proper channel. But he still waited, hoping perhaps that one of the students might do it for him.

Finally the professor leaned forward and inquired whether everyone understood the principles of the various forms of government we had been discussing, if all 'was clear'. One of the students, as if testifying to his ambition to have the matter absolutely clear, finally spoke up.

'Would you mind explaining that point about the direct and indirect vote once more?'

The professor kept on looking at him, as if waiting for a more profound comment. Then, addressing the group, he asked if anyone would sum up this point in clear-cut, simple terms. Someone, over-eager, started off as if reciting a matter so simple that it was hard to find words for making the point still simpler. He was interrupted by another who felt compelled to correct and elaborate, while defending himself against the ambitious interruptions of still another.

'Well, Luke,' the professor turned to the football player when he had run out of volunteers, 'what do you think of our discussion?' The professor's tone implied that Luke might have been withholding his participation for lack of encouragement.

Luke hoisted up his huge body. His features, broadening into a grin, struggled to simulate some aspect of awareness which might be taken as the reflective workings of his mind. He straightened his notebook in front of him. He picked up his pencil and, holding it upright, stared at it as if it were the proxy of his mind and might enlighten him. Then, he looked around the table helplessly, as if he were the victim of a broken, though tacit, agreement, and as such, entitled to rescue.

'Well, prof,' he began slowly, 'a lot of things have been said here today . . . I've been listening, but I don't know what I could add . . . I guess . . .' After each phrase Luke paused, as if waiting for some-one to relieve him. His last pause was resigned. It left any and all interpretation of his meaning to the sympathy of his fellow students and the professor.

'Go on, Luke,' prompted the professor kindly, as if Luke's reluc-tance to continue were entirely due to bashfulness. The professor's benevolent approach seemed to have some effect. There was a shade of anchorage in Luke's reply.

'Well, I guess, it's pretty hard for a guy to take a stand . . . It's all been said here already. . . .'

Serious attention had come, wavered and passed off the professor's features as he waited for Luke's 'stand'. But as Luke's pause dragged out, the professor decided that a word of his own was indispensable. 'That's all true, Luke,' he encouraged patiently, emphasizing 'all' as if Luke had been holding forth at length and he wanted to give him credit for his efforts while helping him along. 'That's all true, I know. But let's have your opinion, Luke.'

'As I just said, prof,' Luke spoke wth surprising promptness, giving the impression that he was at last ready to come out with it all. 'As I just said . . . I think . . .'

'Well?'

29

'I think there isn't much anyone can say or add to what's already been said...'

'Let's forget for a while what's been said in our discussion,' said the professor a trifle impatiently. 'Just give us your own opinion in your own words, please.'

'Well,' said Luke, suddenly smiling, 'I guess I just don't have any opinion on this particular subject.' His smiling, good-natured confession seemed to claim a vague credit for candour, implying that no one could insist that a man have an opinion if he didn't want to.

'Oh now, come on, Luke. You must think *something*.' The professor's voice was almost petulant, as if Luke were spoiling the game by being stubborn. The professor seemed no longer concerned with the gist of Luke's thoughts, but with the elemental fact that Luke *must* think something. It was impossible for Luke to think nothing.

'I guess I do,' Luke said quickly, but without committing himself further.

'Well, let's have it then. Come on. Everybody else has had his say. Now don't hold back. That's what we're here for. So that everybody can say what's on his mind.' The professor seemed to be encouraging Luke to talk, under the assumption that if he only would, there was an even chance that his words might convey something. One opinion was as worthy as another.

'Sure,' Luke said, 'only it's hard for a guy to put *everything* he thinks into words.' Then, as if struck by an idea, he went on. 'Most anything I meant to say, Lee here already said it... didn't you?' He turned to Lee.

'But are you sure you don't want to say something, to add something of your own?' The professor's words were delicately balanced, inviting but not insisting—a tentative conclusion or a last encouragement.

Though Luke had been anxious to drop the matter, he now seemed unwilling to bear the onus of having had nothing to say. He bent forward and with a touch of emphasis, countered, 'Naturally I want to, prof. It's just that I wanted to ask some more questions first, to get it all clear in my mind...'

'Well, go right ahead. That's what we're here for. So you students can ask all the questions you want.'

'Well,' said Luke, 'I'd like to think a few questions over, if you don't mind. Well, I guess that's all I have to say.' And he bowed his head.

The professor, admitting a momentary defeat, turned to the group. 'Now, Shirley. What do you have to say about the comparative merits of democracy and monarchy?'

Shirley spoke at length. Faces around the table acquired a serious mien. The notion seemed prevalent that any second-hand recitation,

30

if pronounced with earnestness and conviction, could be credited as 'my opinion'.

Listening to the haphazard flow of recital and comment, I felt myself part of an elaborate hoax. The students and the professor seemed a group of earnest children playing grown-up. At such moments, the whole campus with its expensive and ornamental lay-out of cottages, clustered trees, lawns and gravelled walks struck me as a meaningless make-believe of which I could not fathom the real purpose, unless I accepted Alex's derisive exaggerations.

In New York he told me bluntly that the whole college idea in his opinion was a joke, 'a voodooism, a superstition, a theatrical remnant of the European heritage still being hung on to long after the umbilical cord with Europe has been cut.'

'Don't let it fool you, the slick campus and those ivy-covered buildings, the caps and gowns,' Alex said, throwing up his hands when I had maintained that no country could possibly progress so far and fast as America had done without progressing proportionately in education.

'As far as this country is concerned,' Alex had lectured me, 'you can take all the professors, past and present, including your Johann Wolfgang Goethe, Friedrich Schiller, *aussi* Monsieur Racine and Co., even *auch* Herrn Wilhelm Shakespeare, and throw all their books out of the window. Or, if you like, treat their collected editions à la Hitler: *Verbrannt* and *Verboten*. It wouldn't make any difference. Business would go on just the same. And remember this, the Empire State Building would go on standing on its base. And as long as the Empire State Building stands, all is well. The rest of the world can yell its head off against America's lack of *Kultur*. The question is: who the hell cares? Nobody. And why should they? All the *Kultur* of Europe wouldn't buy you a meal over here. And why should it?

'Yes, then, why, why, my good man, does anyone bother to go to college, you ask? Why? That's a good question. Why *do* they, really? I don't know. Nobody knows. Oh, they may tell you a lot of crap about getting a background and broadening their minds, but what do people really get out of it? Just ask a guy who's gone to college and then has to make a living, like they all do. Nothing. On a job, a man's background must be anything *but* broad. Just the opposite. In other words, the narrower the better. I haven't read a book in six months. Imagine you have to talk to some boneheaded customer, be nice to him, and you have read a book the night before, broadened your mind, so to speak. Why, you'd feel like spitting in the guy's face. Or committing suicide, if the pay cheque weren't just a few days off.'

Alex snorted in disgust. 'Why, over here a kid of seven knows more about making a living than a Ph.D. in Europe does—all a

31

potential American Croesus needs to learn in a mental way is to read his bank statement and butter up the right people. Why should he bother with calculus and Shelley and all that crap?

'Good Lord, man, do you realize that in this country out of the twenty-five top men—now, don't ask me how much they make, even Einstein couldn't figure it out—out of the twenty-five top money-makers, eighteen, *eighteen* mind you, never had an education. More power to them, I say. Now, don't laugh. A skilled mechanic or a truck driver over here makes more money than the Austrian Prime Minister or the British Poet Laureate.

'Why people bother with college is a mystery to me, really. I don't think even an American can tell you. It must be a modern superstition. But it will pass, *ça passera*. And the Empire State Building will still stand. Oh God, yes, not because, but in spite of these phoney burgs called institutions of higher learning and in spite of these pathetic characters called professors who hawk their academic palaver the way the padres do their prayers.

'All right, all right, you think I am exaggerating. Well, suppose—I'm not saying it happens—but just suppose a student really does manage to pick up something about literature or tries to learn decent English, enrich his vocabulary? When does he ever have a chance to use it, and with whom? He'll be called a sissy and will have to revert to sloppy language just to survive. Anyway, colleges are in full retreat. Who teaches Latin any more? They've learned that the kids won't pay unless they're given a good time at school. Why, except for a few heavily endowed universities, most colleges nowadays are crammed with courses they would be ashamed to teach in a European kindergarten.

'But for heaven's sake, don't get high hat about culture when you get to Florida. It's all pretty harmless if you don't upset the apple-cart by insisting on learning something. The best thing about college is the contacts you make. That's how I got my job. I know, you don't care about that—you plan to go back and be a pasha. But you never know. And if you ever have to make a living over here, don't think you'll get it on a silver platter just because you are the son of your father, went to school in Europe or speak a couple of languages. So, better be nice all around and enjoy yourself while you can.'


IX After Shirley had finished her recital on the merits of democracy versus monarchy, Herb signalled his wish to speak.

'Go ahead, Herb,' said the professor.

'I'd like to ask a question. It's this. In all that's been said about

32

the various forms of government, I mean, regardless, whe
fellow come in who makes an invention? I don't mean th
nical kind that you can patent and all that. Take myself, for
I want to take up medicine, become a surgeon. Suppos
there was a pinched smile of stubborn self-confidence or
—'suppose I hit on a new way of operating, a new kind of
Well, what I want to know is, is there any difference in
forms of government—democracy, socialism, dictatorship
as far as I am concerned? Here, every other doctor can stea
and follow my lead. In Russia, I suppose, it becomes go
property. But suppose it's worth a million dollars. Now, is
difference under what form of government I make my inven

The professor, to gain time, took off his glasses and lea
in his chair. Taking in the whole group with a long glance
'It would be interesting to know what the others have to sa

Elizabeth volunteered to speak. 'I know you can't pa
things, even here in the U.S. But then, that doesn't mean
I guess.' Her voice, which I remembered as high-pitched a
from a date I once had with her, sounded deceptively r
and mature. She looked so sincere and tolerant, as if her sp
at all were entirely prompted by her search for truth ar
But then, most of the speakers in class started off on that n
should an invention in medicine, like Herb says, why sh
worth less than let's say, a mechanic's who figures out a
of engine that saves gasoline or something?' Carried aw
own words, Elizabeth ended on a note of indignation, a
that right must prevail.

The professor indicated the next volunteer. 'Lee.'

'Logically both Herb and Elizabeth are right,' said Lee
quietly and with evident sincerity. 'But considering that
medicine, I don't think that Herb should have the right to
lize his invention or set his own price on it.'

'Why not?' Herb thrust his head forward.

Lee hesitated a moment, taken aback by Herb's fervou
isn't quite like inventing a new engine for a car as Liz
cars, the customer has a choice. He can take it or leave
a man is sick—well, he's sort of flat on his back . . .' Lee s
consciously and, turning reluctantly to Herb, added, 'A
just isn't ethical. No amount of money could justify a di
social responsibility.'

'That's all very well and good,' interrupted Herb. 'But v
it cost *me* a million dollars? I'll pay taxes like everybody el

Luke made a mock grimace at Herb's mention of a milli
His lips moulded into a silent profanity. His gesture
professor's attention.

33

'Luke, were you about to say something?' the professor turned to him.

'No, no,' Luke hastily retracted. 'I was just listening.'

'But every doctor accepts social responsibility before he even starts out,' Lee persisted. 'That's nothing new. Every doctor starts out with the Oath of Socrates . . .'

'Hippocrates,' Herb injected scathingly.

'The Oath of Hippocrates, of course,' Lee corrected himself.

'What you are driving at is just that doctors should be decent and all that,' said Herb.

'Yes, naturally.'

'Like everybody else, only more so?'

'Well . . .'

'Then you think it's all right for everybody else to make a cool million in business and keep it, but a doctor should give it away and struggle along on aspirin and bicarbonate prescriptions. All I can say is that if anybody has such a big social conscience, let *him* buy me off and give the invention free to the public.' From behind the thick lenses, Herb's eyes darted around. His hand passed over his forehead to smooth the tight, wavy hair. He exuded a sort of energy which he usually saved for activities outside the classroom. Herb had a hand in everything that went on at Watson. He was always drumming up people for vespers, trips and dances. He was an editor of the college newspaper, a member of the Student Council, and apparently a friend or agent of the orchestra leader at every dance. Many students carried on with a business at school, acting as campus agent for one of the Lakeville laundry or dry-cleaning establishments, selling subscriptions to magazines, running the food or soft-drink concession at dances or games. Only with Herb, who seemed to be in on everything, it was hard to decide the line between business and philanthropy. He even acted as the manager of the tennis team, though he couldn't play. I used to accept readily enough the towel and cokes which Herb held for each player of the team, but I resented being patted on the back and given a pep talk.

Colour had risen to Herb's face. His voice was edged. 'Suppose I wouldn't play ball and refused to publish my way of operating. What could anyone do? Force me?'

I waited for someone to take up the challenge, but no one volunteered. My vague dislike for Herb got the better of me. Before I was quite sure what I was going to say, I volunteered to speak.

The professor nodded amiably to me.

'This question cannot be settled legally as it stands, at least not the way you present it,' I said in a parliamentary tone.

Herb took his arm down from the back of his chair and faced me

across the table. 'Every question has an answer,' he said, 'and so there must be an answer to mine.'

'Even if there isn't an answer in law, in your case there is one—and I doubt if you'd like it.'

Herb waited, blinking. 'Well, do you know it? If so, I'd be glad to hear it.'

'I may not know the legal answer to this question,' I said speaking slowly. 'But for you personally, I know the answer. It is simple. People like you, who carry such attitudes in their hearts, never make such inventions.'

I looked covertly around, expecting others to side with me, for Herb's persistence had struck many as in bad taste. But there was no response; instead, an air of awkwardness and embarrassment was palpable around the table. Only Lee was looking at me. But not in a puzzled or speculative way as he often used to look at me when I first joined the class; rather with a prolonged stare. There was something incongruous in that stare on Lee's sympathetic features, which were always calm and friendly when he looked at others.

Herb flushed, and after shifting his notebook with nervous fingers, gave a short laugh. 'Well, let's wait and see, let's wait and see. Maybe I'll surprise you some day.' The tentative grin was still on his face when the bell rang.

'You would surprise me, indeed,' I said to him, as I rose with the rest.

Outside the building I saw Lee and Herb standing on the porch. They stopped talking when I came near, with that self-consciousness which betrayed they had been talking about me. I was about to pass, when Herb addressed me.

'Lee here would like a word with you.'

I stopped and faced them both. There was a formal stiffness in their postures—Lee's neat, tall figure clad in well-tailored slacks and immaculate sports shirt alongside the stocky, utilitarian Herb.

'Yes?' I said, expectant, though not knowing what I expected.

'I wanted to ask you this . . .' Lee was trying to sound casual, but a touch of emotion or temper was creeping into his voice, and he paused to collect himself. 'I wanted to ask you this: why do you make it so hard for yourself to get along with the rest of us?'

'I didn't know I was making it hard,' I said, resenting Lee's patronizing tone.

'Maybe you don't know it, but sometimes you sure act as if you didn't care whether anyone liked you or not . . .'

'Maybe I don't,' I said.

'Look. What Lee means,' Herb broke in, 'what he is trying to do is to help you out, sort of, by letting you know in a friendly way that you shouldn't make it so hard for everybody to be friends with you, if you know what I mean.'

'I do not know what you mean. And I was not aware that I needed help. Also . . .'

'See?' Lee turned to Herb. Then addressing me again, 'You are not even listening, or trying to understand what we mean.'

'You think you know everything, don't you?' Herb broke in. 'And you like to sound smart and make others feel small, don't you? All I can tell you is that this won't get you very far in this country.'

'Yes?' I waited for either of them to go on.

'Why do you foreigners always have to get personal, and butt in when it's no concern of yours?' It was Lee who spoke. 'We don't need your big ideas. And we don't want them. We are getting along okay as we are.' Then, as if catching himself being rude or unfair, his tone became surprisingly intimate and conciliatory. 'We're glad to have you people with us, believe me, but you ought to do your share and fall in with the rest of us.'

Lee had spoken with such sincerity that I couldn't help feeling that it was not rancour but a sense of decency which prompted his words. Yet I couldn't make sense out of them. What did he mean—do your share and fall in with the rest of us? What had I ever said or done to antagonize any of them? And the notion that I was the harbinger of 'ideas' was fantastic.

I might have made a joke of it all, or told them that it must be a mistake, if it hadn't been for the righteous and proprietary air which both Lee and Herb unconsciously assumed as they waited for my answer.

'I really don't know why you honour me with your opinions,' I said coldly.

'It's for your own good,' Herb said earnestly, 'that Lee says these things to you. And you should take them to heart if you want to get along here.'

'I have no intention of listening to a lecture on my personal behaviour although I am a foreigner.'

'Oh, for heaven's sake, come off it,' Lee suddenly flared up. 'It's always your kind that causes trouble. This country is okay the way it is. Can you understand that? And we want to keep things that way. Some of us may be hicks and all that compared to what people have in Europe or Persia, but that's the way we like it. We don't want to be any different from what we are. And, we're free to do as we please . . . ,' he added significantly. As I waited for him to go on, he exclaimed with a touch of petulance, almost weariness, 'Oh, why can't you people leave us alone?'

'I shall be glad to leave you alone, and anyone else who wishes it,' I said.

'I wish you would,' Lee said, bitingly, 'I wish all of you would.'

'I cannot take the responsibility for others, but personally I shall be glad to do so. I shall.'

And after I had turned to go, Lee called after me, 'And if you don't like it here, why the hell don't you go back where you came from!'


X  I heard a chair being pulled up at my library table and looked up. A pretty girl, blonde, snub-nosed, and with full cheeks took the seat diagonally across from me. I was not sure whether I had met her before. So many girls, particularly the blondes, looked alike to me, as if they were sisters or relatives. It was not that their features resembled each other's so much, but their expressions did —the way they smiled, walked and talked.

The girl leaned over and whispered, asking if I knew anything about this 'stuff', pointing with the end of the pencil she had taken out of her mouth to the thick volume in front of her.

'What is this stuff?' I quoted her, smiling.

She turned the cover my way. The title was: *Religions of the Modern World*. 'I've got to hand in a term paper on that,' she whispered.

'I am sorry,' I said. 'I don't know very much about religions.'

'But don't you know anything about any of them?' she persisted.

'I wish I did. But I am very ignorant on this subject.'

'Your name is Mohamed, isn't it?' she challenged, with a peculiar emphasis on *Mohamed*, as if to verify a rumour.

'Yes it is,' I said, flattered that my name mattered.

'Really?'

'Yes, really.'

'Well, then you must know something about Mohammedanism, or Islam. That's the same thing, isn't it?'

'Yes it is the same. But do you know much about Christianity that you are so severe with me? Even if your name isn't Maria. Or perhaps it is?' I was pleased at the way I had guided the conversation. I looked at the girl with heightened interest, admiring her ingenuity and originality in hitting upon the subject of religion to instigate a flirtation. It never occurred to me that she could actually be interested in discussing the subject with a perfect stranger, especially when she had a book in front of her which could tell her more than I.

'No, my name is Jane,' she said, rising to the bait.

'Well, isn't that really St. Joan?'

'I, well ... I didn't mean it that way.' She seemed confused. I wondered what way she *had* meant it. A silent warning from the librarian to preserve the No Talking rule must have registered with Jane before I saw it, for she suddenly said, 'We can't talk here. Come on, let's go outside.'

Outside meant the park behind the library. I followed Jane out, noticing that she had an excellent figure, and waited for her to choose a bench.

'It's like this,' she resumed, after we were seated side by side. She explained that she had to write a ten-page term paper on some religion. Any religion would do, and she had chosen Islam. She thought it would be pretty easy, if I would help her out a bit.

'But as I told you,' I said, 'I really don't know enough about it.' I wanted to add that I had left Persia for Europe as a child of eight, and had returned only once since then for a summer vacation.

'Oh, don't be so modest,' Jane chided, laughing as if she had said something witty. 'You must know *something* about your own religion.'

Jane's words raised a question I had never been challenged to answer before. How much did I know, or care, about my religion? In all the years since father took me to Vienna and left me in a boarding-school, religion had rarely risen as a question in my consciousness. I had been too young to remember for long the teachings of the Prophet, the Koran and the religious rites I had learned at home. Nor was the question of religion ever thrust upon me at the boarding-school (though I was the only Mohammedan there) except at the very start, when it had to be decided what to do with me while the other boys attended religious instruction. I was simply given the choice of sitting in with the Catholic majority or with the smaller Protestant class. If I didn't like either, I was told I could join any gym class that happened to be scheduled at that hour for other forms. I preferred the last alternative, and this happy arrangement lasted through my eight years at the school.

Only once had religion threatened to cause friction: when one of the Catholic sisters in the school infirmary gave me an injection, the pain made me swear out, 'Jesus Christus.'

'If you must swear,' the sister reproved me, 'don't say Jesus Christus. Swear by your own prophet, Mohammed.'

I apologized and then added slyly, 'But, sister, isn't swearing bad altogether?'

She nodded, smiling as if I had taken her reproof too seriously.

I wanted to say something of all this to Jane, and to explain why I knew so little about my religion without feeling less about it. But she broke in. Apparently, I had delayed too long.

'If you don't want to help, you ought to say so at least.' She rose from the bench.

'I want to help,' I assured her. I was groping for a solution. 'Why don't you write about the Jewish religion?' I suggested.

She glanced at me suspiciously. 'Do you know much about that?'

'No,' I said. 'What I meant is that you could ask one of the Jewish students to help you. I have noticed they are very good students and would probably know very much more about their religion.'

'Who wants to get mixed up with the kikes?' she snapped out, her features drawing up in aversion. Such an outburst in Europe would not have surprised me; here it did. The persistent claim, implicit everywhere—in class, in the dormitory, in the newspapers—that the virtue of tolerance truly prevailed here had seemed to me really true. To make sure, I once asked a Jewish student whether this were really so. He assured me it was. Now, I wondered, what other answer could he possibly have given me? Suddenly, it seemed not altogether a coincidence that the dozen or so Jewish students joined no fraternity but one; that they seldom scattered in the dining-room, as others did, but somehow were seated never far from each other, near the entrance. Yet instead of contradicting the community's claim, they, too, joined in to say that all was well. I suddenly wondered whether the open intolerance often suffered by Jews in other countries was not a more honourable martyrdom than this pseudo-tolerance, against which a victim was helpless, because everyone denied it was pseudo.

The harsh, almost vulgar tone of Jane's words made me ill at ease. 'Well, *you* wouldn't want to get mixed up with them,' she challenged.

'No, of course not,' I said, anxious to placate her. But the instant these words were out, I felt their full ignominy—less for catering to her prejudice than for compromising some part of my character. I could have said simply no. Why did I have to add 'of course not'? I felt the shame of it, of abusing others just for the sake of playing up to a girl.

'See what I mean?' she took me up. 'Anyway, I bet others in the class have already thought of that. But I'll be the only one who'll have a paper on Mohammedanism . . . that is, if you'll help me.' Jane's large, blue eyes looked at me so trustingly, expectantly, that I couldn't bring myself to repeat my confession of ignorance.

She must have taken my silence for wavering, for she went hurriedly on, 'Just go ahead and tell me a few things. I'll jot everything down, and after I've put it all together you can sort of correct it. Well . . . start talking.' She laughed.

My shame had passed off quickly. I wondered idly why shame dissolves so much quicker when men are facing women than when they are facing each other. 'I start talking,' I said, smiling, 'but not because I have anything to say about Islam, but because I like talking to you.'

'Oh, go on,' she laughed and sucked the end of her pencil.

'Where shall I begin?'

'At the beginning, I guess.' She laughed again. 'How it all got started and all that.'

39

'Islam began in the seventh century with Mohammed. Not me, another Mohamed. The Prophet,' I joked lamely. But Jane giggled nevertheless, a giggle that rose in volume without ever becoming mirthful.

She had flipped open her notebook, and in the rather inadequate moonlight, began taking notes. After a short scribble, she stopped and looked up. 'Is that the seventh century before or after Christ or what?'

'After Christ,' I said, trying not to smile.

'Okay. I got that.'

'Shortly afterward there was a schism.'

'What's that?'

'Well, like with the Christians. First, all were Catholics, then the Protestants started a new branch.'

'You mean Reformation.'

'Yes, something like that, only with us it was more a matter of personalities. There were two sects, and . . .'

'What were they called?'

'Sunis and Shi'ites.' I realized I had mispronounced the last word.

'Sheets!' Jane's giggle rose again in the twilight, irresistible and ingenuous, as if someone had suddenly tickled her and she were enjoying it.

'Why, what is the matter, please?' I asked sharply.

'Oh, the way you said it.' She tried to look serious. 'The soonies and what was the other?'

Her laugh rose again when I repeated the names of the sects. 'Gee,' she said, 'I'm sorry. I didn't mean it. It's just the way you pronounce it. You better spell it.'

'You seem to have all the fun,' I said with mock injury. 'And I have nothing.'

'Oh, I wish I could make it up to you,' she said, impulsively touching my hand. 'I know what. I'll pay you five dollars if you'll write the whole term paper for me.'

The offer of payment didn't shock me as much as the realization that she had interpreted my remark as a hint. 'You would have to pay me in better currency than money,' I said wistfully.

'Well, how else can I make it up to you?' She seemed truly puzzled.

'Five of these,' I said, leaning towards her and kissing her lightly on the lips.

We walked off across the campus, hand in hand, stopping every few steps for kisses. 'Gee, I didn't know,' Jane sighed.

'What didn't you know?'

'Oh well, that you could be so sort of sweet. You always look so serious, I would never have guessed it.' She confided this idea so

40

trustingly that I felt like warning her about myself. At the same time, I was veering her off towards the lake shore.

'Gosh,' she sighed. 'I wish they wouldn't spoil the last weeks of the term with these damned papers. Why can't we do them at the start and get them over with?'

I wasn't listening. I was planning ahead. 'Let's go down by the lake,' I said, kissing her to sway her agreement.

'Okay,' she nodded.

I guided her past the lighted landing where some boats were tied up, and found a darker spot. 'Let's sit down,' I said, trying to sound casual.

Jane stretched out on her stomach, her elbows digging into the grass, her hands cupping her chin. I was scarcely seated beside her when she jumped up. 'Oh! I'm getting my dress all messed up. The grass is all damp.'

I cursed my luck. 'Please sit on my handkerchief,' I suggested for lack of anything better, spreading it on the ground.

'That's no good,' she said.

I was ransacking my brain for some other makeshift when Jane spoke up. 'I know,' she said. 'Let's get a blanket.'

I was as unprepared for her remark as I was for the difficulties it proposed. I couldn't very well run back to the dormitory and walk out in front of Mr. Porter with a blanket under my arm. But I must get one somehow, I told myself. I turned to go. 'I'll be back instantly,' I said, though I had no idea how I was going to manage it.

'Wait. Don't bother,' she held me back. 'Let me get it. Our dorm is much closer.' And she scampered off.

As I waited I couldn't help mistrusting such luck. It was too good to be true. I began to wonder if she might not be one of those promiscuous girls I had heard about, but never met, and I had no ambition to be another bead on her tally. Or, more likely, her running off was probably a trick to break things up. But if she does come back, I thought, there can be no doubt about her intentions. What a pity I hadn't met this girl sooner.

Before I really expected her back, I saw her racing eagerly towards me with both arms held to her chest, hugging something. 'Here,' she said, handing me the blanket, her chest heaving with uneven breathing. 'I sneaked it out.'

'How did you do it?' I couldn't help asking, not a little flattered that she had done it for me.

'Oh, it's easy,' she said. 'Throw it out the window when the coast is clear, and then run down and pick it up.' She had evidently done it before.

The blanket was large enough for us to lie on half of it and to fold the other half up as a cover. I was so sure of myself now that things had come this far, that for a while I was content to hold

41

Jane in my arms, feeling her cheek pressed against mine. I felt her cheek muscles stir and lifted my head. I thought I saw her lips move, but she didn't say anything.

'Did you speak?' I asked gently, partly out of curiosity, but mostly to overcome the impasse of our silence.

She shook her head.

'Why don't you say it?'

'Say what?'

'What you just wanted to say.'

'I didn't want to say anything.'

'But your lips moved,' I persisted.

'Oh, that's just my gum,' she said.

The idea that I had just been kissing a girl with chewing gum in her mouth gave me the odd sensation of having shared her kisses with something or someone else, as if kissing had been only a part of her pastime, supplemented by the gum—or the other way around.

'Would you mind throwing it away?' I asked, almost formally, drawing away.

'Does it really bother you?' she asked. And, as if conceding good-naturedly to some whim of mine, she took the gum out of her mouth and threw it away.

She gave her kisses freely and didn't protest when I unbuttoned her blouse. But farther she would not let me go. For a moment I was alarmed that she, too, might be just another of those girls who liked to play at making love. Yet the fact that she had volunteered to fetch the blanket, and was now pressing and straining her body so close to mine, made me discount all doubts.

The best way to get her undressed, I decided, was to suggest a swim. There was no wind; the lake lay as still as a dark mirror, and we were both sweating under the blanket. I thought I would be at an advantage were I to be prepared first for my own suggestion. A dress could be slipped off so much quicker, and it wouldn't do to have her wait for me. While I surreptitiously made myself ready, her hand prematurely touched my bare skin. She gasped and jumped to her feet.

In the stillness her thin yell remained incomplete, as if caught doubly short, started too late and broken off too soon. It was an exclamation muffled by mistimed breathing, and upset as much as by surprise as by fright.

She stood stock still for a moment. Then, a last protracted 'oooh' escaped her lips, and she ran off among the trees, her girlish gait made awkward by her busy hands buttoning her blouse.

XI I made my way across the campus to my dormitory. A dull, stalking ache in the loins (the same as I had felt some nights after parking with Susan) made me lean a little forward to ease my steps.

About me, the campus was bathed in uneven colours of turquoise, swaying on the borderline of green and blue, and with the transparency peculiar to nights in warm climates. This verdurous half-light seemed to be playing tricks with the foliage of the trees and the shadows underneath.

Ahead, a tree trunk loomed thick and uneven. As I came closer, I noticed two figures flattened against it. The girl's back was against the bark; the boy was kissing her and pressing his torso against hers, while his legs, slightly apart, were planted stiffly back and away like the hindlegs of a horse or donkey when it urinates.

To avoid passing too close, I veered towards the road bordering the front of the campus. Cars were parked there in all the shady spots. Usually I detoured around them, not wanting to intrude upon the embracing couples. But tonight I didn't bother. The couples, locked together in back seat or in front, sometimes in both, seemed unmindful and indifferent of interruption. They didn't trouble to disengage, no matter who passed by. They claimed no seclusion, nor stealth, nor privacy. Only the intruder was aware of his intrusion.

After I had passed the last car I heard my name called. I thought I recognized Carey's voice. But I wasn't sure, and walked on, unwilling to look back or risk stepping up to the wrong car.

In the hall, I found Mr. Porter alert in his chair as usual, as if expecting new company while trying to hold on to what he already had—the premature odds and ends of the evening, students who were reluctant to call it a day. I skirted Mr. Porter's chair, dutifully answering the inevitable inquiries as to how I was and how I felt. Mr. Porter returned my 'Good night, sir' with an insinuating smile. Everybody remained silent as I crossed the hall and climbed up the stairs to my study.

It was too early to turn in. The air in the small study was still warm and tepid from the day's heat. My dictionary and text-book had been left at the library. I tried to read one of Carey's magazines; but I couldn't shake off the remembrance of the couple pressed against the tree and of the others in parked cars.

How did the other boys make out, I wondered? They all seemed so eager for these dates. But it wasn't human to put up with necking night after night. It would be better if all the girls behaved like nuns. Some of Alex's jibes came back to me and I wondered why I hadn't thought of them before. Now, Alex's views didn't seem critical or vengeful enough.

'My God, man,' Alex had said one evening during that first week, 'what wouldn't I give if you were a girl just arriving from Vienna.'

We were gossiping over a drink after a late show. 'You know, I've seriously thought of contacting one of those *demi-mondaines* or *halb-seidene* I used to know in Vienna. We never really appreciated them. We were too young for that. But right now I would gladly go down on my knees or abstain for a while in penance to show my appreciation of them. No, no, this isn't a joke.'

'What? Abstaining?'

'No, no. Bringing one over. Imagine if I had one of them here, for more or less permanent liaison. Let us say, semi-permanent. I'd be much better off and so probably would she. I'd save myself all this idiotic American ritual that ends nowhere, what with holding hands and necking and wetting my pants in the process. And even *if* and *when* an affair flowers, it's such a bloody let-down. I cannot understand it. I simply *can not* understand it. How a rich country like this, hell-bent on glorifying the American girl and spending millions to advertise her long legs and low neck-line—how it has diseffeminated the female. Or can't feminate her better? It's a disgrace. No country or social system has a right to subject the male to such a farce, called here so *à propos* "sleeping with". Maybe they really *do* just sleep together and dream the better version. Otherwise the men would have been up in arms a long time ago, or should have been. For all I know, it's these damned males who have ruined it all.

'Women are like race-horses. If they aren't trained right they turn into nags. And these bitches have all the making of thoroughbreds. Look at their figures. Fantastic, tops, absolutely tops. Those long legs, incredible. When I first arrived I felt like a revolving door. I couldn't take two steps without turning around. You can laugh all you want. But just wait. It'll take you some time to get wise to certain things over here, and women is one of them.

'And for heaven's sake don't let those girlies at college fool you too much. They're the worst of the lot. May all the saints help me, but sometimes I didn't know whether to take these college cuties across my knee and spank them—or rape them. These juvenile, ever-virginal whores, these miniature bitches, sighing and whispering like vampires in the movies just to work your temperature up. And God, how innocent they look the morning after they have given you a superdose of sexual insomnia.

'They've got a society here for the prevention of cruelty to animals. Why, what those girlies do to the guys at college never happens to beasts. Imagine, imagine, I beg of you. Those fellows let themselves be teased for months. For all I know, for years. Holding hands, necking and kissing day in and day out. My God, the guy gets so hot he can hardly wait to be led to the altar, just to cool off. And then, bingo, all he has dreamed about turns out to be just a one-two-three, as if it were a *Turnverein* or some sort of gymnastic.

44

I sometimes think running around so many years with loaded balls does something to them. Eunuchizes them in a way. Look at the males here, there's something missing, I swear. But *I* should worry. Now, as I said, if only I had enough money to do something about that Viennese proposition. . . .'

I heard Carey's steps out in the hallway. I was in no mood to talk. If Carey turned on the radio with its monotonous jazz I decided I would go to bed, though I dreaded lying awake.

'Hello, Mohamed. Fancy finding you in,' Carey exclaimed as if we hadn't seen each other for days. 'How come so early tonight?'

'It's almost late. Twelve o'clock isn't it?'

'Yes, but I saw you walking back more than an hour ago. I was with Lucille. We called out to you.'

'Yes. My watch was more advanced than I thought. I believed it was eleven already.' I felt the vague discomfort of knowing I had lied for something not worth the lie.

'That's tough. That's sure tough. I only wish *my* watch had been *slow* tonight.' Carey's smile turned to a grin as he waited for a matching remark from me. When I remained silent, Carey tried to sympathize with me. 'It must have spoiled *your* evening, though.'

Carey's knowing smile and insinuating sympathy made me wish my lie had been the truth and that I had been spared meeting Jane. At the same time I wondered what Carey would have done with Jane.

'I knew it was early. That's why I called out to you. I thought you'd come over and say hello,' Carey went on. He always seemed a bit uncomfortable if a pause between us stretched out.

'I didn't want to intrude. I thought . . .'

'Intrude like hell,' Carey corrected me. 'We meant to take in a movie but the bill doesn't change till tomorrow, so we just parked. Hell,' he added with a proud chuckle, 'nobody could intrude on Lucille and me. You know we go steady.'

I didn't know what to say. I lacked the facility for small talk so necessary when talking to someone like Carey. I couldn't think of anything to add but 'Yes', half-agreeing, half-questioning, to give Carey at least the satisfaction of acknowledgement, and a chance to expand if he wanted to.

'You bet. Steady as that.' Carey raised his index finger entwined with another. There was a superfluous note in his boast, since no one, least of all I, cared to contest his claim.

I was not quite sure what precisely 'going steady' meant. Neither was I sure how to interpret Carey's claim. There was a childish righteousness in his mention of Lucille which discouraged any implications or *arrière pensée*. Still, for me to accept outright such a protracted courting as merely Platonic would have been unjust to

45

Carey's maturity and manhood. And Carey was anything but raw or bad-looking. He was taller than I, well-proportioned, with good shoulders, and was easy in his movements. His clean-cut features could have stood an additional line of character and personality here and there, but there was nothing about him to suggest that he must limit himself to being Platonic with a girl. Anyway, having a girl 'as steady as that' ought to make consequences inevitable. Nature would take care of that—even insist on it after a while, on pain of revenge.

'How long is steady?' I asked with a touch of sarcasm.

'Oh, about two and a half years,' Carey said rather proudly, and a moment later, he hastily added, 'But nothing *you'd* think. That's got to wait. With Lucille and me, at least. Until we get married.'

'And when shall you get married?'

Carey seriously paused and calculated. 'Another two or maybe three years. Right after college if I can afford it. If I land the right job, that is.'

'Why did you say nothing *I'd* think ever happens between you and Lucille?' I said, vaguely resentful of Carey's presumption in interpreting my thoughts.

'I don't know what you mean,' Carey said with a puzzled look.

'You spoke of going steady with Lucille and then you said that nothing happened that I would think,' I said. 'What are *you* thinking about all the time you are with Lucille? Please answer.'

'Oh, you got me all wrong, Mohamed. I didn't mean anything special,' Carey said, mollifying me. 'Only, you know . . .' he went on uncertainly. 'Well, sometimes foreigners think the worst right away.'

'And when do you think the worst? Never? Never, for two, three, five years, or longer? And why do you call it the worst?'

'Oh, we think of it sometimes. But it isn't so important to us. We can get along without it.'

'*Faut de mieux?* Or preference?' I interjected.

'What's that? I don't know what you mean. Anyway, you can't look at American girls the same as, well, French girls, if you know what I mean.'

'Yes, unfortunately I know what you mean. But tell me, how many French girls have you ever met?'

'None, I suppose.'

'Then, how dare you talk like this about them?'

'You got me all wrong there,' said Carey, who seemed to be growing uneasy at my sarcasm. 'I didn't mean anything bad like that. All I meant to say was . . . and it may sound a bit old-fashioned . . . that we respect our girls too much to fool around with them. And we like them the way they are. We have a good time with them, and we think they are fun.'

'Clean fun,' I egged him on spitefully, remembering the expression which had struck me the first time I heard it as a strange combination of words, qualifying something morally which had always stood by itself outside moral connotations.

'Sure, it's fun. Clean fun, if you insist.'

'Then your fun, your clean fun as you call it, must require a lot of laundry,' I shot back. 'Your fun very funny,' I taunted.

I half expected Carey to tackle me, but he only stood there, his face slightly confused as if trying to untangle a net. He seemed at a loss how to take my sudden hostility, which he had neither expected nor provoked. And I suddenly felt sorry for making Carey the target of my own rancour and resentment.

'I'm sorry, Carey,' I said quietly. 'I didn't mean to interfere with you and your preferences.' Sentimentality got the better of me and I added, 'Perhaps it is better your way.'


XII   From the third story window of the study I shared with Carey I stood one morning watching the campus below, postponing again and again the moment of going back to my desk and dictionary, of turning to face the small quadrangular room furnished in standard sets of twos—two identical desks, chairs, commodes, beds—and Carey's favourite baseball banner on the wall alongside the ever-smiling portrait of Lucille.

I prodded myself to get back to my desk. But the English language no longer enticed me as it had at the beginning, when the mastering of each new word and phrase was a reward in itself. Now, the mere thought of those pages in the text-book, so replete with words I still couldn't precisely understand unless I turned for help to the dictionary, drained me of initiative. I was weary of constantly preaching to myself that there was no short cut to the language, that I must stumble and chew over words with their synonyms and antonyms till their meanings were clear and comprehensible.

But why make it all so difficult and laborious, I nagged at myself? Other foreigners got along well enough with their broken English, which everyone thought so charming. They had no trouble mixing on the campus. Yet I could not bring myself to want to be like them. I detested their precipitate, ingratiating ways of complying with everything American, their thick accents and incongruous gesturings which magnified and distorted all they said and did. I winced at their hasty, idiotic yess, yesses, pleaze, pleazes, sank you, sank yous; and their beootifulls and marrvelooses. They were always so anxious to offer a cigarette and light from their silly *etuis* and lighters. And all of them were so starved for company, so anxious to talk to somebody, that any casual question about their homeland

47

set them off on an emotional recital. They never realized that the question might as well have been about the weather for all the listener cared.

What made foreigners here act like that, I kept asking myself? In any European country, they would have refused to pay such unconditional tributes of praise and flattery to local ways. Here they behaved like needy house guests or poor relatives at a rich man's home. What had happened to their self-respect, character and pride? I understood Janci's position; he was a refugee with nowhere to go. And Salvador, too, who had escaped from a revolution. But the half dozen others needn't make such pathetic clowns of themselves.

I had become so conscious of their ways that I could spot my fellow foreigners on the campus from afar—by the way they walked, by their movements, gestures, even by their slacks which never managed to look like real slacks but like suit trousers with the coat missing. Whenever I overheard them mouth their accursed 'yess, yess, I love it so much here—it's marvellous,' I hastened my steps for fear of being identified with their noxious concurrence and praises. I wouldn't stand for it, if I were an American, I sometimes thought. And yet I often had the impression that Americans courted such flattery, and even liked hearing it, insisted on hearing it. In Persia I would have turned my back on any visitor who tried to please me with such cheery, blatant compliments, though my own country certainly could have used a little flattery.

I turned back and sat down at the desk. But the pages of the text-book, of the dictionary and of my folder crammed with notes—the whole English language—were barren of that beauty and purpose which had driven me on for so many months, daily for so many hours; a labour rewarded by those thrilling moments when a sentence or two, sometimes even a whole paragraph, vaulted into comprehension without the aid of the dictionary.

The cheery words outside my window mocked the printed words in front of me, coupling irony with their challenge. Were I to command all the words in the dictionary, master all the rules of grammar, memorize all my transcribed and translated notes and phrases, would I then speak really the same language they used on the campus? Their way of speaking seemed as remote and alien to the language I was trying to learn at my desk as the words in the book were from my native tongue. And even were I ever to command the language, would I ever want to speak in that smooth and pseudo-intimate way of theirs which seemed for ever attuned to good-will and good cheer, always so warm and sincere, as if rinsed free of all character, temperament and discord?

48

**XIII** 'Why, look you now, how unworthy a thing you make of me! You would play upon me; you would seem to know my stops; you would pluck out the heart of my mystery; you would sound me from my lowest note to the top of my compass; ... 'Sblood, do you think I am easier to be played upon than a pipe? Call me what instrument you will, though you can fret me, you cannot play upon me.'

Hamlet to Guildenstern, Act III, Scene 2

'Hiya, Mohamed! How's everything?' Carey called out with a big smile as he entered the room. He dumped his books on his desk and looked at me as if expecting momentous news. We always met on such a spirited note. But unless I had some English colloquialisms or slang words on hand for him to explain, we looked at each other without knowing what to say next. We both would have liked to talk on, I think; I am sure I would have liked to. But I still lacked a facility for small talk, and he never seemed eager enough about any subject to let the conversation take a serious turn.

Carey turned to the mirror and started combing his hair. When he caught me watching him dent a wave in his hair with the back of the comb, he grinned. Then he turned around and, seeing the dictionary in front of me, he shook his head in mock seriousness. 'How you can stand to pore over that dictionary every day for hours on end beats me!' he said. 'I wouldn't ever open the damned thing if I didn't have to pass English. Only don't overdo it, for Christ's sake. Take it easy, take it easy, boy. You'll catch on fast enough.' And then, anticipating my protest, he added, 'Sooner than you think, I bet.'

'Perhaps,' I said, 'if catching on were only limited to me. But you must understand, it includes many others.'

'I don't get it.'

'How many of my countrymen—how many Persians—do you think the students at Watson College will ever meet in their lives?'

'Not many, I guess.'

'How many Persians do *you* think you will meet?'

'A lot, if I come to visit you in your home town. Got you there, Mohamed. Maybe I could sell them some insurance on the side.'

'You certainly would meet many, but in my country people don't own enough things to worry about insuring them. So I do not think you will find many customers there ... What is that other word for them?'

'Word for what?'

'For "customers". What you always use.'

'Oh, "suckers", you mean. You sure like that word, eh?'

'Yes. It expresses a very frank and honest evaluation.'

49

Carey laughed. 'You pick up the darndest words,' he said, 'and give them the darndest twists.'

'Yes, but to return. You probably will not meet another Persian after me. Now, if I learn English fast, you will think I am intelligent, yes? And if I don't learn English fast, you and everyone else will think that Persians are stupid.'

'Come on, Mohamed. We aren't that hard on foreigners, are we?'

'No. You are all very kind. Perhaps too kind. But you admit that if I learn English fast, you will think I am intelligent?'

'Well, maybe you've got something there,' Carey agreed. 'Any new words today? Anything you want explained? Did you get straightened out on "hardly" and "almost"?'

'Yes, I almost cleared it up,' I said. '*Almost*—that's right, isn't it?'

'What was that? . . . Oh. Oh, yes. "Almost cleared it up". So you got it?'

'I think so.'

'That's fine. Pretty soon you'll have to explain things to me.'

Carey turned to his desk, but then, as if remembering something, he turned back to me. 'Mohamed,' he said in an altered tone, 'I meant to tell you about this.' He picked up a book from his desk and held it towards me, cheerfully but also with a certain embarrassment. 'You ought to read this book. It's a great book—everybody says so. And easy to read.'

It was the first time he had mentioned any reading matter to me.

'Try it,' he said. 'You can get through it easy. It's good style and all that, and maybe it'll give you a few hints that'll help you catch on to the way we do things over here. I can't help noticing sometimes on campus that you have a little trouble.'

I took the book, and Carey said, 'Keep it as long as you want to. I've already read it through. The only book I ever read more than once. But, by golly, it's worth it.' He picked up his baseball glove and cap from the dresser and went out, calling, 'See you later.'

Soon the rhythmic thud of a baseball hitting leather punctuated the silence of the room. Still holding Carey's book, I walked over to the window. Outside, Carey and another fanatic, both equipped with their outsize leather gloves and sporting their special caps, were throwing the white leather ball at each other with exaggerated gestures of preparation and concentration. Back and forth, back and forth. At each relay, the thrower would lean back his torso and lift his left leg as high as he could while initiating the throw with his right arm bent far back. The preliminary movements were always so elaborate that the actual throws disappointed me. However violently the ball was thrown, the other fellow never seemed worse off for it. The catcher calmly lifted his arm, elbow up, palm out, like a bored policeman signalling traffic, and waited for the ball to hit his glove. The thrower, in spite of all his preparation and contortion, seemed to toss the ball exactly where the catcher wanted it. I watched this curious exchange for some time, expecting, as I always did, that their monotonous heave and return would be a warm-up, a prelude to some exciting game in which others would soon join, tossing and catching other balls. An hour later, they were still at it.

That same evening, after dinner, bucked up by Carey's assurance that I was ready to read a whole book in English, I sat down to try it, with the dictionary beside me. I couldn't help being excited. Until now, I had laboured only over single paragraphs and pages— at the most a short story. The large type, the wide margins, and the short paragraphs of Carey's book made me feel bold and confident. It seemed to be conniving with me, enabling me to claim credit for reading full pages, though none of them contained more than half the words on an ordinary page. But the title still puzzled me. I turned back to the front cover and read it again. At first glance, I had thought the book was probably a novel or a saga about friend-ship—perhaps that of famous men. My eyes were caught by the small print of the dust jacket.

'The most popular work of non-fiction in our time. . . . Every page a treasure of wisdom,' I read. 'The making of friends is truly the deepest concern of the world today . . . This is not just a book or a theory. It is a whole new way of life . . . This book will show you how to make lifelong friends, help you be popular, increase your earning power. . . .'

These puzzling statements aroused no reaction in me, except the instinctive certainty that friendship defied method.

I started on the first chapter. Exhilarated by the simple words and ready comprehensibility of the first paragraphs, I read on and on—at first still puzzled, then unbelieving, and, towards the end, sensing a kind of horror I had never known before.

The next morning, I pretended to be asleep when Carey got up and dressed. I didn't feel like talking, and I didn't know what to say if he should ask me about the book. I managed to avoid him the rest of the morning, but he overtook me as I was walking to my last class.

'What do you know, Mohamed?'

'Nothing.'

'Did you get a chance to start on that book?'

'Yes. I finished it.'

'What! Already? Well, what do you think of it? Great book, isn't it?'

'No,' I said curtly.

Carey's face fell. 'You don't think so? . . . I'm sorry.'

'Why are *you* sorry?'

'Well, I thought you'd like it. Everybody else does.'

'That is no reason I like it, too.'

Carey hesitated. 'Well, anyway, it's selling like hot cakes.'

We walked on together, and after a minute or two he said, 'Even if you don't like it, what do you think of it?'

'*Think* of it! There is nothing to think. How can a man think if he is continually insulted? This writer writes of people as imbeciles, cretins. Here'—I pointed to my head—'and here'—I pointed to my heart. 'Even an imbecile cannot be fooled so easily with smiles and flattery, like this book says. And you cannot be or have true friends by smiling and always being nice to everybody. No, you like one better or worse than the other, and smile doesn't make different.'

'What's wrong with liking everybody?' Carey asked. 'You can, like the book says, if you only—'

'Everything. You *cannot* like everybody, exception you are—or want to be—like Christ. And it is not honourable to *pretend* you like everybody.'

'Not honourable?' Carey repeated, surprised, as if I had introduced an irrelevant factor.

I stopped short and looked at him. Could it be that he and I had not been speaking about the same thing, that it was all a mistake? Perhaps I had misunderstood the book, though it was in such simple English. Perhaps the book was a joke, a parody too subtle for me.

'The book doesn't mean what you think—whatever *that* is,' Carey said. 'It just tells about human nature. And human nature is the same in all of us. We all want to be liked, to make others like us, and—'

'Please excuse me from it,' I said, and looked away.

'Okay, okay. Even if you think you're different, a lot of people don't think *they* are. And—well—a smile does go a long way.'

'Yes, from ear to ear.'

'Well, what's wrong with being nice?' Carey said impatiently. 'Try it yourself some time. Also, it's easier. A smile uses only a tenth of the facial muscles a frown does. That's a fact. Try it and see.'

Suddenly, I was sure Carey was joking. I remembered the reference to facial muscles in the book. I was on the verge of laughing, but Carey's earnest air prevented me.

'Look, Mohamed,' he said, stopping and facing me. 'I'm telling you this for your own good. It would help you to get along better in this country. You're too reserved, and some people think you're stuck-up. If you knew what a smile does to your face, you'd smile more often. You look like a different person.'

'Please excuse me if I don't feel like smiling.'

'It's not what you feel, but what you make others feel that matters. Do you like dogs?'

'I don't know. I never had one.'

'Well, a lot of people do. And do you know why? Because you pat a dog, act nice to him, and he'll jump up and wag his tail. It's—'

I interrupted him with a snort of contempt. 'If the dog knew you cheat like that, he would do something else.'

Carey ignored my interruption. 'It's the same with people. You are friendly and smile, and they will smile back. But it's got to be sincere. A phoney smile won't do. You think I'm kidding, but a friendly approach can be worth everything.'

'But if I smile when I don't feel a smile,' I said, 'I feel worse than before. I feel terrible.'

'Just try it, even if you do feel bad at first. *Force* yourself to smile. Practise smiling at home in front of a mirror. Smile to yourself, whistle a tune, or hum. Make as if you were happy. And you'll be surprised. After a while, you'll really feel a bit happier. And then watch how it works on others. Here, I'll give you a demonstration. Watch.'

Mr. Porter was coming down the path. Carey, his voice brimming with interest and good will, called out, 'Hello, Mr. Porter.'

'Oh?' Mr. Porter said. 'Hello, Carey.' His pinched face expanded, as if he had tasted something sweet.

'How are you, Mr. Porter?'

'Fine, fine, thank you. And how are you?'

Mr. Porter slowed almost to a halt, as if hoping for conversation. Carey called back over his shoulder, 'See you later, Mr. Porter.' Then, turning to me with a grin of satisfaction, he said, 'See what being friendly does to people?'

'But that doesn't mean anything,' I protested. 'He is an old man with nothing to do all day. Of course he is glad if somebody notices him.'

'Okay, let's try it again,' Carey said, nodding towards an oncoming figure. It was Johann, a Dutch exchange student. His stiff, unrelaxed stride marked him as a foreigner. Though it was a warm day and his face was flushed with perspiration, he wore a coat and tie. He would have looked even more uncomfortable without them.

'Hiya, Joe!' Carey shouted amiably. 'How are you? What's up? What's the hurry?'

Johann's broad blond face showed for a moment that he was caught in the dilemma of having to answer an unrehearsed question. Then his features relaxed into a childish and grateful smile. 'I am very well, thank you. I hope you are. I am now on my way to the library.'

'Glad to hear it, Joe. Keep up the good work. See you later!'

As we walked on, Carey turned to me, expecting me to concede the point.

'That doesn't count, either,' I said impatiently. 'Johann is a

53

foreigner. Foreigners smile because they think it is polite. They are always glad when they can make conversation. They are lonely and so they—' I stopped because Carey was nudging me and indicating the senior-class president, who was sauntering up the path towards us.

'Hello there, Mort. How's the boy?'

'Hiya, Carey. How's tricks?'

Mort's greeting outdid Carey's in enthusiasm and heartiness. He went on without stopping.

'This is a farce!' I said. 'Everybody here smiles like that. Whatever you say and however you say it, they will all smile. I make a bet. The next one will smile, too, even if you don't.'

'Okay, it's a bet. A pack of cigarettes.'

'No, a carton,' I whispered as the figure of another student approached us.

Carey waited until the advancing figure was almost abreast before he looked up. 'Hello,' he said indifferently, and turned away immediately.

The other student's face, already geared for a greater display of friendliness, relapsed into indifference also. 'Hello, Carey,' he said. There was no smile.

'See? You lost a carton.' Carey chuckled.

'But you didn't call him by his name, as you did the others,' I said.

'But that's just it!' Carey said. 'Use the name along with the smile. It's part of the game. Watch now.'

I felt like rushing up to the oncoming student and warning him not to be taken in by Carey's gesture of simulated friendship. I seemed to have become involved in a deceitful conspiracy. I was being instrumental in foisting a cheap trick on an unsuspecting classmate. Though I knew him only by sight, at that moment he meant more to me than anyone else I knew. Helplessly, I watched the scene played out. In response to Carey's cheerful greeting, the features of the approaching student sparked up in a mixture of feigned surprise, joy, and welcome. The change began with a slight tilt of the head. Then the body straightened up, as if to intensify the facial response. Then, features and voice in perfect accord, he returned the smile and the greeting, rounding them off with 'See you later, Carey.'

Just then, a student overtook us from behind and called out to Carey. When Carey turned around to answer, I was struck by what I saw on his face. It had brightened, just like the faces of those he had spoken to. I felt a moment of triumph at seeing him tricked as he had tricked others. But then I realized how much Carey's expression—so bright with comradeship—resembled the expression he met me with when he entered our room, and suddenly

54

the past months at Watson reeled through my mind. The welcoming gestures I had received seemed no longer spontaneous, but staged. Every word and smile and act of kindness now took on a note of falseness. I wanted desperately to recover one glance, one phrase, one word meant only for me.

We were a few steps from the building that housed our class-room. 'Please wait a moment,' I said to Carey. He stopped. I said, 'Please try it once more for me.'

Carey wavered. 'It's getting late. We better—'

'Yes, yes,' I hastily agreed. 'But please try it once more for me.'

'Okay,' he said, amused. 'If it'll convince you.'

We stood waiting near the door. A late-comer to class was hurry-ing up the gravel path. This time, I did not have the urge to rush up and warn the approaching figure. Any interference from me, even my wishing to interfere, now would have been cowardice. The spectacle must run its course to yield the truth. But in my heart I repeated a mute plea—a plea so fervent that it fell just short of praying, because it was addressed not to God but to another human being. It was up to the approaching boy to redeem for me those who had failed me and those who would fail me in the future. It was up to him whether or not I would ever again trust a friendly face or smile. And when he came abreast of us, I felt the same compassionate terror I had experienced years before when I was reading another book—about how, in the Middle Ages, children sold in bondage had certain facial muscles operated upon, so as to supply for ever a smiling countenance to the master.

When the moment was over, Carey wanted to go in to class, but I held him back. 'Once more,' I pleaded, 'once more.'

'Nuts to you, boy.'

In the doorway he stopped, waiting for me. 'Hurry up,' he said. His voice was kind and cheerful, and his boyish, good-humoured expression so innocent of any trace of evil or guilt that, instead of shouting the insults that were rising to my lips, I silently followed him in.


XIV It was the last day of school. The graduation ceremony was over. All over the country similar ceremonies had taken place this morning, or on other mornings this month, with students dressed up in caps and gowns and one student getting a prize for being 'best all round' and giving his rousing valedictory, as Herb had done here, in praise of America, democracy and virtue. On other campuses, too, there had been fund-raising campaigns like Watson's to raise new millions for more dormitories and more classrooms, for bigger and better libraries and football fields—all aimed at making each college the 'top' in its part of the country.

With a load of books under each arm I backed my way through the swinging doors of the library. Except for the librarian the place was empty. Today, instead of merely moving her lips, she spoke the words of greeting out loud.

'It's hot today, isn't it?' she said as I put the books on the counter.

I knew I should say 'Yes, it is hot today,' but her inquiry had such a personal note that I felt the standard reply inadequate.

'No, it really isn't so hot,' I said, wiping the perspiration off my face. 'It's the books. I changed dormitories, and now I have to carry the books all the way across campus.' I didn't tell her that I had hurried all the way to avoid farewells.

This was graduation day and probably my last chance, except for exchanging good-byes, to talk to anyone. I was anxious that she go on talking so that I might feel prompted to speak up, perhaps even to confide in her why I had moved to the edge of the campus and why I hadn't been able to bear rooming with Carey any longer.

'Do you like it better way over there?' the librarian asked, as kindly as she had been about the heat.

I was suddenly ashamed of the eager, expectant way I had been waiting for her to speak. And instead of telling her how I had really felt these past six weeks, how every time I crossed the campus I had felt as lonely and set apart as an intruder, an exile revisiting what had been a happy, new-found home foolishly forfeited . . . instead of all that, I merely replied, 'Yes, I like it better, much better.'

'I'm glad you do,' she said. And after making sure I had finished speaking, she deftly pulled out a reference card and began checking off my books. When she had finished the first pile, I pushed the other in front of her. 'My, did you read them all?' she exclaimed with polite surprise.

'Yes,' I said, avoiding her eyes. I wished I had been spared the necessity of lying to her. I hadn't read a single book. I had borrowed them week after week as if carrying on a bluff without accounting to myself why.

It was while watching her that I suddenly realized that she was neither as old nor as homely as she made herself out to be, confined as she was to her enclosure and surrounded by her filing cards, her over-sharpened pencils, her telephone and all the other library paraphernalia. It was hard to tell what she might look like in a different set-up, particularly if she would take off those glasses. She always looked so neat, proper and constant, as some homely, middle-aged women do who make fetishes of such virtues. She couldn't be more than thirty-five, and her auburn hair might easily draw a second glance had it not been done up so modestly with the ends cut short as if to prevent them from curling.

I felt a surge of pity for the librarian and her lot, which wasted her and her kindness on unappreciative youngsters like myself. At the same time, she reminded me somehow of those elderly ladies in Lakeville who had invited me along with the other foreign students to their afternoon teas. With those ladies, too, there had been moments when I was overcome by the kindness held out to me. But after several visits, their hospitality had tasted as diluted as the weak tea and as insipid as the store-bought cookies they served. Every time I was urged to come again I reproached myself for not being properly grateful. Yet when I strained towards any such feeling, I recoiled at my own hypocrisy. Perhaps they all meant well— if meaning well for an afternoon over a cup of tea with young strangers who were invariably asked to recite how they liked America can be said to fill the measure.

'We haven't seen much of you lately,' the librarian said.

'No, I have been loffing,' I said.

'It's "loafing", not "loffing". I hope you don't mind my correcting you.'

'Oh no, please. I am grateful. *Loafing*,' I repeated, trying to imitate her inflexion. 'This is my last chance to find correction in America.'

'Why? Won't you be back with us next year?'

'No. I graduated this morning.'

'You did!' she exclaimed, matching her voice by opening her eyes wide.

'Yes.'

'Congratulations.'

'Thank you, but there is really nothing to congratulate. I studied most of the courses in Vienna. Unless you want to congratulate me on my English.'

'I do. I certainly do. You seem to have done very well indeed. So, that is why you dropped everything lately, and preferred to loaf?'

'Perhaps . . .' I smiled evasively.

I wondered what she would think of me were I to tell her what had really kept me away from the library: that Doris, the girl I had met on the train, had sent me a letter a month ago saying she would be coming through Lakeville on a business trip . . .

When I had telephoned Doris at her hotel to make a dinner date, I made a point of finding out her room number. Then, arriving half an hour early, I watched the clerk from the street entrance until I saw him leave his desk, and then raced up the stairs and knocked at her door.

'Who is it?' Doris asked through the door.

'It would be correct to say "It is I", but since my English is even better than correct, I say "It's me, Mohamed."'

'Aren't you early?' she reproached me, as she opened the door. 'It isn't even seven yet.'

'No, but after eight months I couldn't wait one more minute to see you.'

'But why didn't you ring me up from the lobby?'

'I wanted to surprise you. Have I?'

'I guess you did, but I haven't finished dressing yet. I was just going to . . .'

'I am glad you haven't,' I interrupted. 'So I shall have the pleasure of waiting, imagining you making yourself beautiful for me.'

'You certainly haven't changed,' she laughed, and I knew the danger of her asking me to wait downstairs had passed.

'I certainly haven't changed. I didn't meet anyone who could change me. But with you, it's different. I am ready to change into anything—if you teach me.'

'Go on,' she laughed freely now. 'You're giving me that old line of yours.'

'Please remember we were interrupted on the train when you descended. So, we must continue . . .'

'Don't tell me you haven't followed it up with anybody at college?'

'With nobody. Nobody deserved it. I reserved it for you.'

'And you expect me to believe all that? You forget, I went to college myself.'

'Then, you should believe me even more. . . .' I waited to see if she caught my implication.

'I don't get it.' She shook her head. 'Look, I won't be a minute. Just make yourself comfortable.'

She was about to disappear into the bathroom when I asked her for a glass of water.

'Why, of course.' She brought me the glass of water. 'Is that all you drink?'

'It wouldn't be polite to invite myself for something better.'

She looked at me the way people often did when they didn't know whether I were joking or merely being rude. 'Would you care for a drink?' she said.

'I already have one.' I lifted the glass of water.

'No. I mean a real one.'

'If you would be kind enough.'

'Well, what'll you have? Will Scotch do?'

I nodded.

She fetched another glass from the bathroom and then, to my surprise, produced a bottle from her suitcase.

'I hope you don't mind the glass,' she said, pouring out the drink. 'But some hotels are funny about visitors.'

I told her about college, mostly by way of jokes, and when she offered me another drink, I eagerly accepted.

I knew how to hold my beer or wine; but whisky was something else again. I marvelled at the way Doris was gulping down the stuff. At the fourth drink, I knew that I had to be careful. I was still talking on when during a pause Doris spoke up.

'Might as well start for dinner,' she said.

'Are you so very hungry?' I felt awkward getting up on my feet.

'I wouldn't mind having dinner in a nice, cool place. What about you? Aren't you hungry?'

'I am hungry, very much. . . .'

When I kissed her, something in me shrank back from the whisky odour mixed with the sticky sweet of her rouged lips. But I was too eager to mind. And too busy helping her unsnap her dress, which her unsteady fingers couldn't quite manage. Once her body touched the bed, she seemed no longer to care; her stockings were still on and some bracelet or necklace of hers was jutting pain into my flesh. I hadn't anticipated such swift and complete compliance, but now that she had complied, I expected some response.

Doris just lay there, almost motionless, her mouth half open, a sickly tired line hovering about her lips, and for a moment I wondered if I shouldn't have watched her drinking as much as my own. And what a pity it all was to make love in a muggy hotel room with a passive body smelling of drink.

The poor librarian would have been shocked out of her wits, I thought, if I told her any of that. If she would take off her glasses and change her hair-do a little, dash up her make-up a bit, particularly about the lips, she might look a little like Doris. Then, perhaps. . . .

'Perhaps,' I repeated aloud. 'Perhaps, I would have loafed even without knowing I would graduate. I am not really as studious as you think.' I was glad I could confess that much to her. 'But I wanted to learn English very much. It is a beautiful language.'

'It certainly is. And you did very well indeed.'

'Thank you.'

'Now that you are graduated, I suppose you'll be going on to a university to get your master's.'

'Oh yes. I am going back to the University of Vienna.'

'You would rather go *back*?' Her voice and eyes signalled more than disapproval, almost shock, as if I had said something rude. 'I'm sorry to hear that.'

She spoke with such regret, almost sorrow, that for a moment I wanted to tell her, to try to tell her how I really felt about this country, or rather about the little I had seen of it at Watson; how I sometimes longed to stay on and see more of it, and yet shrank from the idea. But when I looked into her eyes, I merely said, 'I must go back to Vienna to finish my studies...' I stopped uncertainly.

She gave me the standard message I had heard so many times this last day of college.

'I hope you liked it here.'

'Yes, thank you.'

'I wish you the very best of luck.'

'Thank you, thank you.'

'Good-bye.'

I left.

XV  Outside, the campus was still alive with students, their parents, and friends who had attended the morning's graduation ceremony. Some students were still in cap and gown. Their black robes and flat, fringed mortars seemed somehow as remote from reality and as theatrical as the page-boy costume I remembered wearing once in Vienna in a ceremony commemorating the founding of the school by the Empress Maria Theresa in the eighteenth century.

I made my way back to my dormitory, skirting the groups of students, visitors and families. I still had to pack.

Alone in my room, I collected in my mind all the stories I would have to tell Alex in New York. And back in Vienna they would think I had made it all up.

Some cars were already being loaded with luggage by the first students to be off. There was a train for New York at two. There had been one at eleven which I had planned to take in order to skip all the graduation ceremony and leave-taking. But I hadn't had the money. I had foolishly cashed in my return ticket when I found myself overspending my allowance. I had written father for more funds, but the passage money I had asked him to wire hadn't come yet. It was overdue by more than a week.

After I'd finished packing I called at the post office for the mail. There was no letter nor telegram from father, so I hung around the campus at a loss what do do with myself. I found myself shaking hands with students I barely knew. The parting words of those who stopped to say good-bye were as impersonal and as cheerful as their daily greetings had been. By the time it got dark I was alone on the campus. After finding the doors to the beanery locked at dinner time, I moved my baggage from the dormitory to

60

a hotel in Lakeville. I still had fifty dollars, so I wasn't unduly worried.

The next morning and each morning after I went to the post office, confident that the bank draft would be there. I knew vaguely that new foreign exchange regulations had been introduced in Persia, but I never imagined that father might not be able to get around them and that I might be left stranded without money for any length of time. I postponed writing Alex because I was over-conscious of not having written him throughout my stay at Watson. When I did write him I described my dilemma as if it were a joke that could only happen in America. There was no reply from Alex. I was too proud to write again and confess that I was down to my last ten dollars. I moved out of the hotel and took refuge on the back porch of the beach house at the far end of the campus, sub-sisting on oranges which were everywhere free for the picking, and a daily loaf of bread. The daily disappointment at the post office and the daily expenditure of one more coin for bread gradually forced me to realize that something had to be done, and not by my father but by me.

# PART II

---

I The idea of finding a job didn't occur to me at first. I had been brought up to regard money as a sort of stream that dried up towards the end of each month, but flowed again at the beginning of the next, when father's cheque arrived. Manual labour I would have thought beneath me. But now, reduced to my last three dollars, I began with a mixture of queasiness and fascination to watch delivery boys, waiters, attendants at filling stations, movie ushers, clerks behind counters—anyone with a job that required no previous experience. By one of those convenient twists of the imagination, I was suddenly able to regard those jobs not as menial and therefore degrading, but as so many opportunities to masquerade—the same as I had done when attending masqued balls in Vienna disguised as a chimney sweep or a valet. Still, I couldn't bring myself to apply for a job as a waiter or delivery boy in Lakeville, where someone might recognize me! The only solution was to hitch-hike to another town. I left my luggage, except for a small valise, at the depot, and instructed the post office to hold my mail until further notice.

The first time I raised my thumb to get a ride I felt I had compromised my pride by this pleading gesture. I was comforted when the people who picked me up didn't hold it against me. And along with this assurance, I experienced for the first time the freedom of anonymity; that total liberty which knows no tie, is subject to no claim—my fate the concern of no one and with no identity other than my face.

An elderly man picked me up near St. Augustine and took me on as an usher in a movie house after listening to my story. I might have stuck to the job and waited for father's bank draft to reach me there, if I hadn't been fired after two weeks on the complaint of a woman customer for whom I refused to fetch some popcorn during the show.

There was still no word from father and I decided to carry on. I had nothing to lose by hiking on. The University in Vienna wouldn't open till autumn and I might as well spend the summer in America as in Europe. Since I wanted some sort of destination, I began to nurse an ambition which attracts many foreigners once they realize that America is rather a continent than just another country—the ambition to cover the country from coast to coast and face the Pacific Ocean.

I didn't do too badly on the road, though there were times when I had to go without food or pass the night at a railway station or bus depot pretending to be a passenger. Lack of food and sleep didn't worry me. I couldn't imagine myself starving or buckling under with exhaustion. My endurance, I felt, was unlimited; and adversity would be as transitory as hunger or fatigue.

By the time I crossed the Louisiana border into Texas, I had learned, after a month on the road, that to hang around any place where loading and unloading were done usually resulted in some work or a ride; that to wash and polish somebody's car was always good for fifty cents or a dollar; and that I must never admit I was a transient when there was a chance for a job. I knew I ought not to hesitate, in a pinch, to walk up to private houses and inquire for odd jobs, but I couldn't bring myself to do this. Instead, I sold, one after the other, for a small fraction of their worth, my Leica, my silver cigarette case and my wrist-watch.

I wrote to the post office in Lakeville a few days before I got to Houston, Texas, asking them to forward my mail to me there, care of General Delivery. In Houston, waiting for me, was a letter from my father saying that he had made an application for a foreign exchange transfer but it would be some time before it was approved. He advised me to try to borrow my return fare—at least as far as Europe, where friends or relatives would extend credit to me.

I couldn't think of anyone in the whole of the United States from whom I could borrow even a dollar. I sold my last valuable—a pair of gold cuff-links that had been a gift from my mother—for fourteen dollars. I knew I ought to turn back and hitch-hike to New York, where I would be more likely to meet a Persian to whom father's name or standing might be familiar and who would therefore be willing to risk a loan; but I hated to pass up my one chance of seeing America, so I decided to keep on.

The next afternoon, on the outskirts of a small town, I got into conversation with another hitch-hiker as we stood together at the side of the road and signalled to the cars that passed. He told me his name was Jim and that he had quit his job as a short-order cook in Philadelphia and was on his way back home to El Paso.

To meet a cook, though a novel experience, lost much of its appeal once I understood that Jim's calling was not a makeshift, but his profession. If Jim had conformed in any respect to my notion of a cook, I probably would have gone my own way. But Jim neither smelled of food, nor looked greasy. He was shaved and his blond hair neatly combed. With his frank, boyish face and spruce appearance he might easily have mixed on the Watson campus. What I

64

couldn't understand was how a fellow with Jim's appearance and self-confidence could put up with such a common profession in a country where all jobs seemed open to a man's ambition—even though he might succeed in opening up a restaurant of his own some day and become a millionaire into the bargain.

No driver stopped for us, and when it began to get dark, Jim suggested we spend the night in the town and take to the rails in the morning. Hitch-hiking, he convinced me, was too slow and uncertain. Riding the rails would get us to El Paso faster, and cheaper, too, since it saved on meals.

I was willing to try anything new in America. Novelty was its own reward. But I shrank from drifting into a situation in which I would be mistaken for a bum. It was not fear of the railroad cops Jim mentioned that made me wary of hitting the rails. It was an unwillingness to compromise my identity. On the road I could maintain a certain form, a certain etiquette towards others and myself. I shaved every day, cleaned my two-toned shoes and kept my slacks spotless. I felt I could never be mistaken for other than what I was. On the road, I also had the freedom of getting off anywhere I pleased. Riding the rails would deprive me of all this. I pictured myself caught in a box car, covered with soot, my shirt and trousers soiled and bedraggled, confronting a patrolman who might take me for a bum or worse.

What swayed me in the end to fall in with Jim's plan was the prospect of having him for company. Jim was the first companion I had found on the road. Those brief encounters with people who gave me rides didn't count, though I met each new driver with anticipation. I never asked myself what I expected of the people who gave me rides, yet I always felt a little disappointed when the ride was over, clinging to the fancy that if the ride had lasted a while longer we wouldn't have parted such strangers after all.

II Early morning the next day Jim and I reconnoitred the isolated freight yard. There was a long train there, which Jim said would probably be going out that morning. We hid behind an abandoned shed from where we could make a run for the train. Jim said we should not get on yet, as the cops sometimes inspected a train just before it pulled out.

No puff of air stirred the heat. The prairie about us was barren save for spots of seared shrubbery. Except for the double lines of rail that thinned and vanished in the distance, this was the first landscape I had seen in America that seemed as primitive as it must have been when the pioneers passed through. Yet, except for moments when trickles of sweat or some noise from the nearby yard made me conscious of my discomfort, I felt strangely contented, unmolested by regrets for being where I was or by any ambition to be anywhere else.

My only diversion was the sound of Jim's curses, which damned with impartial malediction the hard cinders we were sitting on, the implacable heat and the freight train which showed no signs of pulling out.

Though I couldn't quite suppress my awareness that Jim was a short-order cook, my finicky disapproval of him was negated by the wonder that such a fellow as Jim could take it into his head to quit his job 'back east' in Philadelphia and cross a distance the size of Europe for no better reason than 'liking it better out west where I was brought up'. I envied Jim for taking such scope and freedom for granted. And if Jim's horizon did not reach beyond the poles of cooking one hamburger 'back east' and another 'out west' in Texas, still, in his own way, he was following that rainbow of freedom, opportunity and chance which arched over a continent—a rainbow at the end of which so many had really found their pot of gold.

Jim's four-letter curses, though juicy and apt, added to the monotony of our waiting. But I didn't mind. The mere presence of someone alongside me made me strangely content. With a companion, I felt, nothing could happen for the worse, only for the better. I listened to Jim's outbursts, a little ashamed of my condescension but grateful for his company.

A shrill whistle and the clunking of buffers brought us to our feet. Puffs of steam rose and vanished in the air. The laboured revolutions of the engine wheels were taken up by the freight car wheels as they creaked into motion, two by two. When the engine came into view around the bend, I expected Jim to take the lead, to guide me. But Jim remained hunched behind the shed as if afraid of being caught. The engine had already passed the curve nearest us; so had the first cars.

'We must run,' I said.

'If we just don't get seen . . .'

There was no time left for hesitating or planning. Jim started to run, whispering back to me, 'Once we get there, keep close to the cars.'

I couldn't hear what Jim said next. We were running as fast as we could. When Jim was alongside the moving train he tried the door of each car as it passed. None of the sliding doors would give. He stepped back to see how many cars were still to pass.

'If we can't do better with the others, we'd better jump the open car that's coming up. You take front, I take back.' When the open flat-car was alongside, I threw my valise into it and pulled myself over the side-board. As I leaned over to climb in, my breath was

66

blocked by the heavy steam-like heat within. I jumped inside and instantly straightened up for breath, but Jim, from the other end, motioned me to duck.

I almost lost my balance as I crouched on the long metal pipes with which the car was half filled, for ever shifting and clattering. Jim's figure at the other end, like a puppet's, was shaking and jerking in a thousand tiny moves in rhythm with the vibrations of the pipes he was squatting on.

I managed to reach Jim and sat down on my suitcase next to him. Jim poked me in the ribs and with a short, secretive uplift of the chin drew my attention to a corner at the other end of the car. Two silent figures sat there with knees pulled up, back to back, as if hiding something behind and between them. What surprised me was not to find other rail riders in the flat-car, but to find they were Negroes.

Jim's awareness of them—and theirs of Jim—made me conscious of an element of tension, that peculiar absence of ease which occurred whenever whites and Negroes came together accidentally, even though it might be no more than passing each other in the street.

The two Negroes looked at me; then, their eyes veered back to Jim as if relegating me to second place. They whispered briefly with each other. Then their shoulders separated, and the legs of a third figure pushed and stretched forward between them. The third figure was a girl. Her hair was cut short, almost like the boys', and like them she was clad in faded nondescript shirt and denim trousers.

'Hell!' Jim blurted out. 'A bunch of God-damned niggers!'

His outburst seemed to me a bit overdone. What difference did it make who they were? To me, the presence of the three Negroes was incidental, to be ignored. It would have been as anomalous to reject them as to welcome them. They were simply there, and as for me, there wasn't enough affinity between me and the Negroes to call for any reaction or relationship at all. Having never met a Negro in Persia or Europe, my reaction to them lacked any precedent, and could not coalesce into anything more definite than surprise and perplexity.

Watching the three of them in the corner of the freight car, I remembered my first sight of Negroes on arriving in New York ten months earlier. On a busy side street in mid-town Manhattan, amid the city traffic and the skyscrapers, a group of four Negroes, clad in city clothes, seemed as incongruous to me as men dressed for a carnival in broad daylight. Had I seen them in Africa I would have taken them for granted, much as I might have taken other races on their own continents for granted. Even here, the Negroes would have seemed less remarkable to me if they had been dressed in

67

some tribal or native costume. I wondered why they made themselves even more conspicuous by lingering on the street and talking in that lively and boisterous way.

I remembered speculating what country they came from and what language they spoke. After passing them by, I turned and retraced my steps, slowing down as I came abreast of them. Their conversation was too swift and broken-up for me to guess at. It had none of the tell-tale tones and lilts of a language I might have heard before. Yet a word here and there did sound familiar. It was odd. The familiarity was not precisely with the word, but rather as if I were overhearing familiar words, grossly mispronounced, or a familiar accent applied to unknown words. I would have been less confused had I heard the Negroes chattering away in what I might have assumed to be some African tongue, or had I heard them speaking normal, fluent English (but dressed up in native robes, the way I remembered from movie travelogues). Even after I was sure they were speaking English—though with a peculiar accent—I had wondered what sort of visitors they were. They were too old to be students, and evidently too familiar with their surroundings to be tourists.

'They aren't doing anything,' I said to Jim.

'They better not. I'll bash their heads in.' The Negroes watched Jim as if scenting danger.

'If there was another car I'd tell them to scram, those black s.o.b.s.' Jim rose to his feet. For a moment I thought he was going to make a scene. But he merely walked to the side of the car, as if too agitated to stay put.

The dry, dusty prairie surrounding us seemed to be heaving under the oppressive heat. The motion of the car should have created a breeze, but the pace was too slow. As I stood beside Jim the vibration of the car, multiplied by the ever-shifting metal tubes, concentrated on the soles of my feet and, running up my spine, seemed to strike somewhere in the nape of my neck.

But the Negroes seemed contented. They had ingeniously lapsed into comfortable positions. The girl was leaning sideways against one of the boys. His arm curved about her shoulder while his hand groped vaguely about her bare throat. The boy on her other side had nestled his head in her lap. The boys were sharing the comfort and contact of her body without interfering with each other. All three of them were reposing in a peculiar harmony which relieved each of isolation and granted each quiet ease and mutual pleasure. When the reclining boy dozed off, the other drew closer to the girl as if to recompense her for the other's withdrawal into slumber.

I watched them with something akin to envy for the kinship and contentment they shared.

**III** Whenever I leaned back to relax for a moment the vibration of the car rattled my spine and head against the end-board and forced me to straighten up again. The metal pipes on the floor seemed to absorb and double the unrelenting heat of the sun overhead. Perspiration saturated every pore of my skin. I had already used up all my handkerchiefs. They were spread, like pieces of a torn, dirty blanket, under and around me to protect my trousers from the smudgy tubes.

Jim was stretched out on his back. One arm cushioned the back of his head. The handkerchief he had borrowed from me covered his face like a tiny shroud. Slightly askew, it stuck to his sweaty forehead, cheeks and nose. His prostrate body seemed will-less, like an effigy, shaken by the vibrations of the car. He had taken off his shoes and socks and now his bare feet were smudged with streaks of soot and his toes, burned pink and marked off with dark rills of moistened dust, trembled in inane unison with the discarded shoes nearby, which were dancing a mocking minuet of their own— always on the verge of shifting off towards a capricious freedom.

There was nothing to relieve the monotony of the heat and the train's incessant rattle, except talking to Jim. But for him, even listening seemed too much effort. The only way to rouse him was to speculate on the chance of finding water. I nudged him.

'Jim, you better look.'

'Christ, what is it this time?'

'Water, just plain water.' At the word water the Negroes across the car looked up, their faces alert, as if sniffing the air. One of the Negro boys jumped to his feet and wildly looked around, then sat down again, disappointed. 'A row of tanks, Jim, just ahead of us. One of them must have an open faucet.'

'You can't fool me any more.'

'I am not fooling, just look up. The tanks are coming nearer. You better get ready.'

'I'll get good and ready when this damned train slows down.'

'But it's slowing down already. Don't you feel it? Just listen to the wheels.' The Negroes watched.

'This damned train don't even think of slowing down.'

'You are wrong. Just concentrate and you'll feel it. Why, the others . . .' I started to say 'the Negroes' but couldn't bring myself to call them that, 'the others are getting ready to jump off.'

My coaxing and prodding conspired with Jim's thirst, till, mistrusting his own senses, he took the handkerchief off his face, ready to get up. When he caught my grin, he fell back cursing, leaving me to share with the three Negroes this brief distraction.

Once more I got up and walked, first to one side of the flat-car and then to the other. The prairie was as monotonous as the heat and glare of the sun. Wherever I looked it was the same sight. I no

69

longer looked around, but just ahead. I must have gazed too long at the same spot, for after a while the land, as if impatient of the heat and of its own stupor, seemed to stir, exuding traces of vapours which rose into forms and shapes, and like a mirage, began to crowd the vast plain with a great city that stretched beyond the horizon.

Though the sight lasted but a moment, and then dissolved, I couldn't dismiss it altogether as a fantasy. For it might well have been true, I imagined, if the Americans had chanced to make up their minds to build cities here instead of somewhere else. Or it might some day become true; other parts of the country, as barren as this, had been transformed into cities. It didn't matter that this soil was arid, lifeless and isolated now. After almost a year in America, I could no longer take Nature's limitations as relevant.

As little as I expected Jim to remain a short-order cook for the rest of his life, as little was the barrenness of the prairie a barrier to my speculations. Change, I had begun to realize, was not the exception here as it was everywhere else, but the rule, the normal. And everything that avoided or resisted change in America seemed in a way more outdated and obsolete than the antique ruins in my own country. Sometimes I tried to imagine all the changes America must have undergone since its beginnings; tried to add up all the towns and cities I had hiked through, which couldn't have been there a hundred years ago, and to guess how many more there were. I wondered how many cars had passed me on the road, and how many there were in motion throughout the country. I tried to add up the mileage of all the highways that criss-crossed the continent and asked myself how and when did people have time to build them all. Even if every immigrant had done nothing but build roads, working night and day every minute of his life, they still could not have managed to build so many—perhaps more roads than all the rest of the world had built since the beginning of time.

I walked back and sat down next to Jim. Too restless to keep still, I tried again to rouse him into talking.

'Jim, wake up, wake up! You don't know what you are missing. Come on, look up.'

'Christ,' Jim grumbled from under the handkerchief, 'what is it this time?'

'Look up, look up and I'll tell you. Don't sleep away your life.'

'Hell, I ain't sleeping.'

'Worse than that, Jim. Worse than that. You keep your eyes shut. Open them up, open them up,' I almost commanded and, for once, Jim sat up without protesting.

'What's there to miss in this God-forsaken place?' Jim said with a sigh of disgust.

'But it's America, Jim, America.'

'Yeh, I know. You can tell me all about it later.' Jim made ready to stretch out again.

'No, listen. If everybody had acted like you, your America would still be a wilderness.'

'So what.'

'So nothing and everything. You might be riding a horse chasing Indians, or rather, they would be chasing you.'

'Ah, that's old stuff, Bud.'

'Not so old, Jim, not so very old. Where were you born, Jim?'

'I was brought up in El Paso, but born in Arizona; Tucson.'

'Was Arizona already America when you were born?'

'Sure it was,' Jim said as if I'd asked a stupid question.

'I mean, was it officially so? Had it become one of the states of America?' I said.

'I don't know.'

'You don't know!' I said, startled. 'But, Jim, that's so recent it isn't even history yet. You must know it,' I insisted.

'Do *you* remember when the place you was born in became a part of your country?' Jim said peevishly.

'Well, no. Not quite,' I admitted. 'But that happened a long, long time ago.'

'See, then, you don't know your own country either.' And Jim stretched out again, covering up his face.

I wanted to argue that what happened in Persia happened so long ago that it could hardly matter today. But the beginnings of Jim's part of the world were recent enough to be almost personal, even a part of his family's background. If not his father, at least his grandparents must have had a rôle in creating their state. They must have gone through some of the hardships and adventures I had seen in the movies and read about.

In Vienna some of my professors were veterans of the first world war, and listening to them telling their part in it and reading books about those years before I was born, I felt almost contemporaneous with them—so much had their experience permeated the years that followed it. Yet Jim, whose own family must have been participants in the forging of his home state from the wilderness, seemed indifferent to it all, and disclaiming any part of it.

'But Jim,' I blurted out, 'you're part of history yourself.'

'Baloney. My history started when I got my first job.'

I remembered he'd told me of all the jobs he'd had and all the cities he'd lived in and what the pay was. And I dimly sensed that it wasn't a question of dates at all. As in his father's time, what every American like Jim did with his own life counted for more than all that had gone before him. Each seemed to take it for granted that he was on his own and had to work out his own history anew.

71

Whatever history might mean to others in other countries, Jim was absolved of that background which would have conditioned a cook in any other country to think of himself in no other terms, as if such a calling—determined by the chance of his birth and by the past—were his immutable fate and destiny. Jim was free from those collective memories which made the rich walk, talk and act differently from the many, and confined the prospects of the poor. Jim had even mentioned going to California later and riding high with a fancy place of his own. Compared to his ambition—if he only worked hard enough—what did the history of a thousand years, or that of yesterday, matter?

Suddenly I envied Jim, not his freedom of choice, but his assumption that this freedom was a commonplace. I envied him for what he took for granted—the right to make a fresh start; free from geography and time, to choose his own limits and work out his own future.

IV The Negroes were singing and laughing. Their voices rose clear and mellow in the heat, then subsided into a hum and rose again, aimless, yet always in harmony. When I opened my eyes they were on their feet. One boy was circling by himself in motions which I might have taken for those of a ritual dance if I hadn't remembered them from college. His head moved forward and back as he danced along the pipes, his right arm half raised from the elbow pointing a shaky finger at the sky. With the other hand, he was gently rubbing his belly, as if warming up something inside. His gliding steps started off on the heel and shifted over to the instep and toes as he shuffled along sideways and forward.

The other boy and the girl fell in behind him. They danced in silence. Then, without a signal, they turned and faced each other, still circling, their bodies bent low, their hands between their thighs. Their fingers snapped castanet-like sounds in rhythm with each step. Then the girl stretched out her arms and each boy, in turn, pulled her to him, whirled her around, then propelled her back to his partner. Her loose shirt ballooned high, baring patches of her torso and breasts. The flimsy material of her tight trousers clung to her legs along the sweaty contours of her buttocks, thighs and calves. Catching and releasing her, the boys moved ever closer together till the girl no longer was caught by their arms, but was stopped by the sheer impact of their bodies. When they were too close to carry on, they fell into line, and the boy who had started the dance began to move his right arm close to his body, bent at the elbow, in a slow, rotating movement. The girl, close behind him,

72

grasped his elbow and joined his motion. The other boy followed
suit. The first boy clicked his tongue and repeated the word, 'Chuck,
chuck,' imitating the sound of a train's wheels. The word was taken
up by the other two and repeated fitfully as they moved their arms
like pistons. The first boy, with a hissing sound, called out, 'Shee,
shee,' imitating spouting steam. Their rhythm became more pronounced, their voices rose. And soon, alternately rising to yowls and
subsiding into grunts, their exclamations shifted from 'chuck, chuck'
to 'shee, shee' and back again, ever louder and louder, till the words
reached their rhythmic, shouted climax of 'Fuck, fuck' and 'Shit,
shit.'

They flung out the words, again and again, against the sky.

Then, lowering their voices to a whisper, their elbows still working, they moved towards their corner of the car. When the foremost
boy reached the side-board, the girl and the other boy kept on
pushing from behind. The boy who was last, pushed and pressed
his body against the girl's, forcing her in turn to press against the
boy in front, whose torso arched stiffly back to return the pressure
upon the girl between them.

Suddenly, all three slumped down to their knees and rolled over
on their backs. They lay on the floor in a heap, unmindful of the
burning pipes beneath them. Their eyes were closed. Sweat glistened
on their faces, setting off the rosy hue inside their open lips. They
lay still and relaxed, like tired animals in the shade. Faint, secretive
smiles lingered on their faces, as if before going to sleep each had
tasted something sweet.


V   Towards the end of the afternoon the train began to slow
    down. Directly ahead, we saw a group of low, cylindrical
water tanks.

'We got to get some water,' Jim said to me. 'My tongue's hanging
out.'

The three Negroes were running from one side of the car to the
other, exuberant, clowning, laughing. Then, clustering together in
their corner, they began a pantomime. The two boys dropped on
their knees and, moaning and groaning, inched along the floor
towards the girl, pleading with faces and hands uplifted. They
pulled themselves up along her body, while she teased them with
the empty canteen held high above her head.

Jim flipped a coin with me to see whose lot it would be to risk
jumping off. I lost. The two Negro boys were scrambling for the
flask which the girl, giggling and squirming, dangled out of their
reach. Each boy wanted the advantage that went with the risk of

fetching water; the lucky one could drink his fill at the faucet while the others would get no more than a share from the flask. One of the boys suddenly grabbed the flask and jumped off before the train had come to a halt.

I was already astride the plank, ready to jump off, when I saw a black car emerge as if from nowhere. It stopped not more than a hundred yards away, beside the rails.

When I pointed out the car to Jim, he jerked me back. 'Lay low and keep still,' he said. 'Don't stir even if he calls.' Crouching, Jim whirled towards the Negro boy and girl and whispered: 'Copper.' Like a shot, the word sent them to their knees.

Jim's face was so close I could hear his frightened, rapid breathing. The raw sunburn of his face seemed tinged with a strange pallor. We could hear footsteps approaching on the cinders alongside the railroad tracks. Each step seemed to synchronize with the preceding ones into an ascending note of menace. A stick rapped against the side-boards of our flat-car, almost playfully. We lay rigid, and in the bated stillness the knocking sounded excessively loud, boisterous and arrogant.

Then I saw hands gripping the side-board from outside. A grunt brought a giant torso astride the plank. For a moment the man remained astride. Then, lightly, almost daintily, like a rider dismounting his horse, he swung in the outer leg. There he stood, legs apart. 'If any of you s.o.b.s sets foot off this car, I'll beat hell out of you.' All of us stood up.

I was relieved; I had no intention of setting foot off the box-car. I was further relieved when the officer addressed Jim first. 'Where you heading for?'

My mind automatically registered what seemed to me a grammatical error; the man should have said 'Where *are* you heading for?'

'El Paso—my home town,' Jim said, as if he were eager to make a good impression.

'You born there?'

Again I registered the omission in a silent aside.

'Yes, sir.'

Jim must be joking, I thought; surely he couldn't be trying to ingratiate himself with such a man by addressing him as 'sir'. The officer had a provincial accent, and his grammar was inexcusable. I was so intent on remembering the exact wording and pronunciation of Jim's answers, in order to be prepared for my own interrogation, that the officer had to repeat his next question before I realized it was addressed to me.

'Where *you* heading for?'

'El Pazzo, also,' I said. Something odd about the way I had pronounced El Paso lingered in the air. I cursed the language I had studied for five hours a day over the past nine months. My English would never amount to anything, I decided. I might as well give it up if I couldn't parrot a word right when somebody had just finished saying it.

'You a foreigner?'

The officer's voice had an ominous note. So had his appearance. His dark shirt, cut military style, had the crispness of a garment freshly laundered and freshly pressed. Its vertical creases were knife sharp, one running down each sleeve and two down the front. His breeches, held up by a wide belt, were tucked into shiny boots that laced up to the knees. And when I said, 'Yes, sir,' I couldn't pretend to myself that I was joking or had said 'sir' just to imitate Jim.

'Where you born?' he asked.

I hesitated. Should I name the city, as Jim had done, or the country? But the officer had probably never heard of my country, much less of my home town, Meshed.

'I think he was born in Turkey or thereabouts,' Jim said.

'Who asked you?' the officer snapped at him. 'Let him talk for himself.'

I glanced at Jim to let him see I appreciated his help, even though he had backed the wrong country, but he avoided my glance, as if he were anxious to put a distance between us. I suppressed the suspicion that Jim hadn't really spoken up for my sake, but had volunteered information to save the patrolman the trouble of finding out for himself.

'Persia,' I said, 'I mean Iran.'

'Make up your mind—which?'

'You see, officer,' I began, 'my country . . .'

'Don't give me any of that stuff.'

'I am only trying to explain . . .'

'Shut up. You don't have to explain nothing to me. I asked you a simple question, and I want a simple answer.'

I suppressed the errant impulse to tell him that simple questions didn't always have simple answers, and that, unfortunately, there was no simple answer to his question. In 1935, Persia had changed its name officially to Iran—a change that wasn't really a change, because Persians have always called themselves Irani and their country Iran. The very words 'Persia' and 'Persian' don't exist in our language. The whole confusion started a long time ago, when early European travellers transferred the name of the southerly province of Fars, which they called Pars, to the country as a whole. When I told people I was from Iran, they often didn't know what country I meant. But when I said Persia, they knew immediately because of Persian rugs or Persian cats. Maybe the man in front of me owned a Persian rug. He was only a patrolman, but an American patrolman might be able to afford one, for all I knew. I was suddenly caught up in the wild hope that one of my country's rugs had found its way into this man's home. Perhaps, through a kind providence, the carpet had by its weave and design ingratiated its place of origin into this man's liking and memory.

'Persia,' I said.

'Where's that?'

'You know—where Persian rugs come from.'

'What's that got to do with it? Answer my question.'

What was I to say? Where is any place? Every place is in a bigger place. 'In Asia,' I said, afraid of antagonizing him further by silence or hesitation.

'Where did you say?'

'Asia. Continent of Asia.'

'Ah, from the continent,' he said, as if making sense at last of my words. 'How did you come over here?'

'On a scholarship.'

'On what ship, did you say?'

'On a scholarship,' I repeated, with a halting and tentative smile, wanting to gauge his response before letting the smile expand into a grin or fade off.

'Where did you get your entry permit?' he asked, in a voice strangely casual.

'In Vienna, Austria.'

'Thought you just said you come from—.'

In my nervousness I missed the last word. Had he said Persia? Asia? Russia? Prussia? What? I felt my total intelligence insufficient to convey a few personal facts that would allay the man's suspicion and overcome his ignorance.

I looked at Jim, half expecting him to help me out, and then realized that he had grasped as little as the officer where I came from or who I was, though I had talked to him, on and off, since the day before. A peculiar panic rose in me—the panic that is due not to the immediate danger itself but to its assault upon the past. I suddenly suspected that everyone who had asked me about my country and myself—the students at college, the bums on the road, the kind old ladies in Lakeville who invited foreign students to tea and cookies, the strangers who had given me rides—had remained as ignorant about me as Jim, as uncomprehending as the officer, and as indifferent as both. It didn't really matter whether anyone knew where Persia was or what it was called, but it mattered crucially that I should recall one face to whom I, or my words, had mattered.

'Yes, I am from Persia,' I resumed dispiritedly, 'but I received my visa in Vienna. I studied there. I was graduated from ...'

'You say you went to school there?'

'Yes.'

'And you mean to tell me you packed your bags to come over here and hop a freight?'

'No. I went to school here in America also,' I said.

He narrowed his eyes, as if to warn me not to carry things too far. 'Where was that?'

'Florida.'

'University of Florida?'

'No. Watson College.'

'Never heard of it,' he said. 'Got anything to prove it?'

'Well, no, not here with me. I didn't bring my diploma along.'

'That don't surprise me,' he sneered. I was appalled at what I had said, but I had no time to set things right, for he went on, with a knowing air, 'Florida . . . Ever been near the Gulf?'

'Which gulf?' I asked. I wasn't sure what he meant, but I could see he had something on his mind.

'Ever been to New Orleans?'

'Oh yes. I was there several days,' I said with pride. My hitch-hiking had taken me through that city, and I hoped to gain an advantage by appealing to what seemed to me an American penchant for reminiscing, an urge towards nostalgia, which takes hold of two Americans as soon as they discover they come from the same state or city, or have driven through each other's home town, or have relatives living near one another, or have stayed at the same hotel or eaten in the same restaurant. Perhaps the officer had been to New Orleans, too. If I could only remember a few details about that city, it might give us something in common.

'It rained a lot when I was there,' I said.

'I don't give a damn if you had rain or shine. What I want to know is if you're sure you didn't enter the country by way of New Orleans or one of them Gulf ports.'

I caught on at last. He suspected me of illegal entry. I said, 'What allows you to presume that I would bother to lie to you? I entered at New York. Here, I shall show you my passport to prove it.' I turned and stooped over my valise. But before I could unsnap the lock, the officer's boot was resting on top of the bag.

'I better do that,' he said.

I straightened up, outraged, and he frisked me the way I had seen it done in the movies. I was taken off guard and had no time to react, except for shame.

When I found my voice, I said, with all the dignity I could muster, 'If you are looking for a gun, you may spare yourself the trouble. I am not a gangster.'

He didn't look up. He was bending over the valise, feeling through my belongings. Then he straightened up and said, 'Okay, let's have your passport.'

I took it out of a side compartment and handed it to him. He opened the hard cover and turned to the first page, which contained certain particulars about me—my physical characteristics, and the date and place of my birth—written in Persian and in French.

'It says here "Iran".' He pronounced the word 'Eyeran'. 'Thought you said a different country when I asked you the first time.'

'That is correct, officer. I tried to explain to you when you said—'

'Shut up.'

'That is exactly what you said when I tried to explain—'

'Shut up.' He leafed through the pages slowly, curious about all the foreign visas, stamps, and notations. His absorbed attention indicated a simulated, incomplete comprehension. His mind, I could see, was functioning by pictorial impression. When he finished and started all over again, I said that my United States entry visa was on one of the last pages. He was squinting at it, when we heard a voice chanting: 'Coming up the mountain, she'll be coming up the mountain when she comes . . .'

The Negro boy was capering up to the car, swinging the canteen in a high arc of joy and yelling, 'Hey, Crunchy! Hey, Matty! Look, look!' Then, bending back his head, he pretended to pour all the water from the uplifted canteen down his throat.

'Get down! All of you!' the officer hissed, crouching low himself. We all obeyed, taking cover behind the side-board. The voice was still calling and laughing, 'Matty, Crunchy, look, look!' and coming nearer all the time. He was so close now we could hear the shuffle of his feet along the cinders.

The boy pulled himself up and jumped into the car, holding the canteen high like a trophy. The officer's stick smashed the canteen out of his hand. The boy leaped out of reach towards the illusory protection of his friends who had straightened up in their corner.

The three Negroes stood terrified. Their wide stares seemed mesmerized by the officer's presence.

'Come on over here, you bastard.'

The Negro remained motionless.

'Come on over here, you black bastard.' The officer's voice was strangely calm, as if coaxing a child that distrusted him.

The boy moved forward—two slow, unwilling steps. The first step was a fraction quicker and covered more ground; the second dragged to a standstill, as if the boy's will could force him no farther. Some three or four steps still separated him from the officer.

It would have been simpler had the officer stepped up to him. The officer was the active agent. The boy was but the object, limited to compliance. He seemed already to have resigned himself totally to whatever might happen. And if he did not add the third, fourth or fifth step as demanded of him, it was not because of any defiance or any hope of avoiding what was to come, but simply because—

having already subjected himself unconditionally to whatever might happen—he could not find the initiative to advance one more step.

'Come closer!'

The Negro remained still. His posture seemed pliable, as if he were a tree rooted to the spot, but ready to sway with any gust of wind.

The officer stepped forward. The blow was swift and brutal, enough to send anyone to his knees. But the boy's body, as if compliant by instinct, deprived the blow of its power. Like a dummy, he tumbled back with an exaggerated abandon, as if by parading his helplessness, he might pacify the vanity of his assailant.

The boy landed at the feet of his two companions. For a moment, I expected someone—though strangely enough not myself—to say or do something. When the officer didn't follow up his first blow, I assumed it to be the last, and the ugly incident—as degrading to the assailant as to the victim—closed. Still, I expected the other Negro boy and the girl to show some gesture of solidarity or sympathy with their comrade, who lay heaped at their feet with his head and legs drawn up like an embryo. Their eyes were not on the boy at their feet, but on the officer, as if they already knew the worst that could befall their hapless companion, but not the worst the officer might do to them.

The officer walked over to their corner. 'What did I say I'd do?' He kicked the boy's buttocks. The boy's body was wedged into the corner, giving him a brace and depriving the officer's kick of its force.

The officer stepped back a few paces. 'Get up, you bastard.'

The Negro remained motionless on the floor.

'Get up and come over here I said.' He waited. Then, stepping up to the huddled figure, he bent down and dragged it to the middle of the car. With one hand he held the boy's head upright, and with the other he hit it, again and again. Each time he lost his grip, he grabbed the boy and pulled him up again—by his shirt, his arm, his hair, anything that gave him a hold on his target. But the youngster's total submission seemed to rob the blows of their full impact, rendering them monotonous, almost futile. It seemed as if the officer would wear himself out and be defeated by the boy's unresisting inertness.

As I watched those blows, it dawned on me why I didn't interfere: there had been too many other instances when I should have interfered and didn't—instances worse than this, though no blows or insults had been inflicted, no word even spoken, except once in a drugstore in Lakeville, when the proprietor had called the coloured delivery boy 'darkie' as if calling a pet, and a likable one at that. The proprietor and the two customers went on talking. The word had seemed lost upon the boy, too, except for what I thought was a swift shadow passing his soft, withdrawn eyes. It was my first awareness of that protective simulation I imagined seeing ever afterwards in every Negro's face and body when he passed a white man on the sidewalk, when he approached a drinking fountain or a door not marked Coloured, or as he entered through the back door of a bus. He seemed for ever on the alert, while always stepping aside or back, and having to do it naturally and politely, condemned to the pretence of being unaware of his own unspeakable, unceasing degradation. And this pretence was reciprocated by the whites with the corresponding pretence that such a relationship was normal, right and as it should be.

By contrast, the officer's outburst now was almost a relief. It brought the infested issue into the open. Primitive, brutal it was, but natural and free of hypocrisy. The officer's blows had a strange wilfulness about them. There was no longer anything left to attack or punish. The boy lay inert, like a stuffed dummy. Yet the officer kept on striking, as if his target were not big enough, and he were purging himself of a burden. His abandon was a clue to his impotence, but strike as he might, the ties that bound his past to the boy's could not be severed nor undone by his temper. Any show of strength only stressed and twisted the bonds between them; and any concessions made in the name of tolerance and progress, as had become the fashion lately, seemed no better, because such concessions, being conditional, only added to the nameless friction which any loosening of chains must cause—each compromise adding its leeway for rubbing and rawness. And yet, both sides—one to boast of generosity and the other for the sake of extracting more concessions—must pretend in public that all was changing for the better and would be for the best, as I had heard them claim so often over the radio and in the newspapers; as if the past could be bought off and laid to rest by an enforced compromise now that the Negro had to be taken into account as a customer in spite of his colour.

... Or was all this speculation, I wondered, merely a camouflage for my own cowardice, for my failure to interfere? I didn't know. But I did know I could never look a Negro in the face again.

VI  Suddenly the officer ceased. He stood there, panting, feet apart, wiping the sweat off his face and forehead with a large coloured handkerchief.

'You there,' he said, turning and pointing at me. 'Come along with me.'

I turned to Jim, who looked down at his shoes. 'Better do what he says,' Jim said in a low voice.

'Can't you come with me?'

'That wouldn't help you any and might get me into trouble.'
There was a note of irritation in his voice—the irritation of someone who can't get rid of a hanger-on or a child.

I felt like shaking him to make him understand his mistake, to
make him see that this wasn't the time for either of us to think of
himself alone; sticking together was all that mattered, for then
nothing could *really* happen to either of us.

I had meant to ask him how I would ever find him again, if I
should manage to get to El Paso, but I changed my mind. As I
picked up my valise and walked over to the side of the car, my
knees were weak. Suddenly, this miserable flat-car, with its burning
metal pipes, its heat and dust, seemed the only place on earth that
offered me peace and comfort. And I was frightened. It was not
fear of any particular punishment that gripped me but fear of
giving myself over to the officer.

Around us was the prairie, without a tree or a house in sight. I
was in the hands of this local policeman, who might abuse the law
as he pleased. And if he was so dense as to mistake me for a bum
or worse, what might he not do to me to justify his suspicions?

'Look, officer,' I pleaded before jumping off. 'If you would have
a little patience and permit me to explain about my country—'

'You can do all your explaining to the boss,' he said. 'Get a
move on.'

I followed the patrolman along the rails to his car, which was
parked behind some huge vat-shaped water tanks near the rails.
After my ten-hour ride on the freight, the soft, cushioned car seat
was almost enough to make me glad I had been taken off the train.
I leaned back, luxuriating in the cool air of the rotating fan, which
had begun to hum when the motor started. With such comforts on
hand, I thought, civilization and common sense couldn't be too
far off. Caught up in a sudden surge of optimism, I addressed the
officer. 'How long will the train stop here?'

'Long enough to tank up, I imagine.'

'I mean will it stay long enough for me to return?'

For the first time, he looked at me in a personal way, with what
I felt was a good-humoured grin. 'Like hell it will,' he said, and
turned his eyes back to the road.

'But what shall I do if I get back too late?' I was convinced that
I would have no trouble explaining myself to 'the boss', who would
immediately set me free to continue my ride. It was all a mistake
of the patrolman's, and he might as well make up for it by helping
me get back. He didn't answer. 'Could you at least tell me where
you are driving me?' I asked.

'Shut up,' he said good-naturedly.

'I think I am at least entitled to know where—'

'Shut up.'

81

I drew myself up to protest, and he said it again.

We rode on in silence. I was still wondering why on earth these Americans had ever built such a magnificent highway through this forsaken territory when, over a slight rise, a few trees and houses came into view, and, a little farther on, a town. I was relieved; if the train was gone by the time I got back, I could hitch-hike on from here.

We stopped on the outskirts of town, before a small two-storey frame building with wooden stairs leading up to a front porch. I followed the officer up the steps and into a small room. Except for two desks—one, unoccupied, near the door and the other at the far end, where a man sat half hidden by stacked-up volumes—the room was bare. I took it for a waiting room, and looked around, in vain, for a door to an inner office. Straight ahead, two open windows framed the branches of a wide-spreading tree, and between the two windows was a portrait I recognized—the first President of the United States. In spite of the granite jaw and the broad, aggressive forehead, the familiar features seemed drowsy in the heat and the eyes averted from the slab of sunshine that streaked across the dusty frame. Altogether, I felt, the room was too shabby to represent authority.

I said 'Good afternoon', put my valise down, and waited, near the door. My 'good afternoon', I decided, had come off rather well —nonchalant, yet with an accent confident and formal enough to indicate my social level and set a standard of etiquette for the other.

The man behind the desk didn't answer. He didn't even look up. My greeting seemed to linger on in the air, affected and pretentious. I felt caught in a pose; the silence was exposing my words for what they were—not a true courtesy but a pathetic shield for my uncertainty. I wondered if it wouldn't have been wiser and more honourable to say nothing.

The patrolman stepped up to the desk. 'Sheriff—' he began, propping his palms on the desk. I couldn't have been more astonished if he had said 'Your Excellency'. The word 'sheriff' had for me something of the romantic flavour that 'sultan', 'pasha', or 'sheik' might have for Americans. I didn't know this famous breed of men still existed in the American West, much less that I would ever come face to face with one of them. I tried to get a better look at him, but the volumes stacked up at the edge of the desk limited my view to one round, fleshy shoulder and the top of a bald head.

'Sheriff, here's a guy I picked up that might interest you. A foreigner,' the officer added, as if he had bagged special game. His voice, quiet, self-effacing, almost pedantic, was so unlike what I remembered from the flat-car that my attention shifted from the sheriff to him, in surprise. Even his physique, which had loomed frighteningly, now seemed merely of middling proportions.

82

'What's the charge?'

'Vagrancy, sheriff.'

The sheriff's face shifted into view. Dull, drowsy eyes wandered to me with no more interest or animation than they might have wasted upon some spot on the wall.

'That calls for Section 204, don't it?'

'Sure does, sheriff.'

The sheriff turned to me. 'Guilty or not guilty?' The 'not' was all but inaudible, and the question sounded like 'Guilty or guilty?'

I hadn't anticipated a climax so soon. I wanted to avoid committing myself to a direct answer, but my English vocabulary seemed to have seeped away—not just forgotten but lost. This blankness overtook me sometimes when I got over-excited or, occasionally, just after waking up in the morning. At such times, my English was reduced to a few unfamiliar words, remembered by rote and difficult to pronounce.

'Please—guilty to what?' I brought forth at last.

The sheriff pulled down the top volume from the pile on his desk, opened it, and began to read so rapidly and in such an expressionless voice that I caught only isolated words and phrases. '... county of ... state of Texas ... no place of residence ... no destination ... no means of support ... vagrancy ... guilty or not guilty.' His last words sounded like part of the text.

'I cannot admit guilty,' I began haltingly, 'if the charge is not justified. If you had been kind enough to look at my passport, you could see I have a place of residence, which is, naturally, my own country—to be precise, in the city of Meshed, in the province of Khorasan.' I paused, pleased that I had at last found enough English to address him sensibly. Neither the sheriff nor the patrolman looked at me. I went on. 'The officer here must remember. I told him my destination is El Paso. Therefore, I have a place of residence and a destination. Secondly—' The utter lack of response in the sheriff's face confused me. 'Secondly, you must grant that no one could possibly mistake me for a vagrant. No one has so far, and I hope no one will. Also, I have over thirteen dollars. I am sure that this is enough to secure me dwelling and food, either until I reach my destination or at least until I am distant from your jurisdiction. If you wish, I shall take from here a passenger train or a bus, and I hope—I hope—'

I felt I ought to go on talking, but the sheriff's face stopped me. No flicker or expression indicated that he had listened to, let alone comprehended, what I said. I stood and waited.

Finally, he said, 'What did you say?' but without the intonation of a question. I waited, hoping he might add something, but he didn't.

'I said,' I started again, 'that the charge of vagrancy cannot really

83

apply to me.' Carefully, I repeated all my arguments, and ended up not sure whether my second defence had been as good as the first.

'How's that again?' The sheriff lifted a couple of fingers to his ear, which suddenly struck me as enormous. And what did the gesture mean? Was the sheriff hard of hearing? Or outright stupid? And if he couldn't hear, why had he let me talk on for so long without hinting at his infirmity? His face hadn't betrayed the slightest strain indicative of dull hearing—or of a dull mind, for that matter.

In my perplexity, I turned to the patrolman. He glanced towards the sheriff and then back ·at me. 'You ought to raise your voice a little. The sheriff is kind of hard of hearing.'

When I started, for the third time, each argument seemed harder to phrase. My loud voice magnified my awkward pronunciation. I found myself rephrasing my arguments in a way that asked for sympathy. But when the sheriff, taking advantage of a pause, cupped a hand to his ear and repeated 'How's that again?' I glared at him.

'I told you the sheriff is a little hard of hearing,' the officer said. 'You'll have to raise your voice a little if you want him to get the drift.'

'This is a matter beyond hearing,' I retorted. 'It seems neither my English nor my intelligence is good enough to explain myself, or be understood.'

'What was that?' the sheriff said idly, heaving himself forward in his chair.

'Nothing worth while repeating, sir, I'm sure,' I said.

'Well?' He looked up at me. 'Guilty or not guilty?'

'Any way you choose.'

The sheriff leaned forward again. His elbow had pushed his pipe over; grains of charred tobacco dotted the surface of the desk. He propped up his pipe, and when he lifted some papers to shake them clear of tobacco, I saw a magazine cover beneath them—a girl, with hair and dress dishevelled, screaming with terror. Had he confiscated the magazine from some youngster, as my teachers had done with such stuff at school? I missed the sheriff's next question and had to ask him to repeat it.

'The law says here,' he said sharply, and patted the volume in front of him, 'ten days or ten dollars. Well, which?'

'But if I pay you ten dollars, I shall have hardly anything left. I might really be taken for a vagrant.'

'Well?'

I stepped forward, and counting out the money, put it on his desk. All I wanted was to get out of there, to be alone.

The sheriff's hand covered the bills. I went to the door and picked up my valise. 'I hope I can depart now?' I said, forgetting to raise my voice.

'You can get the hell out of here,' the sheriff answered. He turned to the patrolman. 'And make damn sure he stays out.'

The sheriff was not deaf, after all. He had resorted to an unfair trick, and I had been taken in by it. It was humiliating, but I was more upset by his total lack of interest in me, after all the talking about myself I had done.

As I was on the stairs outside, I heard him say to the patrolman in a loud voice, 'Keep an eye on him till he's over the county line. And if he shows up again, don't bother to bring him in.'

VII Carrying my valise, I walked on towards the centre of town, troubled by a sensation stronger than that of being watched but not quite as oppressive as that of being followed. For the first time, I approached an American town without anticipation. I was aware of the weight of the valise, and of the heat of the late afternoon, and of being dirty. When I reached the main street, I turned and walked up it, as I had done in so many other towns, but this time without staring at people and buildings, and without hurrying from one crossing to the next as if each new side street harboured a strange and unexpected vista (until, at the other end of the town, I would be overcome by a sense of irremediable loss, of having missed something—a regret that diminished in proportion as my imagination was drawn by the promise and adventure of the town ahead). I stopped a passer-by and asked the direction of the bus depot. He said the town was too small to have a bus depot, and, trying to be helpful, asked me which bus I meant to take and what my destination was. I thanked him curtly and went on. All I had wanted the bus depot for was to rent a shower for twenty-five cents, as I had done in other places.

The sign 'TRANSIENTS BATHS FIFTY CENTS' above on old building caught my eye. I could afford neither the fifty cents nor the time—it was getting late and I should be on my way—but I was in the habit of having a shower or washing from head to foot once a day, so I went in. After my shower, I cleaned my two-toned shoes and rubbed off the dirt spots from my flannels with the fluid I always carried along. Then I put my dirty linen in the zipper bag, to be washed the next time I had a chance to rent a room for the night. Out on the street again, cool and clean, I felt the luxurious ease that invariably followed a hot and abundant shower in America, and stopped for a leisurely cup of coffee and a cigarette. Then I hurried on.

I reached the highway sooner than I expected. I always over-estimated the size of such small towns, misled by the few buildings of more than average height along the main street. The last building at the edge of town was a gas station. It would have been a good spot—as most gas stations were—to wait for a ride, but I walked on for about a mile and posted myself at the next curve, to give drivers a chance for a long look at my silhouette, marked by my upraised thumb. The sun was about to set. I was sure I had a good hour or two of light ahead of me—time enough to catch a ride. But there were very few cars, and none of them slowed down. The first headlights alarmed me, and after they had passed, the atmosphere seemed noticeably darker. I tried to persuade myself that those lights had been switched on prematurely or by mistake, and I drew reassurance from subsequent cars with their lights still off. Each car that passed bequeathed an ominous note of failure to the next, until the increasing darkness shifted my expectations from legitimate hope to mere luck. I knew by experience how little chance there was of being picked up once darkness set in.

Ordinarily, I would have returned to the centre of the town and found a cheap room for the night, but there was no telling what the patrolman might do if he caught me. I tried to think up alternatives—that I might get a ride yet, that I might spend the night waiting, that I might even return to town without running into the patrolman, or that if he caught me, he might understand that I had at least been trying to get out of town. But all these speculations couldn't cover up the fact that, tired as I was, I was standing there in the dark for one reason only—the sheriff's threat. I decided to wait for one more car and then go back into town.

A car came into view and passed me slowly—much more slowly, I thought, than the other cars had. To check any temptation to temporize—since the car had appeared so soon after my resolve— I picked up my valise and set off towards town. I had barely left the bend of the road when headlights focused upon me from behind. When I looked back, I saw that the car had turned around and was coming towards me. It drew over to my side of the road and stopped.

I leaned towards the window and said, 'Thank you, thank you very much, but I was trying to get a ride in the opposite direction. I am only walking back to town—'

'That's what you think! You stay right here where you are.' The voice was matter-of-fact. It was also familiar. So was the car. And though I could barely make out the face behind the wheel, I recognized the patrolman.

'But that's impossible!' I protested. 'Nobody will pick me up any more, and I cannot stay here the whole night.'

'That's your business. And you better stay put if you don't want me to beat the living daylights out of you.'

He shifted gears, and the car moved on, the sound of the motor rising powerful and indifferent in the stillness of the night. The red tail-lights receded and vanished.

I didn't know what to do. It was as pointless to match my physical stamina against the unknown distance to the next town as it was to walk the one mile back to this town and match my courage against the patrolman, who probably had no patience for such toys as courage and cowardice; to whom the weaker was worse than a coward and the stronger without need of moral props to be respected.

I walked off the highway to the nearest telegraph pole and propped my valise against it. Then I spread my trench coat on the ground and, with the valise as a back rest, made myself as comfortable as I could, resigned to waiting for daylight.

If only I had someone alongside to talk to, I thought, the waiting would take care of itself. I thought of Jim. The other people I had met on the road, for a few minutes or a few hours, had already faded into anonymity. From this distance, college seemed like some pleasant summer resort where everyone is jolly and a collective amiability prevails at the expense of personal relationships. I could think of no one from Watson who would be willing to share my long wait.

And as always when I was alone and wanted to talk to someone, speculations and memories crowded in as substitutes for human companionship; my childhood in Persia, the school in Europe, my stay in America, all mixed in with the recurrent themes of what would become of me if the passage money never arrived and could never be borrowed, and of what my life might have been like if I had never left Persia.

When relatives reproached my father for thinking of banishing a mere child of eight to study in Europe, he said, 'The world can take everything away from a man, but not what he has stored up here,' tapping his wrinkled forehead with his forefinger. It never occurred to him to wonder whether the knowledge and experience I would gain abroad would ever compensate for the loneliness I would find there. He wouldn't hear of sentiments and never said anything about his feelings. In his world, all feeling was safely embedded in centuries of tradition and family ties, so much at peace within its familiar and unchanging boundaries that nothing —no amount of questioning and doubt—could affect it.

I speculated about my father's fury if he were ever to hear of my hitch-hiking, and I had no doubt that some day I would tell my mother about it. Writing her about it wouldn't do; the external details of my daily hitch-hiking were not worth the telling, and as for the rest, her love, the sea of her emotions, would drown any meaning I would try to convey. At the sight of my letter, tears

87

would well into her eyes, and she would mix murmured endearments with benedictions and prayers that her son might be spared pain and want. She would enfold all my hungers in the same embrace, without distinguishing between them. She could only yearn for something specific—for example, for my return. Everything broad and abstract she entrusted to God. The old world she lived in, though never spared its full share of sorrows and wants, knew nothing of that vague, unnameable hunger that haunted the new, where all hungers seemed so richly fed save those of the heart. And her son knew as yet barely more than she did, though sometimes I became alarmed and puzzled when I caught myself, just for the sake of talking and being talked to, addressing strangers for directions I already knew, or entering a store after catching sight of an idle sales clerk who appeared sympathetic, though I had neither the means nor the intention of buying anything.

I dozed, off and on, without quite abandoning the thread of these reveries, until finally the eastern horizon seemed to be growing brighter. Soon, I thought, the first cars would be on the road, and those early drivers, as if unwilling to mar the virtue of their early rising, seldom refused a ride. All I needed to start off on a perfect day was to slip back into town, wash, shave, and change my shirt, if it showed too much wear.

I was up on my feet without actually deciding on it, beating the air with my trench coat to shake it free of dust and wrinkles, when I remembered the patrolman. He was probably fast asleep in his bed. Muttering 'to hell with him,' I made for the highway. For the first time, that American phrase sounded just the way Americans said it.

The sound of my footfalls rose clear and cadenced in the quiet air. There were still a few lights in the town. I watched them for the moment when they would fade off into the dawn, but their dim glow persisted, and the sky seemed no brighter than when I had started out. I began to wonder if I had been wrong about the time.

My palm, gripping the handle of my valise, was sweating, though the bag didn't weigh much and the air was cool. As I switched the bag to my left hand, I stopped, wondering whether it wasn't foolish to go on. But I did go on, doggedly, keeping my eyes on the ground, as if to ward off doubt. When I looked up again, I had almost reached the edge of town. The gas station, white, austere, was immediately ahead. It was closed, and there was a dim light inside. Four shiny pumps flanked the double driveway, like robot sentries, and the rectangular glass of the huge show window caught and magnified my approach in fluid, bluish shadows.

I put my valise on a cement bench and went over to the show window to check the time. The clock on the opposite wall showed precisely midnight. I had the double sensation that sets in when

88

an assumption is proved to be so wide of the mark that the very extent of the error momentarily fortifies the original miscalculation. Pressing my face to the glass, I watched the thin red second-hand of the clock as it ticked off a full round.

Suddenly, the huge plate-glass window seemed aflame. I whirled around, caught in the focus of a searchlight. I had the physical sensation of being exposed naked. My eyes strained to pierce the glare, but it was too strong. I closed my eyes, and it seemed to penetrate my eyelids. As the light came nearer and I listened, I heard the sound of tyres on asphalt. The car stopped. Then the glare cut itself off like magic. A voice warned, 'Don't move.'

The car had stopped exactly in front of me. The door on the driver's side opened with a click, and a flashlight played first over me and then over my valise on the bench. Then a figure stepped forth. It was the patrolman.

Once again, the flashlight circled briefly about my immediate vicinity, then shifted back to me.

'It's you,' said the patrolman. 'I thought so. What you got there?'

'It's my suitcase. I'm sure you recognize it.'

'Open it up.'

I unsnapped the lock and lifted the top. After the patrolman's flashlight had played over the surface of my belongings, it turned to me once more.

'Remember what I told you out there?'

'Yes, I remember.'

'And what did I say I'd do to you if you showed up again in these parts?'

'But—' I hesitated. 'We both thought I might get a ride even then, and so I wouldn't need to come back. I waited and waited.'

'What did I say I'd do to you?' he persisted, like a pedantic teacher who wants the answer given in his particular way.

'You said you would beat the—the daylight out of me. The living daylight,' I corrected myself.

The combination of words amused me, and I smiled. I thought how lucky I was that it was night. If he insisted on carrying out his threat literally, he would have to wait till daylight, unless there was a phrase in English about beating the nightlight out of ...

The blow caught me smiling. Instinctively lifting my shoulder and contracting my neck, I had broken its full force. Still, the impact sent me sprawling. A sharp, shooting pain throbbed about my forehead. I lay there on the ground, as shocked by the patrolman's attack as I was by my own indecision. For I didn't bounce back, as I would have expected myself to do. Instead, I lay there, waiting for some impulse, some overdue reaction, to propel my body into action. All that stirred in me was moral outrage at being hit unawares.

89

'That wasn't fair,' I said, finally, and rose to my feet.

The patrolman neither moved nor said anything. I thought the incident was closed and my moral censure undisputed. I was waiting for some sign from him to confirm this. Simultaneously, I felt a mounting regret that nothing more would happen and that I would be left with the ignominy of not having hit back.

'That wasn't fair,' I repeated. 'If you hit me again, I shall have to retaliate.' That last word, resuscitated from some dictionary page, lingered in the air, absurd, pompous, pathetic.

'So you'll hit back, eh?' There was a faint amusement in his voice. His arm shot forward in the dark and grabbed my shirt collar. The other fist was already swinging, hitting my face and head. 'I'll teach you what's fair. . . . I'll teach you what's fair . . .'

At first, I made the mistake of being concerned with each blow separately—where it hit and how much it hurt. With my arms around my bent head, waiting for the blows to cease, I realized that I must either bear them as best I could, without doing anything that might provoke the patrolman further, or fight back. I closed in, pushed my stiffened palms against his chest as hard as I could, and tangled one foot between his legs.

He stumbled back with a curse, and then I saw the club in his hand. I was caught in a streak of fear. I threw myself against the upraised arm and with both hands clung to it with all my might. The officer's free hand was trying to break my grip, but the instant I felt my hold loosening I made my body limp and dragged him down with me to the ground.

Each pull and curse made me hold on tighter. I was surprised at my own strength and stamina. I no longer thought of the consequences or of the fact that I was actually fighting a policeman. I simply felt like a schoolboy who has got into a fight and must fight it out to the end.

He managed to get on top of me. When the first free blow struck my face, I was relieved that it was with his bare fist. And mingled with the pain of the blows that followed was something akin to pride, as if each blow now testified to my challenge and resistance. I tried to dodge his blows by motions of my head, but something over my right eye was clouding my sight, mistiming my reflexes. I couldn't tell whether it was sweat or blood, but the moisture was thickening. I could barely keep my eyelids apart.

I was still speculating about my eye when a blow, catching me sideways, knocked a tooth out. It stuck in my throat, and a spasm of choking reared my torso off the ground, in spite of the officer's weight on top of me. Then my body went limp.

At last, the blows stopped. I felt myself freed of the patrolman's weight, and managed to rise to my feet, mistaking the slowness of my movements for some residue of self-control. Swaying slightly,

I watched the patrolman brush himself off. I tried to stand upright, but the ground seemed to be shifting and rolling—under one foot more than the other. I looked down. My left foot was on the patrolman's club, which he had dropped in the scuffle. The distance to the ground loomed immense. With all the concentration I could muster, I slowly bent down. When I straightened up, with the club in my hand, the patrolman was watching me. His hand groped towards his hip. When I saw the revolver, I also heard his voice. 'Throw it to me.'

I tried to obey, but the stick weighed my arm down.

'Throw it, you son of a bitch!'

My palm was so moist I was afraid the stick would slip out of my hand. My body was drenched with sweat. I tried to raise my arm for the throw, but the effort was too much. The club slipped out of my hand, my knees gave way, and I tumbled to the ground.

The patrolman, with the revolver in one hand, picked up his club with the other. Standing over me, he said, 'I guess you've had enough.'

'Yes, but you had a little, too,' I said slowly.

I tried to smile, but I felt that my face conveyed no more than a grimace. 'Maybe you wouldn't have hit me so hard if I hadn't hit back a little. So I made it easier for you to beat me up.'

'Shut up. Get up and go on back out there where you was.'

I tried to get up by shifting into a sitting posture first. If I could get on my feet, I could manage the rest. But I seemed to lack the necessary co-ordination. After trying it sideways, by using my hands as props, I shifted into a kneeling posture and then pushed myself up until I was standing.

'Okay. Get going.'

I looked at him, puzzled. He didn't seem to realize what he was asking of me. 'I can't go so fast,' I said, although I hadn't taken a single step.

Something about my voice or my teetering balance must have struck him as queer. He stepped close and, peering at my face, let out a whistle. 'You better wash up,' he said.

'Yes, I think so.' I groped with my fingertips about my eye. It felt swollen and clotty. I wiped the spot with my handkerchief, and saw it was smeared with red.

'That needs washing,' the officer said.

'Yes, yes, I shall,' I assured him. He supported me the few steps to the water faucet. I let the water run over my face. I didn't mind the shooting pain about my forehead; what worried me was the missing tooth, and whether the gap would show. I cupped my hands and washed out my mouth. With the taste of the water a spasm of thirst made me drink in big gulps. Suddenly, I was

91

retching. Supporting myself with both hands on the rim of the bowl, I waited for the nausea to pass.

I heard the patrolman say, 'Here, let me have a look.' His flashlight played over my face. 'Better sit down,' he said.

He led me to the bench, and then got a first-aid kit from his car. I watched him take out a small bottle and a roll of cotton. Putting one knee against the edge of the bench to steady himself, he held up my chin. I could feel his hand pushing my face a little sideways, the pressure of his thumb on one cheek and of his four fingers on the other. Even the wild stinging of the fluid he applied could not detract from my particular awareness of him—of those fingers that rested upon my skin, gently pressing my face this way and that to apply the moist cotton.

I closed my eyes, yielding myself to this sudden bounty of compassion and care, longing for it to last, or at least not to cease too soon. The hand was moving upon my brow. Carefully, the fingers lifted loose strands of hair that clung to my forehead. And with each strand they seemed to lift off so much that I couldn't name.

I was on the verge of crying. Something in me that had been thirsting so long—a thirst I had never quite confessed to myself— took deep draughts of ease from the communion of this human touch. Then I felt his guiding pressure on my shoulders, and knew I was to lie down.

How little the beating mattered now. How often on the road, and even at college, would I have willingly submitted to such bodily pain as that of tonight, if it could have gained for me what was mine now. I could not imagine any pain too great a price for such amends; perhaps there was no other way by which one man could receive and another bestow such largesse—by which they were made so human.

A moment later I was resting full length on the bench, and I missed the contact of those hands. I wanted to call them back, to have them linger on for one more moment. And into my sleep I carried the elation of that fulfilment which, though always sought for by oneself alone, is never found except when granted by another.

# PART III

Blame not him who is out of step—he may be
listening to a different drummer.

THOREAU

**I** The mail clerk at the General Delivery window in the Los
Angeles post office shook his head. 'Nothing,' he said.

I had been so sure of finding the bank draft waiting for me there,
that even after stepping outside I half expected my name to be
called out or to find the clerk running after me to apologize for his
oversight.

I had $2.75 in my pocket. I didn't know which way to turn. I
wouldn't have been surprised if one of the passers-by had stopped
to ask what the trouble was. No one even slowed down or spared
me a glance. I seemed the only still creature in the city, the only
person condemned to wait. Everybody else appeared too busy to
know what standing still was or what waiting meant.

Amidst these eager, rushing people, bent as each one seemed on
some definite goal and purpose, the thought of marking still more
time, of waiting weeks and maybe months longer—the thought of
turning for help to someone (even to a member of my family)
seemed somehow unmanly, almost ignoble. It was there, while
watching the thick traffic and the surge of people in front of the
Los Angeles post office, that my disappointment gradually turned
into something akin to elation: I was to be exposed for a while
longer, left to my own resources, given a greater chance to test
myself—at least to the extent of taking care of myself.

I suddenly remembered I hadn't yet seen the Pacific Ocean. The
imminent prospect of setting eyes upon that sea whose waters
touched neither Europe nor Persia made me forget everything else.
I boarded the bus for Santa Monica; but the commonplace pro-
cedure of buying a ticket and waiting comfortably to reach my
destination was such a let-down that I would have stepped off at
the next stop and hiked on, had I known the road to the beach.
Also, I somehow expected my fellow-passengers to show some
excitement, as I did, at the prospect of seeing the ocean at the end

93

of the line. But they paid no attention, neither to me nor to the view. Even after the bus turned into the palisades, they were still reading their papers or looking, bored, straight ahead; while *my* first sight of the Pacific made my heart beat as if I were the first man to reach its shore.

Below me, terraced houses rose from the cliff sides; and still farther below, the beach wove along the coastline as far as I could see. Long, low waves playfully prostrated themselves in rhythmic ritual upon the sandy shore, which lay there shameless, yellow and naked, tinted by the sun and flattered by the blue of the sky—for ever importuned by the waves, which soaked and embellished with an infinity of patterns and hues the pagan splendour of their own sandy grave.

Each morning I hiked to the beach and back again after the sun had set, though after the first week I vaguely expected myself to make a decision: to hike back to New York, not the way I had come, but by way of San Francisco and Seattle, along the northern border and the Great Lakes, so that I could at least boast of having circled the continent on my own.

But the bright sun and the chance of another day on the beach made me put off a decision every twenty-four hours. I had little trouble making ends meet. A sandwich was enough to carry me through the day. I earned it by picking up empty bottles on the beach after everyone else had gone, and trading them in at a grocer's shop. But I could never find enough bottles to keep up to date on my rent—fifty cents a night for a room which the man who had given me the lift into Los Angeles helped me to find.

He had been a real estate man, and knowing his way about, insisted on making sure that I found a decent lodging for a cheap price. After driving around for a good hour in search of a place for me, he managed to put me up in an old mansion in Hollywood which had been converted into an apartment building. He arranged with the superintendent, whom he knew, for me to have a small room on the ground floor which was slated to become part of the apartment next door.

I was still there after a month, a week behind with the rent. Spurts of rain forced me to leave the beach early one day, and at last precipitated my decision. I pawned my trench coat, paid up my rent and told the superintendent that I would be gone in the morning. That afternoon I washed my shirts and socks, and in the evening started packing.

Through the door of my room, which I had left half-open for a breeze, I heard someone talking on the telephone in the hallway. I was intensely aware of the voice, though not of the words. It was the voice of a woman and she was speaking German with a Viennese accent. Suddenly the past month, my carefree days on

94

the beach, faded into insignificance. I felt like a gambler who has won petty bets, but never had a chance at a big stake. Whoever she was who spoke on the phone, she seemed a last chance sent by fate; I almost prayed that she would be pretty and that luck wouldn't let me down.

I stepped out of my room and walked down the corridor to the phone niche. Though I couldn't see much of her, seated sideways as she was, with her head bent listening, I accepted her as attractive; rather, I knew that had she been unattractive I would have noticed *that* first. When I slowed to a halt beside the booth, she stopped speaking. With her free hand cupped over the mouthpiece, she looked at me with the formal but unformulated frown of the interrupted.

'I thought I should tell you . . .'

'Just a minute,' she said into the filter, and cupping her hand over it again, she looked up. 'Are you waiting to use the phone?' she asked.

'Yes, yes . . . No, no, I mean. I thought only I should tell you I understand German and can't help overhearing you from my room. I would feel very bad if I . . .'

Her smile was an appreciation and a discarding of my precaution. The muffled metallic voice exclaimed something over the wire. She nodded at me in acknowledgement and dismissal.

Back in my room I decided I had made a fool of myself, when I heard her voice from the doorway. 'The phone is free now,' she said.

'You shouldn't have permitted me to interrupt you,' I said, coming to the door. 'You must forgive me,' I went on, switching to German, 'but when I heard you speaking German, I thought it only fair . . . You know, there might have been personal matters . . .' I trailed off, flattering her with the suggestion of secrets, while prompting her conscience to declare itself.

'I have no secrets.'

'You are too good-looking not to have any.'

'Are you Austrian?' she asked.

'No. I am Persian. But I grew up in Vienna.' I told her how I had come to America and started hitch-hiking. 'I shall be going to San Francisco tomorrow.'

'Why? Can't you find work here?' The same question from a man would have irritated me. From her it was charming.

'With my background, I could probably find a good job any time I wanted to,' I said. 'But there are more important things for me to do than go looking for jobs. I must see many things first.'

'Well, I hope you won't be disappointed,' she said in a tone that threatened to put an end to our conversation.

'How can I be disappointed?' I said hastily, almost blocking her way. 'With so much happening every day when I'm on the road.

Why, every day more happens than—well, maybe not every day, but almost every day—than it ever would on a regular job in a month. And I still have the whole northern part of the country ahead of me before I get back to New York.'

'And what will you do in New York?' she asked.

'Oh, by that time my father's money will have arrived, and I shall return to Vienna. Or perhaps to Persia.'

'And if your father's money doesn't arrive?' I couldn't tell whether she was mocking or serious.

'Then, I start hiking all over again, counter-clockwise,' I said. 'But I do not worry about that yet. I have heard so much about the north, particularly about San Francisco. I go there tomorrow.'

'Do you know anybody there?'

'No.'

'Then, what are you going to do there?'

'I don't know. I can't worry about such things.'

She hesitated for a moment and then said, 'I have some friends there. They are Viennese. I could give you their address with a note. They might be able to help you.'

'I don't want any help,' I said abruptly. And to soften the rebuff, I quickly added, 'But I would like to meet your friends.'

She looked at her watch. 'I must be getting along now. Good-bye.'

'Don't forget about the note to your friends.'

'No, I won't.'

'But I shall be leaving tomorrow morning. Early. Very early. When can I get it?'

When she looked at her watch, I thought I noticed a slight frown, as if my request were inopportune. 'I'll write it tonight. You can have it about nine. I'm up in 4B. Good-bye.'

'But you don't even know my name.' I called after her. 'It's Mohamed. Mohamed. Will you remember?'

She nodded and I watched her as she started up the stairs.

'Wait a minute,' I called out. 'What's your name?'

'Marietta . . .'

I didn't catch the last name, but it didn't matter.


II At nine sharp I knocked at her door. When she opened, I caught sight of an elderly man sitting on the couch. He appeared to be about fifty. On the low table in front of him were a bowl of strawberries, a bowl of sugar and a pitcher of cream. He was just raising a heaped spoonful, rimmed with the white of the cream, to his mouth. While she handed me an envelope and wished me bon voyage, I cursed him under my breath.

Back in my room, I berated myself for letting naïveté and optimism lead my by the nose. What rankled was that because of that strawberry-eater I hadn't even had a chance to get to know the girl. I lay on my bed trying to think of something that might give me a second chance. After half an hour, I left my room and ran up the stairs and knocked at Marietta's door. The man was still there, still eating. I wanted to shout at him what a fool he was concentrating on the strawberries with such a girl next to him. Instead, I asked her if she would mind lending me her house-door key. I had already returned mine to the superintendent, I said, but had just now received a call to meet a friend in town. I would slip the key under her doormat when I got back, and I promised not to disturb her again.

In my room I turned off the light and left the door ajar. Stretched out on the bed I waited for the man's footsteps. The chimes of a clock woke me with a start. Through my window I could see the large illumined numbers of a clock on a tower pointing to eleven. I rushed out and stealthily ascended the stairs and listened at Marietta's door. There were no voices, but through the bottom chink, light was spilling through. I knocked, and ashamed of my own hesitancy which had muffled the sound, repeated my knock louder.

'Who is it?'

'I am bringing back your key . . .'

When she opened the door she was standing just beyond the rim of light thrown by a floor lamp. The light was enough to outline her figure, but not enough to show off her features clearly. Her spare make-up was rather a concession to custom than a medium of beautifying her face. Her dark hair, parted carefully in the middle, was plainly arranged. She stood looking at me quizzically, self-assured, but without the brash self-assurance I had found in most pretty girls in America. Also, she was the first girl I had found in this country who was definitely shorter than I—as a woman, I felt, should be.

'I am bringing back the key,' I said again. This recital of the obvious made me ill at ease. I nodded towards the table and spoke in German. 'I see he didn't finish the strawberries after all.'

'Do you want some?' she said.

'If you would be generous enough.'

'Come in,' she said. 'Please sit down. I'll get you a plate.' From the kitchen she fetched a plate heaped with strawberries.

I waited for her to sit down. 'Won't you have some, too?' I said. 'I feel silly eating by myself.'

'I'll have some coffee instead.'

When I finished the portion she urged me to have some more.

'You don't really think I want another portion for the sake of the strawberries, do you?' I said. 'I am just eating on...well, you wouldn't let me sit here if I didn't pretend to eat.'

'Oh, there is still coffee,' she said, laughing.

'You'd better say right now how many cups you will allow me.'

'We'll see,' she said, as if I were being put on good behaviour, and went back to the kitchen for the coffee.

'Who was that man?' I asked as she was pouring the coffee.

'Why?' she said, looking up. Her surprise was also a censure. Then her features softened. 'You don't seem to like him,' she said with a touch of irony.

'No, I don't,' I admitted, taking refuge behind the pretence of frankness to cover up my blunder in asking the question. 'I never like old men, except those who know they are old and don't pretend otherwise. I like them still less when they are with young people. It's almost as if they were trying to cheat the years—by taking something from the young, or else giving the young some of their age.'

'He isn't as old as all that,' she said, making a grimace mocking me for exaggeration. 'A little over fifty.'

'You call that not old?'

'That man, as you call him,' her voice became formal, quiet, almost reverent, 'is a famous conductor and he is my uncle.'

Suddenly, I remembered that face from posters in Vienna. The features sprang into focus in my mind—the sharp nose and impatient eyes; the self-confident, almost arrogant, expression, too self-assured to care what anyone might think of him. It was a face which made of age an irrelevant attribute. But the man on the couch had looked merely old, like any old man, with his grey hair and forlorn face. I couldn't conceive of that famous conductor sitting where I was sitting now, eating what I was eating, and talking to the same girl.

'...and he likes strawberries. Very often he feels quite lonely and then I invite him over and...'

'It was rude of me to ask. I am sorry. It's bad enough to be lonely, but to be lonely and old must be terrible. One could perhaps bear one or the other, but both—'

My words seemed to affect her more than my flirting, as if by talking in earnest about someone else, we had revealed something of ourselves to each other. 'Yes, I'm afraid there's no help for it,' she said. 'But for him the worst is over now. He'll be going back next month.'

'Going back!' I said incredulously. 'But how can he?' I meant to say, how can he *want* to go back. I couldn't believe it. It never occurred to me that anyone might quit America, much less want to quit it—least of all a man like this who had been lucky enough to find acclaim and a position of honour here, for I remembered now reading in the papers that he was conductor of one of the great philharmonic orchestras on the West Coast.

He must be crazy, I thought. At least a little crazy, as well he might be with those deep-set eyes and his aggressive look. Even the way he had wolfed those strawberries had had something intense, almost ferocious, about it.

'Why? Can't he find work here?' Too late I realized I had asked her the same question she had asked me earlier, simplifying everything to the question of making a living. She looked at me as if she had expected better of me.

'No, it isn't that.' She shook her head. I couldn't tell whether her smile was sad or condescending. 'If a man isn't asked to perform, it isn't necessarily a reflection on his art,' she said.

'But I'm sure he was asked to perform. I read about him, I remember . . .'

'Oh, at first they couldn't cheer him enough. But later, everything sort of changed.'

'What changed?'

'Oh, it had nothing to do with music. He says it's because he talks too much.'

'I'm sorry, I don't understand,' I said.

'Well,' she seemed a bit impatient, even wary. 'They don't always like his opinions here.'

'But what difference does that make? Here, everyone can say what he wants to. That's what makes this country so wonderful.'

'You think so?'

'Of course.'

'Hasn't anyone ever objected to something you said?'

'Oh, but they do all the time. But that doesn t count.' And I told her about Lee at college and about a driver who once stopped his car and told me to get the hell back to wherever I came from, because I had said I had never thought of becoming an American citizen since I was already a citizen of Persia.

'Well?' she said, teasing rather than challenging me.

'But you can't really count that. They were just rude, that's all. And I can still go on saying the same things if I want to.'

'I wonder if you could if you had a career to worry about. It isn't as simple as you think.'

'Why?'

'I wouldn't know,' she said. 'Are you ready for your coffee?' She spoke now in the light tone she had used earlier.

'Please, yes. But let me warn you that I shall drink it as slowly as I can.'

'Don't forget, you have to leave early in the morning. Very early.' I was annoyed by the reminder, though she said it so lightly that it might well have been a joke.

99

'Ever since I've been on the road, tomorrow has been a long way off,' I said.

'What made you really take up hitch-hiking?' she said, leaning back and lighting a cigarette.

I didn't like the word *really*, as if I were hiding the true purpose of my wandering. I told her about being stranded at Watson College and how I fed myself on a loaf of bread and oranges; about waiting for the money and, then, of the exhilaration I experienced when I first lifted my thumb at the highway and learned for the first time the freedom of anonymity.

As always, when I had a chance to talk about myself, I spoke hurriedly and with abandon, as if I could never manage to utter all I wanted to say, carried on by the compulsion that I must share my experience in order to possess it more fully myself, growing ever more impatient at my own failure to re-create past events.

'It is true, I was miserable and lost while waiting at Lakeville for father's money. But once I started on my own, I swore to myself I would never let money make me miserable and unhappy again.'

'Did you succeed?' She spoke simply and without irony.

'Yes,' I said with conviction.

'But you need money ...,' she said quietly, almost sadly, as if she were sorry for me and my illusions.

'Money,' I interrupted her, waving my hand, as if it were endowed with a magic that could wave this obstacle aside. 'Look. I have reduced my dependence on money to a minimum, to almost zero. I can go for days on bread alone, or eating nothing if need be. Once a week I wash my seven T-shirts and seven pairs of socks. I shine my own shoes and sharpen my razor blade on the palm of my hand. And then, I can work. People think they get this pair of hands ...'—I held them up as if for witnesses—'... these hands at a bargain price when I wash their cars or windows or load a truck or do their chores. But they don't realize that those few miserly dollars of theirs, once they become mine, are transformed into riches. With those few dollars in my pocket I am richer than any of them. I go where I please, do as I please. These last days when I was stretched out on the beach I looked at those big mansions on the palisades and felt sorry for whoever was living in them.'

Actually, I had felt no such thing, but carried away by my own voice and by the intensity of her attention, I believed I had. And if I hadn't, I ought to have done so. My claims, I felt, were no less true for being late. I could not stop myself from talking, from extolling my vagrant life. I sensed that, for the sake of glorifying my freedom and independence, I was flaunting a reality—the necessity of money, ambitions and goals—which would catch up with me some day and belie these words and claims. But for the moment I felt I had struck upon the truth, that truth born of desire, which no logic or wisdom

100

can negate. Ephemeral as my truth was, it was as true to my soul as hunger and thirst were for my body. And like other truths it would some day make way for new ones. It would wane and die, as the appetites of the flesh do. It would wear off and cease to be truth for me, because the desire and need that nourished it would also cease. Then new desires, or the absence of them, would determine another set of truths for me, born of experience and disappointment, more of the spirit and less of passion.

Marietta listened, caught up by my enthusiasm, as if accepting all my convictions as a pure and permanent mark of my character. And I was speaking to her as if she were the first person I had ever truly spoken to in America. When I left the apartment, I knew that I would not be going away in the morning.


III Half a year later I was still in California. It was, perhaps, as much Marietta's fault as mine that I stayed there. Meeting her and living with her took the momentum out of my keeping on the move. Marietta had no trouble convincing me that no matter how far I travelled, I'd never find a place to match California. Where else was the weather so pleasant, the swimming so near and jobs so plentiful? She soon had it all planned out for me. She would lend me the money to enrol at the local university. I could pay her back later, and in the meantime support myself by giving German and French lessons to other students, and also work part-time for the translation office she was employed in. Everything had seemed so simple and promising. Carried away, I wrote home that I would not return for a while; I could take care of myself.

And it might have worked out if Marietta had left her planning at that. But she kept on planning; and planning not only for immediate needs and the immediate future, but indefinitely ahead—for both of us. When I realized that, I moved out of her apartment.

I had no choice. What had started as a carefree affair threatened to acquire outline and purpose. Each day added its dots and marks. For me these were bright spots, different in colour and for the moment more exciting than those marking my progress on the road; for her they were the beginnings of a new future. She was in her own way perhaps as lonely as I; and perhaps equally adrift, ever since her divorce from the American student she had met and married in Germany. She hadn't been sure what to expect from life in the States—except that it would be different from Europe, and more exciting. But what she found wasn't what she wanted at the age of twenty. Her husband ran a small super-market: his ambition and drive soon washed off any cosmopolitan colouring he had acquired abroad. He expected her to share his enthusiasm, to work the long hours with him; but she wasn't efficient, and her German accent and natural reserve weren't of much help either in handling customers. He told her to stay at home and she did. The end came when her uncle arrived. Her husband took an instant dislike to him and to the things he said. He called his opinions un-American and worse and forbade him the house. Marietta had been divorced for almost half a year when I met her.

Perhaps she counted too much on my accepting her help. She seemed to have geared herself so much to a new future that she could not draw back and continue life as it was: a week after I moved out of her apartment, she suddenly decided to return with her uncle to Europe and rejoin her parents.

With Marietta gone, I didn't enrol at the university. Neither did anything come of my efforts to give lessons or do translations. And finding a decent job was not so easy as I had thought. As a visitor, without first papers, I was automatically barred from most factory jobs.

Without a car it took the better part of the day just getting to Los Angeles and back to Santa Monica, where I had moved to be near the beach. Most of the leads—and there weren't many for which I might qualify—I garnered from the classified section of the Sunday papers. By Tuesday evening I had usually done with them, and few seemed worth all the trouble of going to Los Angeles.

After a month of this, I resigned myself to applying at an employment agency, though I hated to appear there like a peasant with a petition, to let somebody or other look me over to decide whether I was fit to be looked over by someone else who might give me a job.

I paused for a moment in front of the door to the J. J. Brave Employment Agency in downtown Los Angeles to check its name and address with the ad. I had torn from the Sunday paper. Before pushing open the door I rehearsed what I would say and how to say it. But when I entered, the middle-aged woman behind the counter didn't wait for me to speak. She asked if I had come to apply for a job and when I nodded, she said, 'Do you have any particular type of job in mind?'

I eagerly assured her that I was willing to take anything. By disclaiming preference I felt I might make up for my lack of experience, and perhaps better my chances for a job. The woman seemed unimpressed. Her eyes performed no more than their optical function as she handed me an application blank.

I took it to the nearest desk and began filling out the questionnaire by putting down my family name. At the second line, beside the words 'Christian name', I hesitated. What would an employer think when he ran across the name, Mohamed, there? And a line farther on, under Nationality, if he read Persian?

102

I caught the woman looking at me, and hastily filled in my particulars. Next, I was to check one of the professions listed alphabetically in three columns below. I began reading with Accountant, past Dietitian, Mechanic, Radiologist, and ended with Wringer. The list was so long, almost sixty choices, that I felt bound to light on one job for which I might be vaguely qualified. But even after reading the list several times I couldn't honestly check a single one. I left the spaces blank, signed at the bottom of the page and took the paper back to the woman.

'I'm afraid I'm not qualified for any of these positions,' I said.

'What *are* you qualified for?' she said, a trifle impatiently, after glancing at the paper.

'That is just the problem,' I said, smiling. She didn't understand that if I were qualified for anything I wouldn't be standing in front of her. 'I think I could learn almost anything,' I said tentatively.

'Well, I'm afraid we can't be of much help to you.' She didn't bother to give me the usual consolation that most prospective employers did—that about letting me know if something turned up.

'Oh, but perhaps something will turn up,' I prompted her. 'You'll get in touch with me then, won't you? I don't have much practical experience, but I have a little education. . . .' And when I saw her indifference stirring a little, I added, 'I speak a few languages, too.'

She looked back at the application paper. 'Well, why didn't you put that down where it says Special Remarks?'

I took the paper again and went back to the desk. I put down the Maria Theresa Academy and the Foreign Service School in Vienna. Then I cited my year at Watson and the A.B. degree I received there. Next, I added my languages—English, French, German and Persian. I felt much better when I handed the paper back.

This time the woman read it more carefully, though her interest seemed to wane towards the end. She looked up. 'You say you got out of college last June. What have you been doing since then?'

'I have been travelling,' I said.

'Are you employed now?'

'I'm staying with friends in Santa Monica.' I was ashamed to tell her that I had picked up work there as a house-boy, though I really didn't mind the work. The couple who employed me left early in the morning and didn't come home till seven or eight in the evening. Since I had told them, when I accepted the job, that I wouldn't consider cleaning bathrooms or making beds, I had little to do. I spent my days on the beach. But after two months I hadn't saved a cent. Also, I was beginning to get bored.

The woman made a few pencilled notes on the margin of my application blank. I expected now that she would say that part about getting in touch with me if something turned up. Instead, she asked me if I had ever done any selling.

Immediately, I pictured myself at work in a book or antique shop where my languages and education would be useful, or perhaps in an elegant haberdashery. Or a brokerage firm—some place where appearance, manners and polish were indispensable. I tried to impress upon the woman that, though I had had no experience in selling, I was certain I could qualify.

'Then try this place. It's the Genuine Silk Company.' She wrote the address down and handed it to me. 'It's a first-class outfit.'

'Thank you,' I said. 'And, of course, I'll be sure to tell them you sent me.'

'Yes, you do that,' she said drily.

I rushed out of the building. I was in such a hurry that I could hardly bring myself to hear out the first passer-by I accosted for directions. I felt sure this was my lucky chance if I could just get there fast enough. As I hurried up the street, I kept calling myself names for nursing so long that false sense of dignity which had kept me from going to such an agency before.


IV  I found the offices of the Genuine Silk Company on the twelfth floor of a new building a few blocks away. When I entered, the sight of the three men sitting on stiff-backed chairs along the wall boosted my self-confidence. They were evidently applicants like myself, but they reminded me of patients in a doctor's waiting room. They sat motionless, with that self-imposed air of relaxation which stamps those who must wait and, while waiting, dissimulate their hopes and anxieties. They seemed timid and tense, though eager to appear at their best. There hovered about them a touch of apology, of guilt, just for being in this room, for being no better than they were, for having gone no farther and fared no better in life. I couldn't suppress a reluctant sense of kinship with them, in spite of myself, though I resented the degradation their company implied.

I took the chair nearest the door and joined in the waiting. When the commotion of my entrance had passed, I leaned over to the gaunt man sitting one chair removed and asked in a confidential whisper if this were the Genuine Silk Company.

The answer was 'yes' with a formal nod.

'I wonder if this is all the reception we get?' I added, after a pause, trying to inject a flippant note into the overblown ceremony of waiting. 'Did everyone announce himself?'

'We were told to wait,' was the solemn reply.

104

I was glad I had taken the chair nearest the exit door. I began to wish I had the courage to leave then and there.

The door in the far corner clicked open and a cheerful voice could be heard within, calling back to someone else in the room. 'It's okay, Bruce. I'll take over for today.' A middle-aged man walked in with the air of a paternal comrade, sure of his welcome. With a quick, shrewd glance, he took in the four of us who had risen.

'Come on, fellows, pull up your chairs and let's get down to business,' he said, indicating a large table in the centre of the room.

Everyone obeyed, trying not to scrape his chair. I didn't know what to make of it. I had expected the applicants to be interviewed one by one. I still assumed they would be, but guessed we would first hear the general terms of the work.

'My name is Ted Schroeder. You fellows just call me Ted,' said the man, as if he were bestowing a privilege.

The far door opened again. A young man made his way briskly around the table to the exit door. Before closing the door behind himself, he called back to Schroeder, 'See you later, Ted.'

'Okay, Bruce,' Schroeder sang out.

Schroeder nodded towards the door. 'See that fellow?' he said, lowering his voice to a confidential tone, 'He started with the company a couple of years ago. Now, he makes ten thousand a year.'

There was an awkward pause. No one seemed to know what to make of this momentous intelligence—potentially so personal, yet actually so far out of reach as to be almost irrelevant.

'Now, let's have everybody's name, so we can get to know each other,' Schroeder resumed. 'You start.' He turned to the studious-looking man sitting on his right.

'Harry Diemek.' Though Diemek had spoken in a low voice, he seemed impressed how worthy his name sounded when announced in this solemn way.

'Glad to have you with us, Harry,' said Schroeder, as if welcoming him to a private club.

Schroeder looked at the next.

'Frank Begley.'

'Irish?'

'Yes sir!' Begley nodded his beefy face with a bashful air and sheepish grin, as if found out in some creditable quality he had been modestly keeping to himself.

'We can always use a good Irishman, Frank, you bet your life,' Schroeder assured him.

Harry Diemek was polishing his glasses, and Frank Begley now took out his balled handkerchief and wiped his brow. The two looked at each other as if Schroeder's welcome had already placed them in a class apart.

105

'Percy Stuart!' The name was announced prematurely in a high-pitched tense voice. Everyone turned towards the gaunt man whose trimmed moustache only drew attention to the fact that he was the oldest man in the room. Diemek and Begley straightened up a little, as if their chances for the job had suddenly been boosted a notch. Percy's name, the way he pronounced it, his serious demeanour, the fine, elongated cast of his face, the long neck which made his bow-tie seem somehow insufficient—all added up to something incongruous which put Schroeder momentarily at a loss for a remark to fit the case.

'English, aren't you?' Schroeder said at last.

'Yes, sir,' Percy said. For the first time in America I heard the title 'sir' pronounced naturally and not in a self-conscious imitation of an original that had been lost or never known. I wished Americans would let 'sir' stay buried instead of reviving it for potential employers as Begley had done, or for policemen.

'What part of England you from, Percy?' Schroeder asked, his tone a shade less familiar than it had been with Diemek and Begley.

Percy's answer sounded something like a sauce. Schroeder urged him to spell it, as if the letters would convey an intelligence which the word itself had failed to do. Percy began to spell it out, but I was no longer listening. I was steeling myself for my own imminent ordeal. I was the only one left, and dreaded the marketing of my own name.

Percy had barely finished when Schroeder's glance came to rest on me. I couldn't bring myself to expose my own name for Schroeder's commentary. I blurted out the first name that came to me—Alex's. 'Alexander Breuer!' I said.

'Mind if I call you Alex?'

I nodded in a way which left the choice up to Schroeder.

'What country you from, Alex?'

'Rumania.'

'Rumania! You don't say!' Schroeder took me up with that vocal tilt which seemed to welcome everything as good news.

Diemek and Begley also pretended interest. But with them it was a pose; their status was being momentarily blurred by a diverting spectacle. Only Percy held on to his reserve, too polite to exhibit a reaction.

'What language do you speak over there?' Schroeder asked.

'Rumanian,' I said spitefully.

'Oh, I should have thought of that,' Schroeder chuckled. 'Well, glad to have you with us, Alex.'

Though Schroeder had welcomed everyone else with practically the same words, they sounded a touch more personal and sincere, I felt, now that they were addressed to me. I was a little ashamed

106

for having cheated to get my welcome. I should have given my own name and country. To make up for my lie, I said, 'Thank you.'

Schroeder took out a full package of cigarettes, tore off the top and handed it to Diemek next to him. 'Have a smoke and pass it around. Might as well be comfortable. Go ahead. Take one,' he encouraged me. But the gesture too closely resembled a hand-out.

'No, thank you.'

'Non-smoker?'

I nodded vaguely.

'More power to you!' Schroeder exclaimed. 'I wish I had the will-power myself.'

I cursed my bashfulness and hypocrisy. Now I couldn't even smoke one of my own cigarettes. I would have to sit out the interview without smoking.

'Well, fellows,' Schroeder said after waiting for everyone to light his cigarette. 'Let's get down to brass tacks.' He paused a moment; then, looking each of us squarely in the eye, he said firmly, 'All of us are here to make money!' His voice was no longer jolly, but matter-of-fact, conveying a simple, evident truth. 'If I could make more money selling papers or shining shoes—well, I'd be selling papers and shining shoes. Wouldn't you?'

Schroeder's blunt and unexpected announcement that everyone was here to make money struck me with the impact of revelation. I had never thought of a job in such simple, naked terms before. Actually I had never seriously thought about jobs at all. I knew nothing about them, only about professions. The fathers of my school friends in Vienna were doctors, engineers, diplomats or military men; they were respected for their competence and standing and not for their incomes. There was one student whose father was a tea and coffee importer richer than everybody else's father. But there had been no question as to his rank. He rated lower than the rest. And yet, I wondered why I had never before realized that those professional men, too, had been bound to take money into account. Otherwise, they could neither have kept up appearances nor placed their sons in our school. Even my own father, who might have preferred to go hunting and to be reading his Ferdosi all day, had to work all hours to keep the peasants in line and make the land pay enough to afford the luxury of educating his sons abroad.

Though something in me rebelled against Schroeder's over-simplification, I couldn't deny its truth and was powerless to impede my surrender to it. And somehow I wasn't ashamed of my surrender. Schroeder's frankness forced respect. I felt less awkward now at being in this room. And the other three, as if purified by hearing Schroeder's elemental truth, looked the better for it, too, less for-saken, as if rallying around a flag.

'Now,' Schroeder went on earnestly, 'Our job here at the Genuine

107

Silk Company is selling. It's hard work, but hard work is fun, *if* it pays off. Right?' Everyone looked at him with such unqualified consent that no particular avowal was called for.

I was thinking that if I could only keep Schroeder's dictum—that we were all here to make money—in mind, everything would be so much simpler. I would simply work for the money I could gain. I need no longer feel alternately a martyr and a hypocrite where money was concerned. I could stop telling myself I was too good for any of the jobs open to an inexperienced person like myself. I could drop my perverted pride, which had made me run away from interviews and shy away from talking about money.

When my present employers in Santa Monica had asked what salary I would like in addition to board and room, I had been too cowardly to speak up. 'Whatever you think fair,' I had said, as if involved in some shady bargain. It served me right to find only ten dollars in the envelope at the end of the month. With such a pittance I could never hope to save up enough even to bail my suit and overcoat from the pawn shop, let alone make some sort of life for myself.

'Being a salesman is a challenge,' Schroeder was saying. 'Get that straight, fellows. It used to be that all a salesman did was stand behind a counter and wait for the customer to show up. That's old stuff. Today, you've got to go out and get the customer. That's the real revolution that's taken place in the world in the last thirty years. But unlike those foreign revolutions—Communism, Fascism, or any damned ism—ours has been constructive, and as American as apple pie. Now, in the old countries, they may not . . .'

My utter astonishment at Schroeder's manipulation of the concept of revolution, topped by his simile about pie, must have reflected in my features, for he was saying, '. . . Alex, here, may not quite agree with all this.'

I looked at the others, as if calling on witnesses to say it wasn't so. I had been listening with unqualified attention, and with complete agreement. If anything had intruded upon my listening, it had been the fear that Schroeder, with every word he added, was making it harder for me to cling to that evident truth he had established at first.

Luckily, Schroeder was too impatient to wait for an answer. 'Can you imagine this country without salesmen?' he went on. He looked over the four of us on the chance that someone might be fool enough to take this hypothesis seriously.

'I don't care what's produced and how good it is, if nobody gets it across to the man with the pocketbook. . . .' There was no holding him back. He drew a staggering picture of possible consequences— people not buying anything, less demand, less production, and less production, less work. . . .

I had never before thought of economics in such simple, graphic terms. Nor had any of my professors ever mentioned the salesman as an indispensable link in a nation's economy. But Schroeder's logic was so convincing that I was beginning to wonder whether much of Europe's and Asia's poverty couldn't be remedied if someone would only recognize the vital function salesmen had come to perform in the modern world. This idea struck me as such an important discovery that I leaned forward to catch every word Schroeder was saying.

'How good a salesman you are shows up in your commissions,' he said with a challenge. 'I make twenty-five thousand a year.'

He looked it—well-fed and well-groomed as he was. But I somehow expected a man who made that much money to be a bit more solemn about it, not quite as lively as Schroeder who, with his rosy cheeks and blatant air, seemed to do it for sport.

The way he had mentioned the sum of twenty-five thousand seemed no more a boast than a man's claim that he was rising early for pleasure. The faces around the table, though a shade more sombre now, were no longer devoid of self-confidence. Somehow the amount of twenty-five thousand was no longer so impalpable and beyond reach as the ten thousand of the younger man who had crossed the room earlier.

I would be quite content with one tenth of Schroeder's money, I thought, though I was a little ashamed of having no higher ambition. I wondered how the other applicants were estimating themselves, and looked around the table trying to guess which one might make that much money some day and what he would do with it. There was no reason why they shouldn't. The capsule biographies that I liked reading in the newspaper obituary columns always spoke of the poor immigrant or farm boy who had worked his way to fame and riches. Such cases seemed the rule here, not the exception.

I was conjuring figures and fortunes in my mind when I saw Schroeder produce from under the table, as if by magic, a black hand-bag of the type doctors carry on calls. He began to describe in competent but brief terms its sample contents of socks and stockings, underwear and men's shirts, ladies' slips and brassieres, and men's ties.

The sudden and totally unexpected recognition that the job in question was that of a house-to-house hawker, a *commis voyageur*, a *hausierer*, seemed a just, though cruel, joke on the illusions I had fed myself. I envied Diemek, Begley and Percy their absorbed attention. Their faces showed no surprise, and they seemed really interested in the items Schroeder was pulling, one by one, out of the bag.

Schroeder told us the price and described briefly the particular advantages of each item, its patented cut or its special weave, that

109

made it such a bargain. In spite of myself I was impressed. Every item *was* a bargain, much cheaper than those in stores. If someone had offered them to me and if I had had the money, I would have ordered half a dozen of each. Listening to Schroeder, I saw that it was easily possible for a house-to-house hawker to make ten or twenty thousand dollars a year with such bargains to offer. But it was still unbelievable that anyone who made that much money would still *go on* being a hawker.

After displaying the items and folding them neatly back into place, Schroeder held up a small, dark imitation-leather folder which cleverly housed a set of miniature spools, buttons and needles. 'Now, remember, after you ring the doorbell, you step back,' he said. 'It makes a better impression than just standing there, sort of intruding. Then you say "Good morning" or "Good afternoon".' And Schroeder, who had risen to his feet, made a slight bow and held out the folder. ' "Madame, I have a present for you." Don't let them say no. Make them take it,' he snapped. 'Everybody is a sucker for a free gift, I don't care who it is. The first day you do nothing more, understand. Don't rush the customer. But, next day you remind him of the little gift. They'll feel they've got to listen to you because they've already taken the gift. It's a sure-fire starter.'

Schroeder looked around the table. 'Let's see one of you fellows try it now,' he said with challenge in his voice.

I suddenly felt shrunken and panicky. His eyes lingered on me and then passed on, as if, after taking my measure, he had discarded me. He stopped at Percy.

'Percy. Percy, wasn't it? Let's see you try it.'

Percy's restless Adam's apple conveyed a faint tremor to his bow-tie. He fished a handkerchief from his breast pocket and wiped off his mouth and moustache. 'I'm afraid I shan't be a proper example . . .' he brought out at last. His accent seemed too clipped and required too much time to bring out the few words.

All eyes were on Percy, and he suddenly looked, not so much old as obsolete. So did everything about him—his detachable collar, his dark suit, his whole get-up. It seemed as if no amount of brushing, care and good-will could ever vitalize him. And his bow-tie was ridiculous, a symbol of illusion.

'Don't be bashful, fellows.' Schroeder's easy comment struck me as an insult to Percy, no less stinging for being impersonal and playful.

'Harry, you try it,' said Schroeder. Harry Diemek was on his feet before Schroeder had finished speaking. He pressed an imaginary button and then quoted the line about the gift. Percy leaned forward, watching Diemek. When Diemek finished, Percy, to my surprise, spoke up.

'If you don't mind, sir, I should like to try it now.'

I couldn't bear to watch Percy. I lowered my eyes, and imagined him getting up, buttoning his coat, walking to the head of the table. Then I heard Percy's voice and looked up. 'Madam,' Percy was saying, his posture and manner reminiscent of a butler, 'I have a present for you.'

Though Percy's approach was incomparably more refined than Diemek's, it looked incomparably sillier. Percy was watching Schroeder's face. There was a desperate, wanting look in those eyes, pleading for approval.

'That's fine, that's fine, Percy,' said Schroeder without much conviction. 'No need stepping back so far, though. And you got to talk faster if you want the customer to hear you out. Try it in front of the mirror when you get home tonight. All in a day's work.' Schroeder waited until Percy went back to his seat.

Begley, expecting to be called next, shifted to the edge of his chair. I refused to look at Schroeder.

'You get the idea now, fellows?' he asked. All of us nodded.

'Now, listen to this,' Schroeder went on, his voice more incisive, but without losing its quality of friendly attraction. 'For every ten dollars' worth of goods you sell, you get two dollars commission. That's twenty per cent. For sales of a hundred dollars, you get thirty per cent, that's thirty dollars. Not bad, eh?' he exclaimed, as if guessing the busy thoughts of his listeners. 'For anything over a hundred and fifty, you get forty per cent. But wait. That's not all. There's an extra bonus for. . . .'

Schroeder was snowballing commissions into fortunes. I wondered how fair a deal the customer could get with such generous commissions for the salesmen on top of the company's profit—though everything *had* seemed so cheap.

I switched over to my own private figuring. I was calculating how many pairs of socks I would have to sell to earn 1500 dollars. To make the goal more certain, I lowered it to 1000, and finally to 730. That was the minimum, two dollars a day for a year, enough to live on. But 730 seemed so small a goal that I upped it back to 1000 again. That would be enough to buy a ticket home and presents for everyone in the family. What an impressive homecoming it would be, and no one would be able to believe I had so quickly and easily learned how to take care of myself, and on such a luxurious level.

I was still figuring, lowering and upping my total, when Schroeder closed the black bag and asked if anybody had any questions. Compared to the big, secret question of how much each stood to make, Harry's question as to whether he could work part-time at first had that petty note of pointless ingratiation.

There were no more questions. We were all waiting for Schroeder. He leaned forward and with a voice that no longer catered to our agreement, he spoke. 'Success in salesmanship means getting results,'

111

he said, his voice deepening as if he were at last touching on the heart and core of the matter. 'It is nothing more than putting into practice what we all do instinctively and naturally every day of our lives, from the moment we are born.' He paused and drew a breath. 'Why does a baby cry?' he suddenly challenged. 'Because he wants something. He wants milk. How does he get it? He yells. That's the baby's way of *selling* himself, in other words, of getting what he wants!' His voice rose. He chuckled. 'It may not be the prettiest way or even the best. But the baby doesn't know any better. The important thing is, it gets *results*.'

I watched Schroeder closely, waiting for his serious air to break into a laugh. What he was saying couldn't be anything but a joke, I thought. How else can a baby get its milk? Was Schroeder confounding instinct with calculation; or did he mean that instinct was itself a selfish, though natural, design to get what one wanted? I didn't have time to puzzle out what he meant.

It was the same with courting, he was saying. What a guy actually does is try to sell himself to the girl, make her think he's the best she can get on the market. 'What the boy tells the girl may not make sense to you, but it makes sense to her, even if there's not a word of truth in it. And if he gets the girl in the end, why, his approach is worth more than anything Shakespeare put down for Romeo.'

Begley grinned. Diemek and Percy smiled. I smiled, too, though I wasn't sure whether the joke was on Schroeder or Shakespeare. But there was no doubt that Schroeder took the credit for it. And what he said sounded wonderfully true, much more than a joke. I thought of all the tricks I'd played on girls, though never with a thought of being a prospective groom. I leaned forward, intently listening, at this unheard-of marketing of hunger and of love; at the clever insinuation of hypocritical motives for instinctive acts in order to tout hypocrisy as a natural thing itself.

'Let's face it,' Schroeder said. 'Human beings are salesmen by nature. We can't help it. There's always a sales angle in whatever we do, whether we sell a product, an idea or our own personality. Take the five of us around this table. Every one of you wants me to think he's the best man for the job.'

Diemek and Begley put on a show of modesty, though without waiving the possibility that each might actually be the best after all. Percy gazed straight ahead. I concealed my indignation and surprise. I considered myself by far the least acceptable.

Schroeder went on. 'And *I'm* selling something, too. I'm trying to convince you that our outfit is the best there is. Get it, fellows?' he said, chuckling.

He slapped his hand on the table. 'Why, we even do a lot of selling *to* ourselves. Every time you make a choice, say, whether to

112

trade in your car for a new one or to take a vacation, whether to visit old Aunt Martha or old Uncle Charley...' he paused as if to prepare us for the climactic line. 'Well, how do we choose? Do we go by logic? Hell, no. *We do whatever we do in this world depending on what we sell ourselves!*'

He had pronounced the last sentence with a sonorous and heavy beat. Now he lowered his voice and bent forward. 'And do you know what happens to us if we can't sell to ourselves any more? Mind you, not to others, but to ourselves?' He looked me straight in the eye. 'We commit suicide. That's what we do. How do you explain that some people carry on in spite of everything? Some dear one passes away or he loses everything he's got, he's sick and broke and yet he carries on. Why? Because he's sold himself on the grand idea that life is worth living after all. He pulls himself together and hustles.'

Though I had listened to Schroeder with attention up to this point, I had felt, personally, no more implicated than had I been listening to a professor lecture on an unfamiliar topic. But now, the accumulation of his meaning caught up with me, forcing from me the kind of horrified wonder I had once felt listening to a hot-eyed revivalist preacher in Texas, who somehow picked on me, a curious bystander, to threaten with hell and brimstone if I didn't step up beside him 'to be saved'. The words of both were silly, yet sickeningly frightening. The preacher had been talking of the hereafter, Schroeder about the here and now.

If pursued logically and without flinching, Schroeder's premise— that 'selling' runs behind every action of man—distorted all spontaneity of temperament and of the heart to an elemental and cheap connivery, no less reprehensible for being 'natural'.

I was repelled. Yet I was helpless to place myself beyond his insinuations. Memory sided with Schroeder. The little, inconsequential concessions I had made so often in attitude and gesture, particularly when looking for work—though I had half-heartedly recognized and excused them each time—now came back to me and tainted everything I had ever done, every generous gesture and every act of friendship.

Yet I knew with an instinctive certainty that, however guilty I might be, I could never be fully guilty as charged. In that moment I despised Schroeder with a full heart. I cherished all the foolish, thoughtless acts I had committed in my life. But was Schroeder himself guilty? Or was he merely the mouthpiece and partisan of a faith imbibed since childhood—a new faith which indentured all of life, all instinct, into the service of tangible success—at any cost?

'Now get this straight, everybody,' Schroeder was saying sternly. 'We have too many applicants. We can only take the best, those

113

who can live up to our sales quotas. We have a quota for each district. That's to weed out the deadwood.'

Diemek stiffened like a soldier, confident that he could perform his duty. Begley's beefy face flushed, as if he had been caught at something. Percy didn't seem to know what quota meant.

Schroeder now took out some booklets and application blanks from the table drawer and handed them around. 'This booklet will give you background information about our company, and a lot of sales tips, too. Read it carefully and see if you're up to the job.'

Schroeder stood up. 'Well, fellows, I hope you liked my little talk. When you've finished filling out the application sheets, just hand them to the secretary inside. We'll get in touch with you later, after we've looked them over. Well, so long and good luck.' His parting words had such a warm and sincere texture that I felt a little guilty about my own unquiet thoughts.

Schroeder's chair was now empty. Through the window behind it I could see part of the Los Angeles skyline. I knew that in one direction, though I couldn't tell which one, the uneven rooftops of shopping centres, private homes and office buildings spread for over thirty miles to the beach at Santa Monica, and in the other direction, for a hundred and fifty miles south to the Mexican border. My glance ricocheted from the glittering top of the nearest skyscraper to that of the next, and then on and on. When I could see none beyond, I knew it was not because there were no more, but because my sight reached no farther. I knew there were still more cities with towers no less enterprising. I had hitch-hiked through so many of them that I had lost count.

The memory of those towns and cities merged now with the vista in front of me, challenging me again with the same question that had first come up in my own mind, when, half way across the continent, somewhere in Texas in the midst of an arid and desolate plain, a city suddenly rose into the sky, a city I never expected to be there. It was then that I wondered for the first time what impetus had driven Americans to build their interminable highways and countless cities, those I had already passed and those that lay ahead of me. What had drawn them so swiftly across the thousands of miles of unknown territory, building, building?

I knew the answer no better now than I had then. But now I was sure of one thing. Whatever the initial motive, the instinctive thirst, it could never have been the same thing that Schroeder believed in.

Diemek and Begley were busy filling out their application questionnaires. Percy was thoughtfully glancing through the instruction booklet. I waited for him to uncap his pen and start writing. Then, I quietly slipped out of the door. As I waited for the elevator, my heart was pounding for fear Schroeder might catch me

114

in my flight back to the beach at Santa Monica, which now beckoned in my imagination with a beauty and cleanliness I had felt but never understood before. And the ten dollar salary I got there as a houseboy seemed ample recompense. .

Nothing, no reward and no force, would ever make me follow Schroeder, could ever make me believe that what he said was true. And if Fate would ever fool me into his belief and into following his formula for success, I would be no better off and get no farther than the poor drunk I remembered who was tempted by a group of students in the early hours to walk a straight line they had chalked on a sidewalk in Vienna. Some twenty paces down the line they had placed a wine bottle. The drunk tried to walk the line. He tried and tried to reach the bottle, driven not by any challenge to his sobriety, but by his thirst. His doggedness magnified his elaborate efforts into something grotesque. He begged the students to shorten the line, but they would have none of it. Instead, they placed a second bottle at the end of the line, shouting encouragement. Each time the drunk, let down by fatigue and failure, was about to give up, the students added yet another bottle to the reward. A basket was produced from somewhere and all the bottles, a good half dozen of them, bedded in it. Somebody took off his tie and ceremoniously tied a bow around the neck of a bottle. Others followed suit. A woman threw some flowers, and soon the wine bottles propped up in the basket had the festive air of a gala present. And all the time they kept on encouraging the drunk. It was difficult to tell the cheers from the jeers. When the police finally broke it up, only the drunk was angry. He felt cheated of his reward, oblivious to the fact that he could never reach that reward unless the straight line could change into a crooked one to match his steps; or the man he was must change and walk the line laid out by the others.

If Schroeder's was the straight line and mine the crooked, I could as little follow his line as the drunk could follow the crowd's. Even if I wanted to.


V Out on the street every sight and sound—the skyscrapers, the traffic, the rush of pedestrians—seemed to proclaim that Schroeder was wrong: that this vital mass and motion was not fuelled by such cheap and perverted motives as his, but by enterprises and forces too manly and noble for people like him to grasp.

As I walked on, I gradually succumbed once again to that sense of wonder which so often welled up in me when I was walking in an American metropolis; and as if in tribute to all this grandeur about me, I tried to visualize this city as the primitive land it once must have been. Some of the initial stages rose up easily in my imagination; the isolated ranches, the settlements with general stores growing into villages; the dirt and dust roads changing into macadam, the villages, crowding with more settlers, developing into towns and these towns into cities like this one.

But *my* version of this growth always ended up with a city resembling a Persian or a European city, and not what it actually was. I could imagine a Persian village growing into a city like Teheran; and Teheran with more stores, more avenues and more people, some day growing into a city as large as London, Paris or Rome. These cities, too, I could imagine expanding. But to bring them into the line of evolution with an American city—even a smaller one than Los Angeles—required a jump, the addition of an arbitrary element which neither logic nor comparison could pin down.

The American city I had simply to accept the way it was, because it *was* so. The traffic was a bit thicker, the cars a bit longer, but the streets were no wider nor more crowded, and the people not much different from those I had passed in foreign cities. But here there was a throbbing pulse, an infectious, ceaseless momentum which could be palpably felt and which set every American city apart from the cities of Europe. And the skyscrapers, always clustering at the core of the town, rose up as if in testimonial to the spirit that built them—unique and inimitable. Their summits, I felt, rose no higher not because Americans couldn't build them higher, but because they had stopped in order to get on with other work.

Looking up at the skyline, I felt unique among all the people around me, because I alone sensed the marvel, though I could not name it. Other foreigners might think this was all the result of greed, done for the sake of money. They were always saying so. But I knew better. If mere greed could have created this, then other people would have done the same in other parts of the world, for greed is not lacking anywhere. But here one felt an impetus which the rest of the world lacked. My imagination could not keep pace with the trials and labours that must have gone into this spanning and building of a continent, an achievement so far-flung and unique that it dwarfed any other achievement of man. And it had been done not by heroes and great warriors, but by everyone. If the force that impelled them onwards had been no different from the forces that govern other people, their accomplishments would have resulted in no more than an imitation, however much aglitter. But it was a unique force, though no one, not even Americans, could name it nor knew what made it unique.

I headed towards the junction where the south-bound traffic converged into a highway leading to Santa Monica. At the first traffic light past the junction, I stopped. Instead of stepping on to the highway at the next red light and winding my way between the

116

halted cars hinting and asking for a ride, I stayed where I was, my back resting against the corner lamp post. I watched the traffic light change from green to red and back to green again, postponing from one interval to the next my stepping off the kerb to hustle for a ride; the visit to the agency and the interview had drained me of all initiative.

The air was heavy with heat, fumes and exhaust, drying my mouth and making each breath a minute, unpleasant chore. My shirt stuck to my body in patches, and on the exposed skin of my face and hands I felt that gritty unclean moisture that settles on everything that remains still for a moment in the city heat.

I asked myself, as I did each time I made my way back to Santa Monica after a futile trip like this, why I made myself go through all this—this double ignominy of pretence and failure.

Packs of cars, released at set intervals by some traffic light farther back, moved along the road, almost bumper to bumper, until the red signal light in front of me at the crossing brought them to a restless halt. The drivers, impatient of the delay, barely disguised their frowns, their restless eyes constantly checking with the light ahead, diverted only by brief, furtive glances to left and right, as if suspecting the drivers on either side of some unfair design— while feeling suspected in turn. A silent curse seemed to hover on every lip till the change of light released them and they spurted on.

The fitful, yet never-ceasing, passage of the traffic with its discordant sounds seemed to thrust upon my sense a battery of chaotic stimuli which I could not fend off. There was nothing else to distract me. On either side of me the store fronts, with their huge plate glass windows framed in aluminium, displayed the glittering sameness which results when the best and shiniest is exhibited by all. No store could do with less than the others and stay in business. And none could do any better, because they all had the best.

And the cars, too, which at first had appeared so varied in line and colour scheme, seemed, after a while, confined to certain basic models with but a few mixtures of colour. Now, after watching for a long time, it seemed to me that their sameness, their repetitive characteristics, were merely highlighted by the pathetic do-dads each boasted to make it distinctive. And the faces of the pedestrians, like those of the drivers, were set in the self-same expression, as if all were enlisted in some collective goal which everyone was bent on reaching first.

I began to feel like a bystander caught up in a determined mob. The splendid panorama I had conjured up a while ago—as an implicit denial of Schroeder—now seemed no more than a mad conglomeration of cement strips and superfluously tall buildings which served for nothing, in which not a single human being was at rest. I asked myself the why of it all. Why did these people rush

117

and work, and continue to work, to build, to produce still more and more, though they already had such a material surplus and wealth? They had built up the wilderness, they had done it all. And yet there was no slowing down, no resting. This land came closest to what the poor and wretched of the world conceived of as the promised land; here, need and want no longer disfigured the consciousness of man. Americans themselves liked to call their land 'God's country'. And it was. But people who lived in the promised land were supposed to find some measure of peace and contentment, if not joy and delight. Yet the set, harried faces passing me by reflected anything but peace and joy. I felt a nasty, flippant impulse to stop one of them and ask him simply, 'Why?' Why was he rushing, where was he going, what was the errand which impelled him on, and which demanded such uncompromising zeal and intent? What would happen if he just stopped and relaxed, content with the moment, with where, who and how he was?

Suddenly a frightful yell, uninhibited and shameless, rose up behind me. I was taken too much off guard to realize instantly what it was or who might have let it out. I turned around. At my side, so close that our bodies almost touched, stood a child, no more than ten, a bundle of newspapers clutched under his arm.

Blankly I looked at the boy, unable to conceive that it had been his piercing shout which had risen above the traffic's roar to single me out for its target. Just then, the boy launched a new call. This time, the mimicry upon his features was more arresting than the sound of his call. The distended jaws, thrown asunder, strained the features into a stiff mask, distorted and grotesque. The eyes, unable to bear the exertion from the small quivering throat, dilated into a glassy, oversized stare. His head, thrown back, thrust his defiant chin to the fore. With face thus uplifted, his lips torn wide apart, he flung his shout upward to the sky.

His call seemed to last on and on, interminably suspended on the first syllable of *Pa-a-ay-*, then suddenly snapped, like an overstrained chord, on the curt and muffled sound of *per*. The lips clapped shut, the lift of the head fell. The child's face, abruptly delivered of strain, lapsed into a worn and weary mood, as if some mephitic substance had already wrinkled his spirit with the strain of years as yet unlived. His lips puckered into a smile, while his eyes held mine, his glance challenging and amused.

'Did ah scare ya?'

Though his tone precluded doubt, he seemed eager to be assured of his bravado. I nodded.

The boy gave his bundle of newspapers an emphatic pat with his free hand. 'Gotta sell 'em before I can go home,' he said. 'Sold thirty-four already, with six to go.' He jerked his chin sideways to give emphasis to his resolve. 'Gotta sell the rest.'

118

Perhaps I expected him to look thin and poor, too much in need of money to have any choice in what he did to earn it. But he was neither in need of pity or compassion. With legs a bit apart, his strong body seemed ready to bounce into any direction, should a driver or a pedestrian signal for a paper. His jeans were clean, his shoes in good order, and through his T-shirt his strong torso had all the marks of a healthy, lively boy. It was to bolster his pocket money that he was doing this, I knew. But at his age, he should be somewhere else, I thought, shouting other calls, busy with other games, instead of making money.

I was about to turn back to the traffic when a swift, though subtle, change in the boy's face held me fast. It was no longer set and hard like a man's, but naïve, almost wistful.

'Wonna paper, mista?' With his free hand he pulled out a paper and held it out to me. 'Oh, come on, take it,' he said, with that magic charm only a child can summon.

'Yes, I take one,' I said. My foreign accent drew an additional fraction of interest from the boy. I took the paper. Without swerving my eyes from his face, I slipped a hand into my trouser pocket. I tried the other pocket. Suddenly, I remembered the three chocolate bars I had bought at a stand for my lunch, at the bargain rate of three for a quarter. Usually I bought one for a dime. One was enough to kill my appetite.

I offered the paper back to him and lowered my eyes to escape his fixed look. 'I am sorry, but I have not got the dime.' To ease my embarrassment, I added, 'I am really sorry, but I just haven't got the change.'

'I got change,' the boy exclaimed confidently. Pulling out a fistful of coins, he held them out to me, releasing but lightly his tiny, clutching fingers for fear of dropping a coin. 'See, I got it.'

He looked at me cheerfully, confidently. His bright smile, his blue eyes disarmed me with their open, friendly glance. It was his expression rather than any physical resemblance that suddenly recalled Schroeder to me.

'I haven't got a dollar bill either. I really haven't got it.' I caught myself almost pleading.

On the boy's face disappointment hardened into irritation, which he didn't bother to disguise. He eyed me with the self-righteous malice of a victim whose good-will and innocence have been tricked by a joke. A forced laugh, short, superior, unashamed of its contempt—more like a curse not worth the utterance—was all the answer he gave me.

I wanted to reassure him. 'I am really sorry, I really . . .'

'Ah, cut it out!' he snarled, and walked off.

The air felt hotter and heavier than before. Leaning against the lamp post I shifted my posture to avoid the glare of the sun. A

119

deep sense of failure, of utter failure—perhaps waiting for just such a moment—overwhelmed me. I felt myself the helpless target of haphazard and incomprehensible forces which I could not control, but on which everyone else seemed to thrive. A flood of bitterness and animosity, as if suppressed for too long, churned up within me a blinding revulsion and hate, which discharged itself upon everything that passed my eyes or rose in my memories of these past eighteen months.

The shouts of the newsboy traversed at irregular intervals the noises around me. I now waited tensely for each successive cry. Each shout seemed to draw my consciousness towards it, till I found myself concentrating upon that one creature all my shafts of scorn and hate, heaping upon him all my defiance and contempt. My silent curses followed the boy, hurling upon him the malevolent prophecy that each shout pressed forth from his throat was also pressed forth from his soul, though he did not know it; and each would leave an irreparable cleft—as would each smile of Carey's and each gimmick of Schroeder's—upon the spirit, deformities which no wealth nor success could ever heal, which time could not obliterate nor mercy set right. I damned and damned them all till some deep instinct within me quivered and shrank from my own vicious impotence.

I was left conscious of one wish only—to get away; from the noise, from the rush, from the boy and his shouts, from where I was.

At the next change of the signal light to red, I stepped off the kerb. Winding my way between the cars I asked, alternately turning to right and left, for a ride. Each rejection hastened my steps. I heard the noise of shifting gears as some drivers made ready for a new spurt at the imminent change of the light. The thought of having to go back to the lamp post and hear the boy again made me run from one car to the next. Without looking back, I knew the cars up in front had already started to move. I had time to ask one more driver, at the most, two. The first driver shook his head. I leaned towards another. 'Going up, sir?' And when I added 'please', the word tasted to me like that of a beggar.

The driver bent over and unhooked the door.


VI The driver dropped me a mile short of the palisades. Rather than hitch another ride, I walked on. Well-groomed sidewalks along the parkway led to the ocean ahead. A light breeze bore upon me the clean, fresh texture of the sea. I looked forward to my swim, to the feel of the sand under my feet and that of the breakers massaging my body. And when, half an hour later, I rode the breakers and ran along the beach, it was with that primitive contentment which accompanies physical pleasures that surpass anticipation.

In this simple, almost happy mood on my way back to the house, I caught sight of a man just stepping forth from behind a tree a short distance ahead of me along the palisades. As he came nearer I saw that his trousers and coat were ragged and dirty. His shoes looked bulkier for wear and dust. Every shortcoming about him was cruelly set off by the pure light of the afternoon, and magnified, as it were, by the prosperous backdrop of palm trees and well-kept lawn. His features were set in an expression of sulkiness, a resentful though impersonal frown. He seemed well past middle age. But his shock of unruly hair and the spring of his walk signalled a much younger man, no more than a few years older than myself. Everything about him marked the derelict, and prodded the imagination to conceive of his appearance as worse than it actually was—his beard a bit rougher, the skin unhealthier, his walk less controlled and his clothing shabbier.

When we were abreast, I looked away, as if instinctively avoiding the necessity of acknowledging him. I didn't even turn around when, after passing him, I heard him muttering behind me. Only after his steps faded off, did I turn to look after the lonely figure whose springy gait, even in the distance, seemed to brag of his indifference and defiance.

All the way to the house, I couldn't get the man out of my mind. I kept wondering why he didn't loaf on the beach rather than pound the streets. On the beach he could spare himself, at least, the burden of his clothing. He could swim and sun himself and wash off his ugly mood and, perhaps, recoup his bearing. I dreaded to think of what my own days might be like without the boon and solace of the ocean.

When I entered my room over the garage, the first thing that caught my eye was my employer's coat, which I had borrowed (without asking him) for my visit to the employment agency. I had been too much in a hurry to take it back into the house when I changed into my swimming trunks an hour earlier. If Mr. and Mrs. Meyer had come home in the meantime I would have to smuggle the coat into the house somehow. The necessity of facing this chore set off such a tantrum of self-abuse and self-ridicule in me that I just stood there, feeding my temper at the sight of the coat hanging on my solitary chair.

A year ago I would have been ashamed to wear such a coat, with its padded shoulders and loud design. Now I had come to a pass where I had to filch a coat for a day, while my suits, shirts and dinner jackets were gathering dust at the Lakeville railroad depot and I didn't even have the few dollars to send for them, provided they hadn't been auctioned off by now. I didn't even have the twelve dollars to get my one remaining sports jacket and my trench coat out of hock. Twelve dollars. I had given away that much in tips over a week-end at college. In other countries twelve dollars might spell a sum of money, but twelve dollars in America! It was absurd.

I aimed the towel through the open door at the rack in the bathroom, and sat down on my bed. In the twilight, my oblong room with its low ceiling seemed even smaller than it actually was. The wall opposite held my gaze till every crack and spot upon it was accounted for. My eyes followed a water-stained streak down to the floor, to the threadbare rug with its worn fringes at the entrance and at the bathroom door. The cumulative shabbiness of my room overwhelmed me. The sagging bed I was sitting on, the ugly table, the single straight-backed chair, the rug, would probably have all been thrown out if it hadn't been for me. And all that I owned was exposed by the open closet door—a pair of shoes, some dirty T-shirts, socks and a pair of jeans on the floor; two shirts and another pair of socks on the shelf above; and my solitary pair of slacks dangling from the hanger.

I caught myself thinking of the bum again. Except for outward appearance, both of us led essentially the same lives. Mine was as planless and as precarious as his. I carried on from day to day, at best read a book, while he indulged in cheap wines and whiskies, and in his own brand of indifference and devil-may-care which wasn't much different from mine. He bummed for hand-outs while I played the house-boy for ten dollars a month—thirty-three cents a day—a job even the bum would scorn. Point by point, shade by shade, all distinction between his life and mine disappeared, till for an instant, I seemed to see myself walking down the street with the bum's appearance superimposed on my own.

VII  Again I told myself, as I had done so many times since Marietta left, that I must force a change. Even a change for the worse was better than what I had. I would no longer drift, nursing false hopes that by luck I would run into a good job accidentally or that the next driver who gave me a lift would offer me a job at the end of the ride, as Mr. Meyer had done. I must quit at the end of the month; and I was more determined than ever not to write to father, as I had sometimes been on the verge of doing. I must make my own way.

I speculated on how much I might earn a month as a dish-washer or selling ice cream. But even the best I calculated was petty compared to what Schroeder had held out as commissions this morning. Just because I had taken a dislike to the man and his talk was no reason to reject the chance he offered. I must have been dense this morning, I thought, to pass up the chance. It was God sent, even if I had to play the clown and ring doorbells for a while. I could keep my job with the Meyers and do the selling on the side. With room and board taken care of, all my commissions would be pure gravy. With no more than two or three sales a day I could save up hundreds of dollars within a few months. Then I would be free to make plans for myself, perhaps buy the second-hand car I had always wanted. Or I could go to South America, or hike back to New York by way of Canada and the northwest. I could enrol at the university in New York, or even go back to Vienna.

I changed into slacks and shirt and, grabbing Mr. Meyer's coat, rushed out into the garden. The house was dark. After making sure the Meyers weren't home, I took the coat upstairs and put it in Mr. Meyer's closet. On my way down, I haphazardly checked whether any ashtrays needed dumping, and pushed two chairs back into their places. This was about all I ever did, except for washing the breakfast dishes, and those for supper, if there were any, which was seldom, because Mr. Meyer liked to brag how late he worked; and Mrs. Meyer was his secretary. I sometimes wondered what pleasure they ever got in owning their nice house.

The kitchen was the nicest room in the house. Large, airy and handsome, it had quite a different character from a European kitchen. It was a pity not to use it for anything better than making sandwiches or heating up canned food. Everything—the stove with its many knobs, the spotless white sink, every drawer and utensil—was not only pretty but handy and practical. Sometimes it seemed to me that, in proportion as kitchens became practical, beautiful and modern, the less they were used for what they were designed for —cooking.

On the kitchen table were two cans and an apple—my dinner. That meant the Meyers would be out for dinner. I knew one of the cans was soup, the other stew. I couldn't complain. Except for a steak or a roast on Sundays, the Meyers themselves ate the same. I didn't feel like bothering to open the cans and waiting for the stuff to heat up. All canned food tasted pretty much the same, anyhow. I buttered and salted some bread and, munching it in front of the kitchen window, looked out into the garden. It was getting dark.

Now that I had decided upon a plan for tomorrow—to go to Schroeder—I didn't know what to do with the empty evening ahead. I called up a girl I knew from the beach. A man's voice answered. Either I had the wrong number or it was her husband, who should have been at work on the night-shift at the airplane factory. I called up another girl, but there was no answer.

Eating what was left of the buttered bread, and then the apple,

I kept on looking out of the kitchen window as if the silence or the darkness outside might offer an idea for passing the evening. I knew I ought to do something—take a walk, clean up my room, pick up a book or go over to the library to get some new books before it closed.

I sensed my restlessness for what it was—the forerunner of one of those climaxes of loneliness that sometimes overwhelmed me. The first one had happened on the road, the night I was beaten by the patrolman. Since then, they had come upon me at unpredictable intervals. And the longer the interval the more surging the onrush. Then, loneliness would engulf me, as if some inner dam had given way, carrying off—by way of revenge and punishment—all pretexts and subterfuges that could help me maintain my self-respect and my claim that I was not lonely; that I was self-sufficient and needed no one else. It seemed as if some force I could not control were bent on extracting from me the one confession I had to withhold—the confession of loneliness.

Tonight, instead of trying to control or counter these initial warnings, I acknowledged them with a kind of specious sentimentality, in the hope that by admitting to a little loneliness as a bribe, I might soften or even divert the attack—and hoping, too, secretly, that some interference or distraction would intervene and dispel it altogether before it could strike me.

I let the hot water run over the knife and plate I had used, and after drying them, put them back in place. When I glanced around to check that everything was in order, my eyes caught the large crayon marks on the two cans. From where I stood I could easily make out the price marks, 18c and 31c. That made 49c, not enough for a movie. I could try to turn them in at a grocer's, but I would need more. I took an empty paper bag from under the sink and put the two cans in, then took two more of the same cans off the shelf. I had left so many cans unopened on other nights that I felt way ahead in the game. Ninety-eight cents was enough for a movie if I could turn the trick at the grocer's.

I walked towards the business centre of Santa Monica, past the quiet residential streets. Suddenly, the cans broke through the paper bag. Their clatter multiplied and reverberated upon the sidewalk, the stillness magnifying the drumming noise as the cans rolled off the kerb. I looked around, apprehensive that the noise might have alarmed the nearest residents. No porch lights snapped on, no voice disturbed the stillness. I collected the cans and walked on.

Two blocks later a voice called out behind me. 'Hey, wait a minute!' A black car pulled abreast of me. Then, the policeman stepped out.

'What you doing here, Bud?' The voice was casual, almost conversational, but I resented the familiarity.

124

'You have every right to ask me that question,' I said, 'but no right whatsoever to address me as Bud.'

'Okay, okay,' the policeman laughed. 'You want me to apologize?'

'No,' I said, feeling foolish. 'Of course not.'

'We got a call at the station about some disturbance around here,' he said. 'If you give me your name, I'll be glad to address you as Mister, so you won't take offence.'

I gave him my name and address and told him about the cans falling, making up a story about the grocery having delivered the wrong cans.

'You're sure touchy, Mr. Mehdevi. That was the name, wasn't it?' he said, before returning to his car. 'But no harm meant.'

He got in and closed the door and touched his hat. 'Good night. We aren't so formal in this country.'

'I am glad you are not,' I called after him. 'Good night.'

I watched the car disappear, feeling self-conscious and ashamed of my childishness, and of digging out this old stand-by of formality and etiquette to belittle Americans. It may have been excusable at college, when I really did take offence, and in New York soon after my arrival when I stalked out of the drugstore after the clerk said, 'What's yours, fellow?' But after eighteen months here, this was a cheap way to buck up my pride and dignity.

The first grocery I passed was closed. Another, farther down, was just closing. The blinds were down and the lights in the window were already turned off. When I entered, I recognized Mr. Novak. He was bent over the counter next to the cash register. Novak's was one of the stores I had canvassed for a job.

Novak's large head promptly turned my way. His long, sharp nose sniffed the air and the dark eyes with their bushy brows hid that suspicion which all storekeepers seem to feel for late customers.

I explained my errand. I had bought the cans here some time ago, but needed the cash now, I said. Would he please take them back and refund the money?

'You bought them here, you say?'

The moment I said 'yes' I realized I should have covered myself by saying 'I guess so' or 'I think I did', though I scorned such hedgings in others. Very few people had said 'yes' or 'no' outright to me in this country, and I was beginning to understand why. It was safer not to.

'This ain't stuff bought in my store.' Novak pointed his pencil at the cans.

'But you carry this brand,' I protested, pointing to a row of cans on a nearby shelf.

'Sure I do. Every store does. But these cans didn't walk out of this place. I ought to know. I don't mark my prices that way,' he said, putting his finger on the crayon marks.

125

'You recognize me, Mr. Novak, don't you?' I said, to thaw his suspicious and impersonal attitude. 'We met a few weeks ago when—'

'Sure I do. Never forget a face. Or a name either.'

Every time I heard such a claim, I wondered why people cluttered up their minds and memories with names and faces, when the human beings who bore them really didn't matter. A subscription salesman who had come by the Meyers' house a second time could even spell my name a month after I had given it to him. He bragged about this, as if I should feel flattered and as if he deserved praise.

'Well,' I said to Novak ingenuously, 'I thought Mrs. Meyer bought them here. You know I work for them,' I went on by way of further identifying myself. 'They left me over the week-end a dozen cans for lunch and dinner, and they haven't come back yet. I need the money badly and I don't know anybody to borrow from. These cans are all I have. If you don't want to take them, could you, at least, hold them and lend me the few cents till the Meyers come back? Would that be all right with you?'

'What you need money for so bad all of a sudden?' His suspicion was no longer uncompromising, but seemed conditioned upon the answer he would get.

Confessing to the movie wouldn't do. Motives must always be adjusted to the listener's pitch, as if the listener's credulity and judgement—and not facts—made them true.

'I have a terrible toothache, Mr. Novak,' I said, touching my cheek. 'Ever since this morning. I thought it would pass, but it didn't. That's why I still have so many cans. I couldn't eat.' My confession sounded so disarming and sincere that I was taken aback, less at the skill of my lying than at the shameless, shifting allegiance of my sincerity—an allegiance I had always thought reserved for truth only. 'My dentist is in Los Angeles and I haven't got the bus fare. I have already called him up. That's why I said I bought the cans from you, though it wasn't true.'

Novak made the common mistake of accepting a lie for the truth just because it confessed to another lie. With a quick glance at me, he opened the cash register.

'Is that all you get to eat?' He indicated the cans as he pushed the refund money across the counter.

'Mostly yes,' I said in a low voice. I caught myself conspiring with his pity, though I had nothing more to gain from it, and it was none of his business what I got to eat. But the temptation to warm myself in the glow of his concern was too great to resist. Perhaps it was so great because nobody else seemed to care. 'Anyway, pretty often,' I added with a false smile.

Novak took out three portions of hamburger meat and wrapped

126

them up. 'Here. Take it. A man's got to eat right. You'll need some-thing to fill you up after that tooth is fixed.'

'Thanks, but I couldn't accept it.' At first, it was pride which made me refuse. But then, it was something more, a sense of guilt—not for having tricked Novak into refunding the money, but for having tricked him into being generous. I was on the brink of telling him the truth. It would have been the simplest thing to do, as honourable issues are always simplest if faced instantly and without equivoca-tion. I missed the chance, and a moment later no words or expla-nations seemed adequate.

He urged me again to accept and I picked up the package. I couldn't spoil his gesture of kindness. When I thanked him, the words grated upon my tongue and ears. The least I could do was swallow my pride for his sake. I was at the door when Novak called out after me.

'I may need a helper one of these days. Drop in next week and we'll talk about it.'

I wanted to assure him that, after what he had done tonight, I would rather work for him than for anyone else. But my plan for getting ahead flashed into my mind. If I went to work for Novak I'd probably be unable to save more than ten dollars a week. It would take me a year to save up enough money to give me any leeway—money to take up my studies again or to follow up my good intentions about making a place for myself instead of just drifting. With Schroeder I could save it up in a few months.

'I'm sorry, Mr. Novak, but I already have lined up a new job starting the first of the month.'

'Okay. Good luck, fellow.'

On the way to the movie theatre I promised myself that some day I would write Novak a letter telling him the truth, and send along a present with it. I felt a bit consoled by this good intention, not realizing that all such intentions have their fatal flaw in the assumption that a failure involving another human being is retriev-able or reparable.

I sniffed at the meat package I was carrying. It was good meat Novak had wrapped up, not that faded, mixed stuff that went by the name of hamburger. I could go back home and make a feast of it—chop some onions, add an egg, a dash of flour and knead it all into a sort of *kebab*, with rice steamed up for *polau*. The idea of such a meal conjured up such essences that my stomach prodded me to turn around.

But what fun was there in feasting by myself? The better part of any meal was company. I kept a look-out for someone needy to whom I might offer the package. But everyone I passed looked much too well-off for such a hand-out. I suddenly realized that, except for the bums on the road and city drunks, I'd never met an American who might even resemble a destitute. At the last corner, before I reached the movie, I dropped the package into a refuse basket.

The foyer of the theatre was crowded. Rather than enter and join the crowd, I stayed on the sidewalk. Waiting outside, I almost had a change of heart. Marking time at the movies was a poor way to spend an evening. I might still make it to the library and with any luck run across a good book to take home. But even the best book wouldn't be enough for tonight. I could drop in at Homer's— a fellow I knew from the beach who ran a gas station. Or I could look up Elkins, the architect who had given me a ride a month ago. Both had always welcomed me when I called. But dropping in on them tonight, I felt, would be cheating their welcomes, for I wouldn't be visiting them for the sake of seeing them, but in order not to be alone.

The third bell rang in the foyer. I waited a while longer, after the crowd had gone in, to make sure it would be dark when I entered, to spare myself those idle glances which fasten on a new-comer and follow him to his seat. But when the usher showed me in, my impulse was to turn back. The lights were on and a searchlight flooded the stage where a man was just announcing a special attrac-tion tonight—a programme by the winning team of the Greater Community Barber Shop Quartet Contest. I slid into the nearest chair. Two more searchlights converged on the stage and picked up four men from the shadows in the wings and led them to the centre. Self-conscious in their dinner jackets, they looked like waiters dressed up for their first jobs.

I looked down to spare myself the embarrassing sight of them. They began with a song I remembered from college, about a moun-tain and a railroad—the same song the boys sang in the dormitory after some party that had broken up too soon, or when they had had a drink too many. I used to dread getting caught up with them and having a fraternal arm thrown across my shoulder. Now, looking down, I could easily imagine four of the students on the stage, huddled close, heads leaning together, with mouths too wide open or lips barely apart, their features simulating that sentimental camaraderie which they felt their song should inspire—and so deadly serious about it all.

When I looked up, the four singers *were* huddled exactly in the centre of the stage as I had imagined they would be. Only this quartet looked so much sadder for being so much older. Their postures of sentimental gaiety, like their song, were but an imitation of what I remembered from college, though the fellows at college had seemed scarcely less pathetic for trying to revive and imitate a spontaneous merriment of which they had never known the original.

128

One man in the group struck me as familiar. A moment later he stepped forward, or possibly the others stepped back. Carrying the tune solo now, he stood pin-pointed in the glare of the stage light, which changed colour in spirit with the jolly rhythm he was singing.

I recognized Schroeder. I seemed to see only the jolly grimacing of his features, without hearing the sounds which moulded them. What was he doing up there, I kept on asking myself? I didn't have the answer, but I was sure Schroeder did, or thought he did.

I got up and pushed past those sitting next to me, and made my way up the dim aisle, bent on reaching Novak's store before it closed for the night. I would tell him I'd changed my mind and would take him up on his offer of a job.

VIII A year later my prospects weren't much better, though I had passed through almost a dozen jobs since I had left the Meyers. I was sorting sales bills in a back room on the sixth floor of the Woolton Department Store in Los Angeles. It was the dullest of all the jobs I had had.

Compared to sorting sales bills, the other jobs I had held since leaving Novak's grocery seemed exciting in retrospect. Every now and then, I looked at the five fellows who were sorting with me, seated around a large table, and searched their faces for some hint that one of them might feel the way I did about the work. Their faces reflected neither impatience nor contentment. Only when one of them caught himself in a mistake did his features momentarily quicken, as if this minute variation, this particle of roused initiative were a welcome novelty in the routine of sorting.

Whenever I caught myself in too many mistakes, I, too, forced my attention back to my work; but each time I did so, the renewed concentration seemed to penalize me. Then, the lifting of each sales bill, the checking of its number and colour before slipping it into the right pigeon-hole, became a disproportionately demanding task.

To ease the strain, I tried to think back, or ahead—sometimes retracing in memory the past two and a half years since I had come to America, and sometimes projecting myself into what might happen tomorrow, in a week, in a month, should by some miracle money from home arrive after all.

But I had played this game too many times. Neither my memories nor my prospects would yield any stimulation. Tomorrow would repeat yesterday and today. I would come to the Woolton Company and start work at 4 p.m. and get off at midnight. Then, to tire myself out so I could sleep, I would walk all the way to my rooming house, telling myself along the way that something must change, that I must get up early in the morning and look for a better job.

But the next day I would sleep late, and by the time I had shaved, dressed, had my coffee and read the paper, it would be time to start off for work again.

I felt years older since moving to Los Angeles from Santa Monica three months ago, and thought of the beach with something akin to homesickness. I even nursed the memory of working at Novak's store—the ever-fresh air of the open store front, the green and red of the vegetables and fruits arranged row upon row like flowers, kept fresh by mechanical sprinklers. If only Novak hadn't shown such a blind spot when it came to taking sides between a customer and myself, I might still be there. But Novak wouldn't even hear me out when I tried to explain that no man could stand being told by every female shopper to be 'sure to put the tomatoes on the top' (as if I were a moron sure to put them at the bottom of the bag) without sassing back once in a while.

But Novak had repeated over and over, 'I don't care. It's the customer that counts.' I gave up arguing and stepped back behind the counter alongside Ned, the cashier who punched the cash register as fast as a typist at a typewriter, and never blinked an eye or dropped his smile when a customer wanted her total checked over again. Ned winked, grinned at me, and said out of the side of his mouth, 'Yes, sir. Kiss their ass and be sure to say "Thank you, ma'am".'

After that, Ned's phrase rose up in my mind whenever a customer rolled up her shopping basket and I stood waiting for Ned to punch the prices on the register before placing the groceries in the shopping bag. The shoppers always seemed to look at me as if expecting me to remember Ned's motto, and put it into practice. I knew Ned was right, but I also knew I couldn't face those females another day.

After quitting Novak's, I called myself a fool, worrying what I would do when my final pay cheque ran out, and wondering how I would ever find another job. But at the last minute, a job did turn up, as it always did—driving a laundry truck, clerking in a liquor store; then, as helper on a moving van, at a hamburger stand, in a small factory, at a freight yard shifting loads to trucks. Each job started out as a little adventure, but after my pay cheques helped me pay up my back rent and increased my solvency, I began to chafe at the burden of repeating the day's work, till I felt almost relieved when I got fired or had a chance to walk out.

After getting fired from my last job in Santa Monica, as a soda jerk, for making the sandwiches too thick, I moved to Los Angeles. There had been no reason for me to make the move, or to think I would fare better in the city. Perhaps, the notion of denying myself the beach, as some sort of penance, which might in turn oblige fate to treat me better, had something to do with this abrupt decision.

That I had survived these past three months in the city was sheer

130

luck. Looking for a cheap boarding-house the first day, I passed a flower shop. The cool, pleasant half-light within, where a girl was arranging flowers in vases, was so tempting that I stepped inside without knowing just why I did so. The girl stopped her work and approached me. 'May I help you?' she asked. I didn't know what to say, and when she began to talk about the flowers she had just been arranging, I confessed that if she really wanted to help me she could give me a job. There was no opening. I thanked her and was at the door when she called out after me to wait. She wrote down an address and handed me the slip of paper. 'If you want so much to handle flowers, try this place. Wright's wholesale.' She told me they had needed a helper last week and the vacancy might still be open.

The job at Wright's was the pleasantest I ever had. It was sorting gardenias and orchids, which I picked up in a small truck at seven each morning from the greenhouse, a good hour's drive in the countryside. Back at the wholesale house at ten, I unloaded the thin, plywood boxes and joined the others in sorting. We were usually through by one, and if there was nothing left to do, Mr. Wright let us go. When I left the warehouse I was quite content and cocky at having done a day's work and still having the afternoon free.

Compared to sorting flowers, sorting sales bills at the Woolton Company was a poor substitute. Looking at the faces around me at the table, I wondered if I looked as pitiful as my companions did. In the light of the low ceiling lamp their faces had a sickly pallor— slack and pasty. I could never feel as healthy and alert on this job as I had felt on those early mornings when driving my little truck back to the store, with the aroma of the boxed flowers mixing with the fresh country air that pressed in through the open window at my elbow. Sometimes when a traffic signal stopped me on the way and I saw a pretty girl waiting for the bus, or about to cross the street, I leaned out and threw her an orchid or a gardenia. The girl's pert, pretty face, at first startled, would light up with a smile. And as I drove off, we would wave at each other and I would think to myself that none of the thousands of flowers in the back of the truck, which would be bought by retailers for corsages, bouquets, parties and funerals, would ever fetch such a surprised welcome.

I wouldn't have minded being bawled out by Mr. Wright for giving the flowers away. Somebody must have recognized the truck and told him about it. But then, Mr. Wright started talking about other people's property, as if I had sold flowers by the dozen for my own gain. At the end, he abruptly asked what had happened to my button. Why wasn't I wearing the button, like everybody else did? Everybody meant also Mr. Wright, who wore it on his lapel. It bore the legend 'Wright grows them right'. This slogan was printed across the boxes, the wrapping paper, and also headed the store front.

I hedged for an excuse, and mumbled something about having lost the button again. Mr. Wright stumped off to his desk, took out a button from a drawer and tried to pin it on my shirt.

'Is wearing that button part of my job?' I said, stepping back.

He stood there staring angrily, as if he couldn't make sense out of my words. 'You bet it is,' he flared up.

'I am working for you, not advertising you, Mr. Wright,' I said. 'If you are satisfied with my work, that should be enough.'

He called over his shoulder to his secretary to make out my pay cheque. Turning back to me he snapped, 'You needn't come back tomorrow.'

I told his secretary to deduct half a day's pay, because I was quitting right now.

All the way to the bus stop that day, I upbraided myself for making such a fuss over wearing a button. I was still calling myself names when I recognized Percy, one of the applicants at the Genuine Silk Company, waiting for the bus. Though a little thinner, Percy had a confident, almost jaunty air about him, quite different from the nervous, hesitant fellow I remembered. He recognized me at the same moment and we shook hands. Each of us seemed to assume that the other was working for Schroeder. But I said it first.

'I am afraid this being a house-to-house solicitor wasn't quite suitable for me,' Percy informed me, as if my assumption that he had taken the job were not quite proper. I assured him that I had felt the same way about it.

When I asked him how he was making out, he told me he had found a spot to his liking with the Woolton Company Department Store. A note of smugness crept into his voice when he answered my question about how to go about landing such a job. I wanted to press him for some pointers, but the bus was pulling up, and the best I could do was ask him for the name of the man who did the interviewing.

'Spielman, sixth floor,' Percy called out rather curtly from the stair well of the bus.

For once, getting a job was easier than I had expected. It was simply a matter of filling out an application blank and being interviewed by Mr. Spielman. Though he hired me on the spot, and probably would have hired anyone who could read and write—for those were the only requisites necessary—he first studied my application blank with the silent thoughtfulness of a man weighing a momentous decision. When he cautioned me that the job was temporary, I felt a little sorry for him for assuming that I, or anyone, could ever consider such work in any *other* way. Still, after he said that I could report for work at four that afternoon, if I wanted to,

I was a little dazed at my luck. I was quite unaware that my being hired had nothing to do with my background or education, so laboriously listed on the application blank and upon which Mr. Spielman had made some complimentary comments. It was simply a consequence of the semi-annual sale.

Though I had only been at the Woolton Company two weeks, it seemed like two months or two years. Each day, waiting out the eight hours seemed harder than it had been the day before. The wall clock was always lagging behind my notion of Time, and there was nothing else in the room worth my attention. Sorting the sales slips did not require more than a fraction of my brain. My hands could do the sorting almost reflexively, almost but not quite. And though my mind was idle, it couldn't roam too far, for then my sorting got mixed up or ceased altogether.

Whenever I looked at the others, I wavered between grudging admiration and contempt. I alternately cursed and envied them for their calm, patient, uninterrupted sorting. In the glaring light from above, their faces appeared inscrutable, both stupid and profound. Only with Percy did I feel an unspoken intimacy, because I caught him checking with the clock almost as often as I did.

Only seven minutes had passed when I looked at the clock again, instead of the hour I had guessed. It showed 6.12. For an instant I thought the clock had stopped. To distract myself I glanced through the items listed on the larger sales bills to see if there was anything there which I would have liked to buy. Some bills were as high as $80, $100 and even $150. Who could afford such bills, I wondered? There were too many of them to have been paid by rich people only. Where did all the money come from? I could well believe the company's boast that the average turnover was $500,000 a day. Multiplied by 365, that made approximately $180,000,000 a year— a bigger sum than the annual budget of some foreign countries.

The next time I looked at the clock it had jumped fifteen minutes; I felt as if I had cleverly tricked it into moving faster. I decided to concentrate on sorting, forbidding myself a look at the clock till I was sure a full half hour had passed.

But such a spurt of concentration, after a short while, required too much energy. It left me weary and fatigued, a forewarning of the desolate exhaustion that would trail me at midnight when, walking home, I felt more spent than I had after a day of the hardest physical labour I'd ever done—mixing cement for a tile layer.

After an hour of mixing cement I had felt as if my backbone would crack the next time I straightened up to carry two bucketfuls into the house for the mason. Carrying the buckets to the first and second floor could still be managed, but getting them up to the third floor I had to set my teeth not to knuckle under. Yet, after a day's work with the mason I felt tired but not weary, as I did now after barely two hours of lifting and dropping small pieces of paper into pigeon-holes.

The only other work that had affected me the way this sorting of bills did was the one factory job I ever held. It was in a plastics factory. From the work bench next to mine a steady supply of horseshoe-shaped forms popped into a basket beside me. My job was to press the shapes evenly against a rotating brush to file off any rough edges, and then to throw them on to a moving belt which carried them away.

For four hours in the morning and four hours in the afternoon my gloved right hand picked up the horseshoe shapes, and after my left hand joined the right, they pressed the thing against the whirling wire brush while my right foot pressed a floor button to increase the brush's speed. I envied the others their casual, natural way of attending to their tasks, and when the day's work was done their bearing and talk had no hint of tiredness or depression. They walked out towards their big, shiny cars as if contented with their lot and the day's work. And Mac, who picked me up each morning on his way to work and dropped me in the evening (charging two dollars a week), switched on the radio as soon as he got behind the wheel.

Sitting alongside him in the car I kept asking myself how a man could go on performing the same motions at the same machine every day for fourteen years as Mac had been doing. His work was no less monotonous than mine; his machine was bigger, had more buttons and levers, but he, too, sat on a stool like mine and his motions didn't seem to require more brain. There must be millions of workers like Mac, whose days and work were conditioned the same as his. It didn't occur to me that unless such hosts of men performed precisely the kind of mechanical work Mac did, neither he nor the others could have afforded what each of them had—the big car, the modern house, and all the electrical gadgets that brought their existence up to date.

When on the second Monday Mac tapped his horn outside my boarding-house, I told him I wouldn't be going to work. He thought I meant it just for the day. 'What's the matter, you sick?'

I told him I was, and after I said the words, I had the eerie feeling that what I had said was much closer to truth than to the lie I had meant it to be.

IX  Now I forced myself to go on with sorting the bills, refusing to look at the clock. But I stole a glance at the faces around the table. They had turned wearier by shades—greyer and pastier. Across the table, Percy's face seemed longer and bonier

134

than it ever had. His neck, too, seemed longer and leaner. And his eyeballs seemed to protrude more, as if his bow-tie were but a pretty noose drawing tighter by the hour. Only his moustache, still groomed and clipped, seemed stubbornly asserting his claim for a place in the race of the living.

Now and then we looked at each other, two people who might otherwise never have exchanged a glance or word. Our silent glances repeated the same message: 'How much longer till the supper break at eight?'

I decided to visit the wash-room. When I pushed back my chair, Percy looked up, startled. His eyes were so expectant, so hungry for a word, so hopeful for that message that would permit him to put a stop to his sorting, that I could not disappoint him by silence. On the spur of the moment, I said, 'Dinner time, let's go!'

The bony face lighted up as if responding to a blessing. The sallow skin seemed to bloom. The bulging eyes in their hollows shone. And an expression of blissful relief, like that of a sick man miraculously restored to health, expanded over his drawn features. When Percy bent forward to follow my example, pushing back his chair, he glanced sideways at the clock. It showed only 6.35, nearly an hour and a half short of dinner time.

Percy fell back into his seat. His features relapsed, the skin fading into its previous greyish tinge. A re-transformation, as extreme as the first—but now bringing into cruel perspective the aspect of a man to whom sickness and not health has become the normal—drained that face, leaving it naked, bereft of all guards. (And yet, at that moment, Percy's face had a touch of that pathetic greatness which is sometimes apparent in a man who has, haphazardly, become a mirror of the many.)

At the same time, Percy's change of expression, perhaps for being so swift and distorted, struck me as irrepressibly comic. I burst out laughing. And Percy, either in response or in self-pity, began a slow, hesitant smile. His upper lip tentatively drew up above his large, flat teeth. It quivered, then joined the stretched lower lip in a wide smile that turned into a chuckle and then into laughter. But his laughter sounded so odd and sad that I stopped laughing.

Behind me I heard the voice of Spielman, who had evidently observed the whole scene. He asked me in a casual yet studied way to come with him to his office. I couldn't help granting a certain justice to his summons, ominous as it seemed. For I felt instantly guilty, not for having worked less, but for having pretended less and, with my bad joke, for having interfered with the pretence of the others. Yet, as I followed him across the room to his office, my conscience revolted against this self-reproach. I felt that peculiar ignominy which comes with the acceptance of guilt—not for a

135

transgression—but for some unruly trait or spontaneous action closer to virtue than to a fault.

His office was a cubicle partitioned off from a row of others along the hallway. After I entered and closed the door behind me, I had that sensation of over-proximity I sometimes experienced when stepping into a crowded elevator. Spielman was already seated behind his desk. He was twirling a pencil and looking at me as if trying to formulate a difficult thought well before expressing it. Behind his desk, he cut a less impressive figure than he had when looming up so unexpectedly at my elbow.

'How are you getting along?' he asked, innocuously.

I assured him I was getting along fine.

'Do you think you have been doing as well as the others?' His voice, reflective and almost kind, seemed to ask for my judgement on myself in order to help him find the right answer. For a moment, I actually wondered whether I had been doing as well as the others. I said I was sure I had.

'I thought so!' he exclaimed, as if my words had confirmed his private opinion. 'And you think your work good enough as it is, don't you? Well, let me tell you such an attitude won't get you far. I would still be a clerk in the stockroom if I hadn't always tried to work a little harder than the fellow next to me.' He paused in tribute to himself. 'A man can always do better, if . . .'

He began to talk about his rise with the Woolton Company. At once, I listened with that impulsive admiration I couldn't help feel for any American who had worked his way up. I tried to imagine the frail, almost studious figure of Spielman struggling with wrapping, packing and shipping packages in the stockroom alongside brutes who scoffed at him—something similar to the way Fritz, the driver of the moving van, had razzed me about my flannel slacks and two-toned shoes, only worse. I imagined Spielman sticking it all out and working his way up, step by step, till now he had an office to himself.

But I felt sorry Spielman hadn't risen any higher in return for all the work he had done. Inwardly, I pleaded with him to go on talking, hoping he might cite some adventure, some joy or triumph or sorrow that would have been additional recompense for his labour, more than his name and title lettered on the door of this cubicle.

He was sitting straight and stiff behind his desk, as if conditioned to that posture by the restrictive space of his tiny office, his presence a mere supplement to the grey, metallic furniture—a desk, two chairs, a lamp and a telephone. It was arranged so austerely that, for a moment, I felt as if I were a visitor to a cell, a monk's or a prisoner's. But his face reflected neither the quiet, peaceful glow of a celibate's, nor the resignation of a prisoner's. His horn-rimmed glasses and his crew-cut gave him a superciliously boyish look,

136

though his face actually had nothing youthful or aspiring about it. Neither did it have any of the marks of maturity beyond a touch of grey at the temples and a few wrinkles around the eyes and mouth, marks which seemed rather blemishes than signs of dignity, wisdom and experience. He seemed to have lost his youth without recompense, to have aged without having been granted any of the rewards that justify the loss of youth.

For the first time the American magic of rising up in the world failed to answer me as a measure of man. Somehow it didn't seem to matter to me whether Spielman had worked his way to foreman or to president. It seemed to me that the road he had travelled, and which so many others set out on, was a sterile trek whether it led him higher or not. I even thought, perversely, that he might have lived a richer life and been better off if he had remained working in the stockroom. I didn't know whether to admire him for having risen to what he was, or pity him for having nothing better to show for his labours.

A faint colour had come into his dusty cheeks, as if he had been carried away talking about himself and had said more than he meant to. He had risen to his feet, and so did I, thinking the interview had come to an end. It was then that he reproached me for not being fair to my employers, for not being loyal to the company. . . .

He had used the word loyalty to me once before, when he had hired me for the job. I had thought everything settled when he told me to report for work at four that afternoon. I had said good-bye and was at the door when he called me back.

'I forgot to ask you, are you now or have you ever been a member of a foreign political organization?' He sounded so sonorous that he reminded me of a movie I had seen where the clerk read out the words about speaking the truth, the whole truth and nothing but the truth as if they were his own. I would have told Spielman it was none of his business, if his words hadn't sounded so silly and if I hadn't needed the job.

'Why no, I never have.' I could have added that I might well have been a member of some such group, as so many other students in Austria were. The only reason I hadn't joined one group or another was because there were so many and I could never make up my mind which party to join.

'Were you ever a member of a club with political affiliations? Were you ever a member of any club?'

'Yes. The red-blue-red Tennis Club in Vienna.'

'And this club was a purely social or sport club?'

'Yes. Tennis.'

'Then how do you explain the colours, red-blue-red? Has that any significance?'

I told him I couldn't possible know why the club had chosen

137

those colours. It was the oldest club in Vienna and the one nearest to my apartment.

He seemed to accept my explanation. 'Then, please be kind enough to sign this paper,' he said, pushing a form towards me.

The paper asked me to swear that I had never been a member of the Communist party nor of any subversive group, and that I had never been a member of a group advocating the overthrow of the U.S. government. The phrases were familiar to me from newspaper stories about investigations. I didn't finish reading the text.

'Is this really necessary?' I asked Spielman. I couldn't help smiling.

'Of course, you don't *have* to sign if you don't want to,' he said reasonably. 'But we have made it part of our policy to give our employees a chance to express their loyalty to our form of government by signing this statement.'

I couldn't understand why loyalty to the government wasn't taken for granted, but I had the distinct feeling that if I didn't sign, my refusal would be taken as an expression of disloyalty. I signed.

I was puzzled, though, why Mr. Spielman or his bosses might think revolutionists would start sorting sales bills at the Woolton Company. Or did they make themselves the guardians of national loyalty? If they did, it might all end up with every company and person trying to be more loyal than the next, until everyone began thinking he wasn't loyal enough if he didn't do his share in making sure that everyone else was as loyal as he was. Nobody seemed to realize how they degraded the concept of loyalty by handling it this way, just as they degraded the flag by draping it all over the store front to boost their semi-annual sales.

When Spielman spoke of loyalty to me this second time, I asked him if he was taking issue with my work.

'I do not think you can work very well if you *laugh* so much,' he said, as if laughing were one of my shortcomings.

I looked at him sharply. Above the dim light of the desk lamp, his face had a mask-like, putty-like quality, as if it might melt or decompose in a stronger light. I felt that if I were to rub a finger hard across his cheek, I would leave a streak, as on wax. I tried to imagine Spielman laughing, really laughing.

I left his room without answering him. But it wasn't till after I had rejoined the others at the sorting table that the full implication of his words—that I was laughing too much—caught hold of me. My hands were shaking. I tried to shrug Spielman off.

I tried to remember when I had really laughed last, and couldn't. A sudden dread and fear that I might never again laugh, really laugh, took hold of me; and even more, the fear that—should I by some miracle feel like laughing in the future—I might suppress the impulse for fear of displeasing. And any other spontaneity still left in me would be bound by the same censorship. I had to take a stand. Each slip of paper that I kept on sorting was mute proof of my helplessness, of my cowardice. I sensed, without actually challenging myself, that real cowardice for me no longer consisted of cringing before another man—as I had almost done in Texas—nor of compromising some part of my honour and self-respect as I had so often done by whining about my luck in order to seek sympathy and companionship, but of turning tail in a dilemma like this one; which, insignificant and inconsequential in itself, would, if let go unchallenged, finally mutilate my instinct, the last refuge of my self-respect, in the name of reasonableness.

Staying on would be only common sense, but it would spell defeat for me. And my victory, if escaping defeat could be called victory, and if a real victory would ever be, would be crowned with a shrug by others and rated no better than a quixotic gesture.

I sorted the bills faster and faster, expecting the continuity of work and time to bridge the interruption, to tide me over and lead me safely back into the collective routine. But all the while I was holding off the only alternative left to me—to walk out, to quit. All the reproaches that had followed my quitting other jobs kept crowding in on me, warning me not to be childish and silly. This job was temporary, anyway, another ten days or two weeks. I reminded myself of past pilgrimages to agencies and interviews. The wisdom of hanging on to what I had was evident. But wisdom was not enough.

If I could keep on sorting for a while longer, I thought, all might be well—past and forgotten. Spielman would forget, probably had already forgotten what he said. Even if he had spoken to me in front of the others, they, too, would forget. By tomorrow, or even sooner, after dinner, I would probably have forgotten, too. But did I *want* to, and *should* I forget?

Once more I looked at the heads around the table, spotlighted by the low, bright ceiling lamp. They were bent low, as mine had been. I felt I ought to shout a warning. I looked at the clock. It was a few minutes after seven. I put down the batch of bills I was holding, pushed back my chair, and without responding to Percy's inquisitive glance, walked out of the room, past Spielman's office and down the corridor to the service elevator.

X  The night exit let me out on a side street. I walked past the Woolton Company show windows that stretched along the whole block towards the avenue. Each picture window was as large as a room, each different in content, layout and lighting, and among them, they displayed almost every item needed or wanted to make life comfortable and pleasant. Each held the message that all this would come true for me if I would ransom it with a down payment of a few dollars.

Though I slowed down as I came abreast each window, I wouldn't have stopped altogether if I hadn't caught my face reflected in a large looking glass that was part of one display. It was not my reflection, but my expression—so different from what I had expected —that stopped me. What I saw was a dull, set face without a spark or any sign of awareness, a face with a vacant, listless look like a sick animal's. About the cheekbones the skin was stretched taut, pulling the half-open lips into an odd shape, as if they were on the verge of smiling or of crying, but had forgotten how to do either and why.

For a moment, I thought something might have provoked me to smile, though I couldn't remember what it could possibly have been. I moved a hand to touch one cheek. The flesh felt knotted, hard, as if my teeth were on edge. Suddenly, it seemed to me I was looking at someone else's face in the mirror and I whirled around, as if caught in a shameful act. There was no one behind me. Quickly, I walked on.

In a moment I had reached the avenue, which opened into a large square that was a blaze of lights. Advertisements, three, four, ten storeys high, spelled out and blinked their messages with such powerful neon that the sky above was pale and colourless and the stars blotted out. Each ad. competed with the others for attention, but their clashing glares and contradicting claims seemed to cancel each other out. Yet their light and colour gave a festive, almost gay air to the buildings and to the crowd.

Such a profusion of light and colour still stirred in me some atavistic notion of festivity. I remembered all the lights of Teheran being lit up for the Shah's coronation. But compared to what I saw about me now, those lights had glittered no brighter than so many candles. And the Prater in Vienna on a summer evening, with all its honky-tonkies and the Riesenrad lit up, had been no more than a collection of lit-up toys.

I walked on in the direction of my boarding-house. For another block, advertisements brightened the façade of the avenue. Then they petered out into solitary store signs lighting no more than a single name or trademark. Now that there were fewer signs, I began to read a few of the names and slogans, for company. But after a short while, my mind spelled them out automatically; there were too many of them to grant me pause. As soon as I had acknowledged and shaken off one ad., another took its place. I tried to look aside, up and away, even across the street, seeking doorways, windows or building fronts with grace and interest enough in themselves to hold my attention. But all were as monotonous and grey as the cement

140

I was walking on. It seemed as if the house fronts, the very street itself was only there as a sombre background against which the signs would better show up. Except for the signs, there was no light anywhere, no sign of life.

I walked on faster; but the faster I walked, the more slogans, names and legends crowded in upon me, till, as if forced to give them their due, I began to recite each like a litany. I seemed powerless to ignore them or do otherwise, as powerless as I had been as a child when listening to the prayers of my classmates at school in Vienna at bedtime. Then too, at first, I had thought their loud, collective praying unwarranted and silly. At home everyone had prayed silently and alone, Hearing the evening prayers at school—the Catholics kneeling in front, the Protestants standing behind them, and I at the last—my eyes had roamed over the praying figures in front of me searching for some distraction. But after listening every night for years to their collective prayers, I sometimes caught my mind and lips, though perhaps not my heart, joining silently in their beautiful, sonorous chorus of *'Pater noster qui est in coelum, sanctifetur nomen tuum, adveniat regnum tuum. . . .'* But never had I been caught up by their suggestiveness against my inclination and will as I was being caught now by the impersonal, mechanical ads. which could mean nothing to me.

At the next corner was a snack-bar. I abruptly entered. My first reaction was, once more, how immaculate, sanitary and functional even such a small, third-rate place could be in this country. Everything was bright, colourful and spotless—the walls, the mirrors, the gleaming counter, the skillets. And best of all, the waitresses in their pretty, proper uniforms—so quiet, quick and efficient. But I missed the pleasant murmur of conversation, the informal relaxed atmosphere I remembered so well from cafés and restaurants in Europe. Here, the customers hunched over their plates, barely giving me a glance when I entered, nor did they look at each other, for that matter. I couldn't tell from their faces or expressions which ones were hungry, with appetites, waiting for their orders, and which ones had been fed. All were equally indifferent. And as for the ones who were eating, there was something as efficient, rapid and imperturbable in their eating as in the quick, impersonal way they were served. The only conversation, the only speech, was that of someone placing an order or asking for his bill.

I took a stool at the counter. Facing me was the mirror and all around it were tiny placards, lit up in miniature like the signs outside, extolling brand names of soups, coffee and bread. I looked away to avoid spelling out their messages. But there was nothing else to substitute for them, only surfaces of aluminium, plastic and glass. I gulped down my coffee, paid, and left. There was no release from tension here.

Rather than put up again with the signs along the avenue, I took the next cross street, and at the next corner turned again, following the street that ran parallel to the avenue. Though only a block removed from the traffic and the shops, the street I was on might have been miles away. Everything was quiet and calm. The wide sidewalks were flanked by tall trees, their thick summer foliage shedding pools of shadow that melted into ever-changing patterns with the stirring of the leaves. The houses on either side, though not as large as those in Santa Monica, looked spruce and attractive, set as they were in their small and well-tended lawns and flower beds, each ending up in a strip of lawn at the sidewalk. There were no fences or walls, only a few low, flowering hedges, as if the residents felt themselves such good neighbours that none wanted to mark himself off, nor cared for the sort of privacy which made people in other countries go to such length to obstruct the view with walls and fences.

XI   I had been walking for ten or fifteen minutes along the quiet street when I noticed at a corner street lamp that I was on Mariposa Avenue. I remembered passing along here once before, when I had tried to look up Mr. Wellbourne, the man who had given me my ride into Los Angeles and who had been so helpful in finding me a place to stay. He had given me his address in parting and urged me to look him up. I had written to thank him, but hadn't tried to get in touch with him till I had moved to Los Angeles. I had thought that he might know of a job for me, but the afternoon I finally got around to calling, no one had been home and I had never gone back again.

Walking on slowly, I kept track of the house numbers. I was sure Wellbourne's house was farther down the street—somewhere in the 600 block—and that I would recognize it, though most of the houses looked alike with their porched fronts, identical lawns and two-car garages. It wasn't easy to make out the numbers, either. Some of the houses were dark, though it couldn't be much later than seven-thirty. Faint music came through a few of the open windows and sometimes I caught sight of silhouettes—imagined or real—in the darkened rooms.

When I came up to Wellbourne's house I suddenly remembered the number, 666. It was one of the few houses lighted up. Through the large front window I could see two young people, a man and a woman whom I didn't recognize, seated in armchairs. The woman was leafing through a magazine. The man was staring straight ahead —at what, I couldn't see. The woman then closed the magazine and she and the man looked at each other as if one of them might

142

possibly wish to say something. But their lips didn't move. They seemed to have that detached, almost bored, look people sometimes have in waiting rooms or at railroad stations when they have failed to strike up a conversation with each other.

When I walked up the three short steps to the door, I saw the woman's head perk up as if she had been listening for me and had caught my approaching steps. I had scarcely rung the bell, when the door opened wide and the woman said, 'Oh, come in, come in. I'm so glad you could make it.'

Before I could say anything, she added, 'You are the television repair man, aren't you?' She seemed annoyed at the possibility that I wasn't. 'We've been waiting for the repair man all afternoon.' She spoke fast and a bit out of breath, as if still hoping that I might be the man she expected.

'No. I am sorry. I came to call on Mr. Wellbourne.'

'What is it, Pat?' a man's voice called out from the room to the left.

'It isn't the repair man, after all,' she called back without turning around. 'Somebody is asking for Mr. Wellbourne.'

The young man, her husband, stepped into the hall; after taking a small apron off and placing it on a table, he came up beside her.

'I'm sorry. Mr. Wellbourne doesn't live here any more. He moved to Beverly Hills,' he said to me.

'I'm sorry to have bothered you,' I said, wondering why it seemed that everyone I met in California soon moved to a newer or larger apartment, or to another house, changing addresses the way they changed clothes or cars. 'Do you have his new address?'

The man hesitated for a moment and then asked, 'Are you a friend of his?'

I told him about Mr. Wellbourne giving me a lift and helping me out, and explained that I hadn't had a chance to look him up sooner.

'He moved to Beverly Hills,' he said again, placing a certain emphasis on the name as a country man might accent the city he soon planned to go to himself. 'But if you wait a minute I'll get his address for you. Come in, come in,' he said, and led the way to the living-room. 'We're a bit mixed up tonight,' he added while looking through some papers on a table near the telephone. The woman asked me to sit down and smiled a brave smile, as if trying not to show how worried she was.

'Our TV set is on the blink,' she said, 'and the repair man hasn't showed up yet.'

'He was damn well supposed to,' the man said, jotting down something on a piece of paper. 'Here's Wellbourne's address,' he said, handing the slip to me. 'A fine fellow, Wellbourne is. We bought this house from him five months ago. He was a friend of yours, you say?'

I had said no such thing. Again I told them how I had met Mr. Wellbourne and how nice he had been to me.

'You say you were hitch-hiking?' the man asked. 'You must have seen a lot of our country. What do you think of it?'

I began to talk, and they kept asking more questions about college, about Persia and Vienna, and then about me, with that running indiscriminate curiosity that accepts all answers and all information with equal enthusiasm and pleasure, content with the bright surface of facts. Except for mention of Mr. Wellbourne, I seemed to be repeating the same tale I had been forced to give so many others—but brought up to date.

Yet, each question was put forward with such show of interest, that I couldn't help feeling they were really curious and sympathetic. Several times I tried to stop talking, but they urged me on. Yet whenever I answered a query too much at length with too many digressions, or whenever I inserted my personal reaction or opinion, I could see a wavering of their attention, as if my answer were too much of a good thing. Sometimes they cut me off with a new question.

The woman, Pat, excused herself and returned immediately with a coffee jug. She was pouring a cup of coffee for me when her hand stopped in mid-air above my cup. She seemed to be listening. 'That must be him,' she said, putting the jug down and making for the door.

We heard the doorbell ring, but Pat was already at the door, saying, 'Come in, come in,' just as she had said it to me. She led the repair man in.

'Sorry to be late, folks. But that's how it is,' the man said, as if the fault were not his and nothing could be done about it.

'We've been waiting all afternoon,' Pat said. She told him in some detail that she had quit work early just to make sure she would be home when he arrived.

'I did the best I could, ma'am.' The repair man was polite, but firm. 'By rights, I should be home watching my own set. I've been on the go all afternoon, and with still another call to make.' As he talked he kneeled down and disconnected the set, pulling it away from the wall.

'You think you can get it fixed tonight?' Pat asked.

'Can't say yet. Maybe. If it's nothing that needs parts.'

'Let's hope you can fix it,' the husband said. 'We sure hate to miss the High Spot show. It's our favourite programme. An anniversary show tonight.'

'Same here,' the repair man said. 'I only hope I can get home in time to catch the show myself.' He spoke in a matter-of-fact way, neither trying to show off nor trying to please. In this exchange, if anyone could be said to be trying to be ingratiating, it was Pat and

144

her husband. They seemed anxious to please, as if their attitude might sway the repair man's favour and influence his efficiency.

The repair man said something about a wire and a contact that I didn't understand. A moment later, he straightened up, closed his tool kit, pushed the set back against the wall, plugged it in and turned a knob. The screen lighted up.

'Oh, that's wonderful!' Pat exclaimed. She seemed so overjoyed and jubilant that I expected her to clap her hands. 'Would you care for a cup of coffee?' she asked the repair man.

'Mighty kind of you, ma'am.'

Recognizing his accent as Southern gave me a boost, the same kind of secret superiority I felt when catching on to some slang phrase or colloquialism which other foreigners couldn't get. It made me feel a shade more American; in any case, less foreign.

'But I got to be on my way, ma'am, if I want to make it home for the big show,' the repair man said.

'Well, thanks a million,' Pat said, giving him a bright, grateful smile.

'How much do I owe you for the job?' the husband asked.

'That'll be twelve fifty.'

The husband's hand was on his hip pocket to draw out his wallet. It stopped there. 'Twelve fifty!' He tried to sound even more incredulous than he was.

The repair man nodded.

'That's a bit steep, wouldn't you say?' The husband's eyes narrowed, as if to convey the secret that he could hold up his end against the repair man, if driven too far.

'That's the rate. Five dollars minimum charge per visit. Extra for time.'

'What time?' said the husband. 'The job took you all of ten minutes!' The husband's voice rose tentatively to the offensive.

'Time it takes to get here and back to the shop.' The repair man spoke unhurriedly, as if repeating a set phrase.

'But you said you had another call to make. So you aren't going back to the shop!' he accused the repair man. 'And probably you came here after making other calls on your way or you wouldn't have been so late.'

'Maybe so. But that's what our rates are.'

'How much do you charge for time?' the husband asked, warily, trying another tack.

'Five dollars an hour.'

'That still doesn't add up to twelve fifty. Five dollars minimum and the five for your hour getting here and home. That still makes only ten.'

'It's after six. That's time and a half.'

The husband's figure seemed to slump a bit as he drew out his wallet and paid up.

Pat said it wasn't fair. It wasn't their fault he was late. They had been waiting all afternoon—at least she had, because she had quit work early.

The repair man didn't bother to answer. He put the money in his pocket and rose to go.

The husband's face showed self-reproach, as if he had been out-smarted. And Pat's face was sulky, as if her good-will and honesty had been taken advantage of. Only the repair man seemed unruffled, with the calm of the sure winner.

Watching the three of them, I couldn't help but remember what Ned had said to me at Novak's about the women shoppers prowling around with their pocket-books—weapons more merciless than swords. Now, for once, the rôles were reversed. The TV repair man was the only one who could pull it off. And the more the customers liked TV, the more they were at his mercy.

The husband took the repair man to the door, and I didn't hear either of them say good-night.

When he came back, I rose to go. But they insisted that I stay to watch TV. The husband switched off the lights and Pat adjusted the dial. I glanced at them on the chance that we might go on talking, even with the show on. But both remained silent, their eyes on the small screen. They seemed so calm and contented that, in spite of myself, I felt some envy rising in me, though I couldn't determine precisely for what. The husband couldn't be much older than myself, and yet he already had everything that was thought necessary for a happy, full life—a pretty wife, a nice house with all the comforts and a two-car garage in a nice district, probably a good job and some money in the bank. And he had all this while still young enough to enjoy the fruits of life to a degree that was beyond the capabilities of most men old enough to be his father. But he seemed to take it all for granted, to be hardly aware of his good fortune, or of his pretty wife. In the dim light of the screen, the two of them sitting next to each other, their heads immobile, seemed more like brother and sister than husband and wife. Both were blond, of equal height. Both had blue eyes, small heads, and she, too, wore slacks. And they seemed as oblivious of each other as they were of me.

Comfortable as I was in my chair, with a cup of coffee at my elbow and my cigarette glowing in the dark, still I would much rather have talked and listened to them than watch the tiny screen. I hadn't even had a chance to ask Pat and her husband where they worked or any of those questions that come up naturally in the course of a conversation. I leaned back and joined them in watching, resigned to accepting the substitute of the TV show for human company.

The story line kept virtue triumphant against odds that would have crushed any man or woman but the heroes and heroines of the story, though they were not the strong, the mighty, the talented or the rich, but men and women anyone might have for neighbours. The characters might easily have been the repair man, Pat or her husband, Mr. Spielman—almost anyone I'd met touched up a bit with the brush of forbearance, forgiveness and faith, and with some physical improvements to make the men appear more male and the girls more feminine.

Watching the show I gradually identified myself with the screen characters, weaving into their story those thoughts and fancies of my own that rose up in me when I was alone. The heroes seemed so simple, so human and yet so great. Compared to their trials, my own seemed peevish and irrelevant. Their reward was a greatness of character and of the heart which gave me a sense of guilt for having underestimated so badly my fellow men.

Yet as soon as the first story was over, I felt a tinge of shame for letting my aroused emotions wallow in the tricked-up substitutes of joy and sorrow projected on the screen. I turned to Pat and her husband, sheepishly, checking to see if they had seen or guessed my reactions. Both were still looking at the set and listening to the commercial. The faint light from the screen did not reveal their expressions, but there was something about their faces and hands, their motionless postures, that resembled victims of a trance.

I felt forewarned when the next show began, confident that I wouldn't let myself become involved again. In the darkness, vision and sound conspired against me. I was too weak to resist. Even the notion of resisting, of denying truth and reality to what I saw, turned against me, as if I were denying those human beings projected on the screen the compassion and sympathy they so fully deserved. The strain of checking my sentimentality and of having it succumb again became too much to bear. I longed for the show to end so I could get up and go and be myself again.

At the next commercial I got up and insisted I must go. Pat switched on the light and I thanked them for the evening. Both of them urged me to stay, at least for the next programme, the High Spot show. Though I was on my feet and the lights were on, I almost wavered. I thanked them again for the evening and I was still talking when I noticed their anxious glances towards the TV set, keeping check with the show that was about to go on. Their next words were no longer really urging me so much to stay as to make up my mind quickly—to stay or to go, either way, but to make up my mind instantly before the show started. And when the husband took me to the door and stepped over the threshold, his handshake and parting words were hurried.

Outside I turned in the direction of my boarding-house. The street lamps seemed brighter, now that almost all the houses were dark. There were a few cars parked along the street, but none driving by. Nor was a single pedestrian in sight. The absence of all motion and the silence made me self-conscious of the sounds of my own footfalls.

Suddenly, from all directions at once, a triumphant voice rose up announcing the High Spot show and the name of the star, followed by a short crescendo of music. Then the happy-go-lucky voice of the announcer was heard again, coaxing, yet compelling; and hurried, as if there might not be time enough to transmit all that he had to say and all that his listeners were waiting for. I didn't catch the sponsor's name, for the house I was passing was dark *and* silent. But at the next house, as I passed, a blast of applause greeted me, its repeated echoes rising and ebbing along the street, till it was overtaken by roars of syncopated laughter.

Ahead of me, more house lights were being turned off now. From almost every house I passed, laughter floated out through the open windows. Sometimes I heard the live laughter of a voice or two mixing in with the recorded laughter of the studio audience.

Passing the houses I couldn't help listening, and beading together the comedian's wisecracks. I found myself slowing down when I thought a climax was due, but the tagline was usually drowned by a chorus of premature laughter before it reached me.

Volleys of laughter pressed upon me from all sides. I turned down the next side street and then turned again. But here, too, the metallic vibration of broadcast laughter and applause dogged my steps. I wanted to get away from it, but some compulsion—a sense of wonder not unmixed with terror—kept me going along the same street, while the incongruous question grated upon me: why was it I had never seen or heard them laugh together in daytime, in the open, on the street, in restaurants, in stores, at work—anywhere, any other time?

And I began to imagine millions of listeners all over the country, like wound-up puppets, responding simultaneously to a ready-made stimulus on cue, sharing a ritual, joined together in a national ceremony that was a substitute for what they no longer could or would find in each other. And by accepting this substitute for real joy and laughter, they were forfeiting the chance and the grace of ever finding such companionship in each other. Each new paean of laughter that burst out upon me sounded less human than the last. This was not human laughter, but the laughter of the insane and of the damned who must laugh without joy, with only their lips and throats. I imagined shadowy figures within the darkened houses all over the country leaning back their heads on command, the knotted chords of their throats throbbing in unison to the same stimulus which compelled and condemned them to laugh alone in the anonymous company of millions of others, alone like themselves—because they could no longer share laughter with each other.

Abruptly, I turned back to the avenue. The advertising posters beckoned as a pleasant, harmless diversion. When I reached the avenue I was almost out of breath. I would have taken the bus home, for I suddenly felt tired and spent, but the street numbers reminded me that I was only half a dozen short blocks away from the crossing where I would turn off to my boarding-house.

Ahead of me I could already recognize a familiar landmark, Sam's famous Car Clinic, a double lot wired along the front with streaks of neon, advertising 'Sam the Car Doctor'. Each of the two lots extended a whole block, and each was packed with row upon row of second-hand cars. Flooded by encircling searchlights, the metal and glass of the vehicles glistened in shifting rainbow colours, heightened by sparkling refractions. Only the white cardboard price tags remained constant, sober and unchanging.

On my way to work I always walked by Sam's place, and I often slowed down to eye the cars, speculating which car I liked best and which I might afford some day when I had earned enough money to make the small down payment. But tonight, all I wanted was to get back to my room at the boarding-house.

Long before I had come abreast of the first lot, I heard Sam's loudspeakers, which, suspended like trumpets all along the street front of Sam's two lots, were extolling Sam's honesty, his friendliness and integrity, hailing passers-by to enter just for a look, for a moment, no obligation, just for a try. Sam's voice tonight seemed louder and more persistent by the time I had reached the first lot. He recited bargains at a faster clip tonight, with barely a pause— pleading, inviting, cajoling, insisting, as if bent on slowing me down. With each step I made, Sam seemed to think up a new lure, a fresh gimmick, a better bargain.

By the time I had passed Sam's first lot, I felt as if I had been walking and listening for hours without gaining on Sam—as if he were walking beside me or as if the ground were receding under my feet in the opposite direction. The second lot seemed to stretch ahead of me interminably. All the time Sam's loudspeaker seemed either immediately ahead of me, beside me, or catching up with me, repeating the same injunction to buy, to buy, to trade, to trade, to take, to take—a car, any car, any car!

I was unable to obey, for lack of money; but I was equally unable to defy or shut off his command. And still his slogans kept on drumming into me. I tried to walk faster, but I couldn't. My legs

149

were too heavy. My torso seemed to share my impulse to hurry on, while my legs, up to the thighs, dragged themselves in dull pain—as if they were mere stubs and my efforts at haste were bruising them against the raw asphalt.

'I must reach the corner,' I kept on repeating, till I heard myself say, 'I don't want a car, I do not want a car. I do not want to buy. I do not want to trade.' I kept on protesting even after I had turned the corner and stood in front of my boarding-house.

When I let myself in and shut the door behind me, the safety of the silence around me made me stand still, listening. The silence was like a benediction. I bowed my head in gratitude; I felt a relief akin to that of struggling out of a nightmare. I let the silence bless me, and blessed it in turn—the double grace a creature grants himself when there is no one to give thanks to and no one from whom to receive blessing.

By the time I reached my room, dry, racking sobs had got the better of me, without my knowing why or what for.

# PART IV

I was preparing myself for a new world with my eyes
already open to comprehend it and with a troubled
soul, fearful of becoming lost in it.

MILOVAN DJILAS

I Walking up Fifth Avenue to the Persian Consulate to renew
my passport for my return home, I was half-glad, half-sorry my
makeshift life of the past few years was coming to an end. Father's
transfer had, at last, caught up with me in California. He must have
assumed I had lived on credit all this time, for the amount he sent
far exceeded the price of my ticket to Persia. After paying my way
to New York and having two suits made to order, I figured I had
enough money left over for the passage home and a couple of weeks'
stay in the city. Walking up the Avenue now, dressed up and with
money in my pocket, I felt my old self again, as if resuming the
identity I had dropped when I started hitch-hiking from Watson
College.

And just as, in former days, I had expected when I was broke that
some passer-by would recognize me for what I really was rather
than for what I appeared to be, so now I half-expected someone in
the crowd to notice my good fortune. But people pushed by as they
had done in other cities, self-occupied, and with something of the
adolescent in their shameless rush. I felt myself the only one not in
a hurry, the only spectator.

A big trailer truck pulled up at the crossing while I was waiting
for the traffic light to change. The driver's face was tensed up; the
few moments of idling at the crossing were too brief to give him a
chance to relax. He seemed to look down upon the shiny cars and
taxis around him with the same amused condescension, almost contempt, that I remembered experiencing when driving a truck through
a big city. I would have liked to step up and tell him that of all the
jobs I had had, I liked truck driving the best because it left a man
alone. When he changed gears to pull off, I raised a hand and waved
at him, but he didn't respond.

Walking on, I slowed down each time I came abreast a store in which I could see people doing the same work I had done—a liquor store, a drug store, a news-stand—and watched them through the plate-glass windows. Their faces seemed no more familiar to me than those of the people hurrying past me on the street, but their postures and movements were. I controlled an impulse to step inside one of these stores, to let on casually that I wasn't such a stranger after all and knew something about their trades; I knew the profit margin on hard liquor was forty per cent, on wine only twenty-five. I knew that youngsters were a headache at the soda fountain and seldom left a tip, never a large one; that at the news-stand the fifteen-cent magazines were delivered for eleven cents, the twenty-five-cent ones for nineteen. I might add conversationally that I was leaving the country for good, and so have a chance to say good-bye to someone. I would hide the fact that I felt a little sorry for them all, because their jobs were not masquerades as mine had been, and they had no one to bail them out.

Fifth Avenue, the sidewalks thick with pedestrians, stretched far ahead as if on a moving belt flanked by stationary skyscrapers. The impact of New York—so unlike that of any other city—was as strong as it had been when I walked this same avenue the day of my arrival in America. Again and again, I looked up until the towering heights struck me as senseless, overdone. One skyscraper or a group of them, I felt, might be more imposing than the Sphinx, more spectacular than the Eiffel Tower. But a whole avenue of skyscrapers ceased to have any relation to the monumental or the unique. I had to take them for granted, and I still couldn't.

At Rockefeller Plaza I took the elevator to the Persian Consulate on the twenty-second floor. The lettering on the door spelled in Persian and English 'The Imperial Consulate General of Iran', beneath the emblem of the rising sun behind a lion holding a scimitar in his right front paw. I read the Persian words slowly to myself, while the English word 'Imperial' lingered on, strange in my mind.

When I entered, the secretary told me the Consul was busy, offered me a seat and asked me to wait. I sat down and opened the newspaper I had bought on the way. But after a while something incongruous about the place intruded upon me. Was it the Persian rug, the framed miniature prints and enlarged photos of Persepolis along the walls above showcases exhibiting mosaics salvaged from some antique mosque or palace—all intended to transfer a breath of Persian atmosphere into an office in the midst of New York? Or was it the presence of the blonde American secretary? Pretty though she was, she seemed to lack life and lustre amidst such surroundings, her trim presence a required adjunct to her aluminium desk and electric typewriter.

A large portrait of the King in Imperial regalia, his chest full of medals, was facing me from above the entrance door. His large, dark eyes, thick eyebrows and black hair were instinctively familiar to me, more familiar, though I had never met him, than the face of any American I had known. Yet familiar as the portrait was, it was strangely removed in relevance and time, as if this young king were more a contemporary of other Persian kings—Darius, Xerxes, Cambyses—than of mine.

I thought of the portraits of other kings I had run across in Consulates when travelling in Europe during my student days; the long, wooden face of the King of Sweden; Zog of Albania with his shoe-string moustache; the kings of Italy, Belgium and England, all of them self-conscious as if no longer sure how a king was supposed to look nowadays, now that royalty, in spite of royal birth, was no longer taken for granted. I wondered what glory there could be in being king of poor people. And compared to America, all other nations seemed poor.

The very notion of royalty struck me now as a little humorous, and also a little sad. Kings died no better than they had been born, at best no worse. And I remembered the joke about the American who refused to change places with a king because a king had no chance for promotion.

Suddenly I felt sorry for that young king. It was the same impulsive sympathy I felt for people born rich in America. I couldn't help pitying such people for all they missed compared to those who had risen on their own and proved their mettle in life.

I tried to remember whether I had ever met an American born rich, but I couldn't think of any. All the employers I had worked for had started out with some job such as they had given me. There had been Mr. Benson, who now owned a fleet of trucks, Mr. Howley, a chain of liquor stores. Mr. Wright managed a dozen greenhouses and possessed more land in California than my father did in Persia. Every one of them had risen on his own.

Often when I compared myself with such people, I felt a vague resentment against fate. Father's wealth, by placing me too high, debarred me from ever starting out at the bottom. It deprived me of the chance to match myself evenly with others, and denied me those adventures of the heart and triumphs of spirit which can only belong to those who begin life with nothing.

By leaning my head back against the thin partitioning that separated the waiting room from the Consul's office, I could hear a faint murmur of voices on the other side. Though I couldn't catch a single word, except for intermittent exclamations, I followed the rise and fall of intonation the way I might listen to an indistinct but nostalgic tune. It didn't matter what was said in the next room.

153

I was content with the recognition of Persian sounds. And as I listened on, the soft, melodic flow of the language struck such an intimate chord in me that, in contrast, all the contacts I had had in America seemed but pathetic imitations, pitiful make-believes. I saw now how thin was the thread of friendship and understanding I had tried to weave between myself and others—in college, on the road and at my jobs, compared to the sudden and unbidden sense of kinship I felt now at the mere sound of my own language.

I wished the Consul's door would open and he would call me in. My lips, on their own, formed the long-forgotten formal phrases of greeting, and the replies I would make to his welcome. The Persian words I summoned for rehearsal rose haltingly at first, but soon reached a flow too personal and rich for the formalities of greeting the Consul. The words hastened on in my mind to the next stage of my journey—when I would meet my family again.

My imagination conjured up scenes of home-coming with a haste I could barely keep up with. The scenes rushed by like the leaves of a family album too quickly turned, miraculously revealing among the old snapshots of the past similar ones of the very near future. Each picture was flying by too quickly to yield precise recognition or to be savoured in full.

Only the road leading from the outskirts of our town over the two and a half miles to our estate was clear and precise. The double rows of birch trees (each two rows separated by a tiny stream) which father had planted along the road when I first left home to study abroad, were now, after thirteen years, tall and leafy enough to shade the road as father had intended. For my arrival, both stream beds, usually kept dry save for channelling the precious water to the adjacent fields, would be flowing full. Peasants, stooping over their work in the fields of cotton, poppy and wheat would look up at the passing car, then straighten up until I had gone by, their figures etched by the glaring sun against the level wasteland stretching beyond to the far-off hills. Amid this plain stood our walled garden with its melon beds, fruit trees and clusters of poplar and willow trees, laid out with the informality only very large gardens can afford.

The moment I passed the gate of our garden and caught sight of our house with the family waiting at the entrance, the sequence blurred. Only after my mother and father had embraced me and re-entered the house did the scenes sharpen into focus again. I would wait for my older brothers and sisters to precede me into the house, but on this occasion they would insist on my preceding them, though I was the youngest. Inside the doorway, in the cool carpeted hall, stood the servants, the male servants lined up against the wall with their hands folded over their waists. For once they might feel bold enough to look up without being directly addressed. Further

154

back, near the archway to the dining-room, I saw among the veiled figures of the female servants my old nurse, her thin body shaking with sobs of joy.

As I moved towards her I suddenly recognized the male servant, about my own age, standing last in the line. He was the son of our cook—the most exciting companion of my childhood when, during the summer days, we trapped birds and raced our donkeys at the back of the garden. Impulsively I stopped and held out my hand to him. He bowed his head and touched my hand. I was too late in withdrawing it to escape the kiss.

His kiss spoiled the picture. The pageant of my home-coming was irreparably tainted. I could not weave fancies within a scene that included hovering servants bowing and scraping to me. I recoiled from the prospect of another human being endowing me with superior qualities I had done nothing to merit, and at a way of life which conditioned so many to take their subservience as the natural order of things.

Sitting there in the Consulate waiting-room—this room with its rugs, prints and broken tiles in which I had felt more at home than in any room I had called my own in America—I suddenly felt alien to my own past life. Something had happened to the identity which I had always considered my true one and which I had always thought waiting for me to pick up whenever I chose to, on leaving America. I saw now that it was no longer mine, that I could never be at peace with a life not of my own making, nor with a job, a government job probably, that would be mine because of my father's influence and standing, and with a salary supplemented by an income from one of my father's farms, where peasants worked with primitive tools from sun-up to sun-down to supply me with a car, a house and tailored clothing. Such a future would be crippling to my manhood.

Even the intensity of my love for home could not solder the rupture between my memories and what I would now feel and see when I reached home. I dared not ask myself outright whether I could fit again into the pattern of life back home. I knew that I couldn't. Nobody could, or nobody should after seeing America, except at the price of his self-respect.

I was caught up in a sense of double identity—or rather of double anonymity. I seemed on the verge of abandoning one identity without having as yet acquired another. I didn't have the courage to cut myself off from the old one, nor the strength to risk committing myself to the new. As I tried to cling to both, each seemed to cancel the other out. I didn't know what to do. All I knew was that I couldn't go home, at least not immediately. But neither could I stay here for ever, and remain myself.

155

The voices in the other room were louder now, almost distinct. I saw two shadows close to the milky glass panel of the Consul's door, one of them bowing lower than the other.

'May your shadow never shorten,' one was saying.

'Your bounty is too great,' replied the other.

'May God be with you. . . .'

The phrases proper to leave-taking struck me to the quick, as the murmurs had previously done. It seemed they were being spoken to me, that it was my own leave-taking from home. Yet coupled with meaning and occasion now, the Persian words seemed as unreal as the King's portrait over the door, and as remote from the world as the poet, dead these many centuries, who had first uttered them.

I saw the door handle pressed down and, quickly stepping up to the secretary, I told her I could wait no longer. Without giving her a chance to detain me, I hurried out of the room.

# PART V

You can't have Falstaff and have him thin.
GEORGE SANTAYANA

I I was alone in the office in the downtown financial district of
New York when the elderly man came in. I took my feet off the
desk and, folding my newspaper, got up, annoyed at the interruption. The lunch hour was the only time of the day I had to myself.

'I hope I'm not disturbing you,' the man said, with that show of
modest courtesy which some elderly people affect to disarm their
youngers; knowing how difficult it is to reject them without appear-
ing to reject their virtue, too.

He introduced himself as Mr. Webb, and offered me a subscription to the *Wall Street Journal* (for the office). I told him the boss
was out, and that I was an assistant and . . .

'I understand,' Mr. Webb agreed, with the pacifying but self-
confident smile of a kindly doctor facing a difficult patient. He then
went on to ask me 'as a favour' to spare him a few moments of my
time.

I could hardly pretend, as he implied, that my time was so
valuable that I couldn't spare him a minute. I listened without
encouraging him, feeling a bit foolish—as I always did when I had
to listen and it didn't matter what was said. Once I tried to interrupt
Mr. Webb to save him from wasting *his* time. But then I let him
carry on. After almost two years in this Wall Street office, I had
learned that the worst blow for a man like Mr. Webb was not the
rejecting of his product, but the cutting off of his sales talk.

Yet, the routine approach, so natural to others, didn't come easy
to Mr. Webb. The more he talked, the less sure he seemed of his
lines, as if worried about bungling his cues. From pressure and
aggressiveness, he shifted to subtlety, and then back, without advancing his argument. He seemed afraid to pause, as if apprehensive
that the first moment of silence would, like an invisible eraser, undo
all he had already said. His voice rose a pitch at each new argument, becoming almost petulant, as if battling a stubborn listener
who purposely didn't want to understand.

Mr. Webb took out his balled-up handkerchief and wiped his forehead and cheeks. His expression, momentarily off guard, relapsed into fatigue. I suddenly guessed why Mr. Webb had come in during lunch hour. He had nowhere else to go. All the restaurants in this district were too expensive for him, and lunch at the crowded counters couldn't be made to take up more than fifteen or twenty minutes. There wasn't a bench or park chair for miles in the Wall Street area for a man who just wanted to sit down. I knew, because I had so often looked for one.

It was the way Mr. Webb slipped into the chair I offered him that made me decide 'to pay for the subscription myself on the chance that the office might okay it later. I signed and paid for the order, and expected Mr. Webb to rise and go. But, after carefully putting the money in one billfold and the order blank in another, he stayed in his chair.

'You think a man my age should be doing better than selling subscriptions, don't you?' he said, a smug note getting into his voice.

Though I had thought no such thing, I had no choice but to make a denial, which sounded false.

'A lot of people think I'm a has-been. I would be, too, if I hadn't anything better to look forward to. But I have!' he added with an emphatic flourish. 'What I'm doing now is just a makeshift, to tide me over.' He leaned forward in a confidential way. 'You know, I worked my way up twice before, and I'll do it again.'

I had met so many people in America who had worked their way up that I was no longer surprised. Everybody had. The building was full of them. I, myself, had risen within two years to a relative position of responsibility in the import-export business simply by sticking to one job and trying to do it well. But this was the first time I had met a man who had done it more than once.

The fact that Mr. Webb was starting out—at sixty or more—for the third time added suddenly to my awareness of him. I no longer saw him in terms of subscriptions. He might as well represent a hundred thousand dollar deal. I searched his face, his voice, his gestures, for some quality of greatness, some trace of a crowded eventful life. The clear skin, the cheeks a bit too rosy for a man his age—yet so particular to older people in this country, as if the flesh had fed and survived at the expense of some inner quality—and the lively eyes, unfaded, shrewd, though without depth; the voice purposeful, yet without resonance and timbre as if attuned long ago to some standard key—everything about him was barren of maturity. I would have liked to ask him about his previous careers. But his blithe, boosting talk so similar to the business talk I was forced to hear daily, snuffed out my speculations.

'Why, sir, if I were your age, if I had your years ahead, I wouldn't worry for a moment; I would be so sure of myself. You could put me at the end of the line, and I'd catch up, just the same.' Mr. Webb waited for a rebuttal. Now that he spoke about himself—not about his product—he was so convincing I couldn't help but believe him. I was sure if Mr. Webb had been in my shoes, he would be much farther ahead than I was, God knows how much farther.

'Why even the age I am now, I can do it. I know I can.' He repeated the claim, as if the brief formula of assertion said often enough vouched for its truth and success. 'If nothing goes wrong, too much against me, I mean,' he qualified himself with a modest smile. 'But given half a chance, I'll do all right. Why, you may not recognize me in a couple of months, I'll be riding so high. No sir, I haven't given up yet. I believe in it more than ever. Why, I could get myself a better job any day—on a regular salary, I mean. But in the long run I'd be the loser. Nobody ever got rich on a salary. I know; I've tried it both ways. I'm handling these subscriptions because this kind of work happens to fit in with my plan—to start a new distribution company. I have my own ideas on that. All I need is a little more time. This, here, that I'm doing is just to tide me over,' he repeated with disparagement. 'But it's all right. If I just hold out for a while longer I'll be over the hump. That's why each subscription means so much to me right now.'

The longer he spoke, the harder it was to keep up my faith in Mr. Webb's future. The dark suit he wore seemed to remind me of the suit I had worn on my first job in New York—the research job I got through the man who had the apartment above me in the village. It had been my only suit. I had postponed picking up the other from the tailor till, one day, I no longer had the money to pay for it. Each night I brushed the suit, cleaned it and dampened the shiny spots. But after an hour's wear next morning, the shiny spots were out again.

'You see what I mean, don't you,' Mr. Webb was saying, a bit more insistent now, as he put his sample newspaper back into a folder.

I nodded. I was relieved, not so much by the prospect of parting with Mr. Webb, but because his departure would release me from simulating sympathy, understanding and agreement—from all those emotional counterfeits everyone insisted on extracting from me— even over the telephone—in the name of business and sociability; without their becoming any richer for it, but leaving me so much poorer. It was because of these ransoms I paid that by the end of the day I felt exhausted, bankrupt, having spent more than I had to spare.

Mr. Webb suddenly seemed to remember something his con-science might never forgive him if left unsaid. 'And thank you for the cigarette.' I instantly offered him another. 'No, no thank you. You may be getting short yourself. Well, if you really want me to.'

He thanked me twice and very much. 'And let me wish you the very best of luck and good-bye.'

Mr. Webb was half way across the room when he turned and walked back again. 'If I may ask you a favour. . . .' There was again that patient, reasonable note in his voice. 'Next year, a month or so before your subscription runs out, you'll be receiving a renewal slip from the company. As a favour to me . . .' he paused, as if giving me a fair chance to refuse even before he had put the request, 'please cancel it. Then, I can come around again and renew your subscription. That is, if you let me. That'll give me the same credit, you see, as if you were a new subscriber. I probably won't need it any more by then,' he added. 'Sure I won't.' He smiled, as if the possibility of his needing it were the most unlikely thing that could happen. 'Pretty sure I won't, even if I'm still with the same outfit. But you never can tell, can you, and it won't hurt to make sure.'

'I am afraid *I* won't be here next year, either,' I said. I felt awkward for placing my prospects on the same level with his. His attentive expression forced me to add, 'The office will send me abroad soon.'

'That would be wonderful, wouldn't it?' he exclaimed.

He seemed on the verge of congratulating me, so that I quickly added, 'Yes. But it isn't a hundred per cent sure yet. Though almost.'

'Oh, but I do hope it will turn out the way you plan. I really do. Well, good-bye.' We shook hands again. 'And the very best of luck to you, and maybe we'll be seeing each other again, though for both our sakes, I hope not here. But, in case you're still here and I'm . . .'

He walked to the door, his back straight, his head held high. Even his suit looked better. He was half way across the room when I quickly stepped over and opened the door for him, as if to make up for having privately discounted all his chances, and for grading him no better than a pathetic old fool who deluded himself into hoping he would not be back next year.


II Closing the door behind Mr. Webb, I felt secure from ever meeting him again. I'd be far out of his reach in a year's time—in Persia most likely, on my own, running a branch for an American import-export firm. A decision about my assignment was due soon. I had been waiting for it for a year; now, it was a question of waiting just a bit longer.

I couldn't keep my mind on the paper I was reading. I thought of Mr. Webb, chipper, but blind to the odds, carrying on, day after day, harnessed to his illusions. His showing up again in a year's time seemed so fated that I inadvertently glanced at the door, half-expecting his small head, topped by his shock of grey hair, neatly combed, to peer in as if looking around a corner. And, after recognizing me, pretending surprise at still finding me here.

I banished this possibility. I might be here another month or two, even six months. But not another year. I was bound to have a decision soon, either from this office or from one of the larger companies I had broached the idea to.

This near-certainty and imminence of success, which had bucked me over doubts and discouragements before, somehow failed to spring up spontaneously this time. Matched against Mr. Webb's conviction, my own seemed pallid and wavering. It had a tinny ring, as if worn out and abused by too many appeals. It no longer had the power to hide altogether the fact that I was no nearer my goal now than I had been a year ago when I first expected to be sent abroad. I still had no commitment from any company, large or small —only vague encouragements and good cheer. I let them boost my hopes and prospects, instead of doing the boosting myself, for I dared not disbelieve them.

To buck myself up I marshalled again all I had gone through in New York, as if by presenting an account I could force or shame fate into sticking to the bargain; the weeks and months of postponing my return home, until my initiative was paralysed and I no longer had enough money to book passage home; my making the rounds of agencies and scanning the ads. till I felt I was re-reading the same page of the same paper over and over again every day; the brief euphoria at finding the research job, which had led me on to this one. And now the waiting, after having hit on what seemed the ideal solution for me—to get a job with a company that did business with the Middle East and which might open branches there.

The sheer waste of waiting had filled the credit ledger. But the surreptitious, piecemeal waiting of the last six months was wearing me out. Each day seemed longer and harder to wind up than the preceding twenty-four hours. I felt a part-time prisoner doing time from nine in the morning till six or seven at night, and my off-hours seemed intervals of convalescence rather than of freedom or pleasure. Each week was one more part-payment towards my goal; and too many had already been made to throw up the game now, for each might be the last.

These instalments, though I tried not to add them up, snowballed today into an aggregate so enormous and staggering that no reward could ever make up for them. Compared with the drain of energy and the blunting of temperament this waiting had extracted from me, my actual work (that seemed to count for so much at the office) and the labour I had invested in learning the business thoroughly, in making contacts, getting to know the ins and outs, even teaching myself shorthand and book-keeping on the chance I might start off

161

with a one-man office abroad—all seemed mere pastimes more suitable for an adolescent than for a man.

Such an ominous reckoning ought to have roused me to new resolves, induced an upsurge of purpose and will—or to have given way to panic. I felt nothing of the sort. Even the prospect of facing Mr. Webb in a year's time—or worse still, of awaiting him, though he, on the road to success, would not show up—left me indifferent. Success itself now seemed but a borrowed bait I had been dangling in front of my nose to make myself carry on. What glory could there ever be in the exporting and importing of goods from one country to another, in buying and selling, in crowding my time and imagination with the details and ceremonies of business?

I had to admit that my enthusiasm for my project had never been really more than lukewarm and opportunist—vague and sluggish compared to Mr. Webb's single-mindedness. And Webb's drive was no exception to be mocked at. Everybody in the skyscraper I was in seemed to be driven by the same impulse, their lives given to getting ahead, to the mastering of producing and selling more of the same product. And if they hadn't been infected by the same compulsion which drove Mr. Webb on, they would not have been able to carry on day after day, year after year, for a lifetime, the same pursuit.

Instead of feeling left out and unfit, I felt a peculiar surge of joy at discovering that I seemed to be the only one spared this bondage to illusion; as if I had suddenly recognized that all wishing and ambition, if allowed to dominate life unconditionally and to enlist all other impulses in its service, must become an unshakable harness, a blinding illusion—but imperative in order to generate the energy and faith required for the pursuit of the goal. This was the price they paid for dedicating their manhood to success, for wishing only for what success could give them—a bargain as exacting and fateful as Faust's, only they paid the forfeit in advance and never tasted what they had bargained for.

III I left my desk and walked over to the open window. The street below was already in shade; so were the buildings across the way except for their upper storeys, where the sunlight still blazed in patches upon the window panes. At one of the windows a girl was sitting on the window-sill with her back resting against the frame, her head tipped a bit sideways and out, her face held up to the sun in the sad, hungry fashion of city people, whose sunning is stalked by the knowledge that it must be brief.

Beyond the buildings across the street, I could see from my window on the fifty-sixth floor the tip of Manhattan Island, the

162

Battery. The harbour seemed no bigger than a toy model with toy boats floating upon it. Only the smoke from their smoke-stacks hinted at motion. The incoming boats, as if guided by invisible hands, miraculously avoided collision at the narrow mouth of the harbour with the outgoing boats, which, farther out, dotted the surface of the ocean like a seaborne caravan. Each dot that vanished in the distance was soon replaced by the emergence of a larger dot at the harbour mouth.

They all carried freight, I knew. Passenger boats left from midtown docks. There could be ten, a hundred times as many outgoing boats if the rest of the world could afford to buy their cargoes. And still, all their cargoes would amount to no more than a fraction, a mere sample, of what America's factories could produce—factories of which I knew nothing save the names of a few I had run across on bids and bills of lading. And their output was managed and channelled from such skyscrapers as I was in, where the offices with their telephones, typewriters, teletypes and secretaries were all geared to the same end as the factories' smoke-stacks and machinery.

My imagination had never before conceived of all this together, but only in parts. All that was spread below me now, along with what I had seen when hitch-hiking, and all the cities and farms and factories that I would never see but could imagine, were the outcome, I realized, of plans and ambitions which, when conceived and begun, must have had less substance and reality than Webb's ambition had. And if Webb's was an illusion, then all that spread out in front of me was illusion, too. I shrank from this profanity. Instead, a humiliating and impotent envy possessed me—the envy that is not for the rich setting of another's table, but for his appetite; not for his wealth, but for the talent and the qualities that went into the making of it, even for his greed and folly, without which nothing might have been begun and accomplished. Now I envied Webb his stubborn drive. His success or failure no longer mattered. By virtue of his struggle he was superior to me. In contrast to his faith and stamina my own efforts were bland and cowardly. Compared to him I was a sick man—too weak and irresolute even to grapple with life, let alone master it.

Across the street, the girl was still at the window. The sun was almost past her, barely touching that half of the window frame she was leaning against. Her body was in shade, but by lowering one shoulder and craning her neck out, she managed to keep her face in the sun. Against the vast, abstract façade of glass, aluminium and cement with its geometrical patterns of window frames and grey strips, that one solitary human head reaching for the sun had an irresistible appeal and grace. Her features were relaxed in an unconscious, almost vacant smile from which all awareness had

163

seeped out, save perhaps a plea that the sunny moment would linger on for a while longer.

I guessed her a secretary who had exchanged her lunch hour for a momentary place in the sun—one of the thousands of girls who, briefly, each morning, with their gay dresses, good looks, quick chatter and tripping feet, enlivened the windowless corridors of the skyscrapers into a brisk bazaar before beginning their daily routine at the typewriters and telephones; a routine which taxed and wasted their chic, their kindness, their instincts and good cheer.

I could not remember when, exactly, I had faced the sun as she was doing now. But I remembered the spot. It had been at the corner of the avenue in Greenwich Village where I boarded the bus to work on sunny days, instead of taking the subway. A short line of passengers was waiting for the bus, and rather than crowd in with them, I stood back close to the nearest wall. It was as I stood there that an unwonted kind of warmth, along with a vague sense of well-being, stirred in me. The sun was shining on my face. The top of my head and the skin of my face had already absorbed that degree of heat which unstiffens cold hands held out to an open fire. I closed my eyes and, tilting my face up full to the sun, leaned back against the wall.

When I heard the bus pulling up, I thought I would wait just a moment longer, and then make a dash for it. Then, I decided not to stir. The next bus would be by soon. With closed eyes I listened to the brief scuffle of people boarding the bus. With my head resting back and the sun in my blind face, I began to feel absolved of all frowns and strains, tasting a contentment I seemed to have forgotten still existed. It made no demands upon me, except for my wish that it last on. And it would last, on condition that I didn't move.

A hand touched my elbow and a voice offered to help me board the bus. When I opened my eyes, the voice stopped in mid-sentence.

'Why, I thought you were blind,' the elderly stranger said quickly, drawing back and eyeing me reproachfully, as if I had deceived him into a show of kindness. I didn't know what to say, and hurried away to look for a taxi.

The girl at the window seemed to have moved closer to the edge, and to be leaning out farther. Taken up with courting the sun, she seemed oblivious to her precarious balance. Another fraction farther out, and she would risk a fall. A single glance down and she would, I was sure, draw back in panic. I felt an impulse to shout a warning to her. But the longer I watched that immobile, sunny face, the less certain did I feel of my impulse to shout. Her small, dedicated, up-turned face seemed entranced in a communion that had stolen upon her, like faith upon an unbeliever, holding her now in its inimitable spell. Were I to rouse her, I would bring her back to no better a reality than the man who had disturbed me at the bus corner, rouse her to nothing better than her typewriter, telephone and routine.

I leaned out to gauge the distance down. We were at about the same level. To see the base of the building on her side, I had to lean out—and farther out, still, to see the sheer drop on my own side. The converging pattern of glass and cement added a peculiar abruptness to the precipice. Past the half-way mark, each storey below me was a shade darker. Further down, the windows of the lower storeys glowed with light. The narrow strip of the street was buried in deep shadows as if it were the beginning of yet another abyss, where some miniatures of men somehow threaded their way across. They gave me the sensation of being so much higher placed than any building could ever place me; and the distance down to the street seemed so immeasurably greater than it did when seen from the ground up—a distance so great that a falling body would, after the first quick rush of air and alarming intake of breath, lose all fear of falling. For the fall would be so prolonged and drawn out that, after a short while, it would not feel like falling at all, but rather like a long glide towards an end which would for ever recede. And when the end did come, it would come too suddenly to be taken into account . . .

Quickly, I turned around when I heard the office door open behind me.

IV It was Miss Collier, the secretary. She came towards me, a paper bag in her hand, smiling as she always did when she handed me my lunch—a sandwich and a carton of coffee. I paid her with a dollar bill and she, as always, had the right change ready.

Back at her desk, she put her gloves in the left-hand bottom drawer. Her routine of settling down to work—unvaried and predictable from the moment she entered till she fluffed up her rich, blonde hair with the palms of both hands, closed her make-up kit, put it in her handbag and then put the bag beside her gloves in the left drawer—made me feel each time that I had won another bet, which I would much rather have lost. Even the sight of her tall, trim figure as she walked over to the rack in the corner and reached up to place her hat upon the topmost peg, didn't make up for my feeling of disappointment.

Self-conscious about her height, she seemed always a bit tense while on her feet. But to me, though I was a few inches shorter and never cared to stand next to her for long, her height seemed natural and requisite for displaying the full proportions of her body. A shorter figure wouldn't have done it. It wouldn't have given her limbs the scope and flow they needed to be shown off at their best. And when she walked back to her desk, it was with a light, forward tilt, with a soft break at the knees, which gave her movements a forward, prowling fluidity so in contrast to her prim, upright posture once she sat down at her typewriter.

I felt like asking her to hold off her typing for a while, so I could eat my sandwich and read the paper in peace. The other secretary and the clerk would be back soon enough, and the bustle of the office would start again. But I said nothing. I watched her as she went about her work. Unless I looked out of the window, there was nothing else to look at, except the desks, the filing cabinets and the telephones and the solitary rose Miss Collier kept in a thin, tall vase on her desk.

Watching her back and her pretty, curling hair, I asked myself why I had never flirted with her—neither on impulse nor by calculation. Yet she was one of the prettiest girls in the building, and the place was swarming with attractive girls. The information girls in the lobby, the bevies of elevator girls, the secretaries I passed in the corridors—there were so many of them, and most of them so pretty, that if a girl caught my eye it was because she was homely.

I would have had no qualms about dating a girl who worked in the same office with me. Rather, I knew it would be wiser not to, but also knew I was too weak to resist temptation. What puzzled me was my utter absence of interest or initiative, this failure to feel tempted. Was it my fault or hers? A few years ago, meeting a girl like Miss Collier would have been an adventure. Now, I spent eight hours a day with her in the same room, day after day, and never looked at her as a man should look at a pretty girl. If I thought of her at all, it was to congratulate myself on what an efficient secretary she was.

I wondered what an affair with Miss Collier would be like. Probably I would feel no more intimate after going to bed with her than after the first kiss—as had happened with other girls in New York. I might be wrong. She might be the exception. But if she were, how could she stand this deadening routine of office work? There was something incongruous, unnatural and perverse about such a pretty, graceful creature being linked for so many hours each day to the typewriter; and speaking to men and being spoken to by them, as if neither she nor the men counted for more than adjuncts of the business routine.

Added up, how many months and years had Miss Collier sat on a swivel chair facing her typewriter? How many miles had she typed, how many words exchanged over the 'phone, without identifying herself with a single word in print or sound of her own? Added up, the mechanical components of her life must be staggering, inside the office and out. From the moment she got up in the morning, used hot water, pushed the button on her toaster, plugged in her percolator and took the subway and finally rode up the elevator to the fifty-sixth floor until she returned home in the evening, turned on the light, used hot water again, snapped on the radio or the television and managed a dinner from what there was in the frigidaire—there was no real relationship between her human needs and the satisfying of them. By contributing little thought and no feeling to the satisfaction of her elemental needs and desires, some part of her nature was bound to atrophy. Though outwardly she might remain prettier and more youthful than her more primitive sisters elsewhere—more slender, more chic, better dressed and with more comforts, yet in some essential quality shared by all women, she was bound to be the loser—without anyone knowing the why or the how of it. Yet, girls all over the world would want to be like her— perhaps at any price. I remembered the timeless drudgery of my Persian nurses; of the woman who attended the samovar, serving tea to us and to the guests—a full-time job—from dawn till late at night; the red hands and fatigued faces of so many women in Europe. Miss Collier was their queen; their American counterpart whose emancipation had overtaken anything votes or rights could give her. Was she the forerunner of a new breed (of her sex) or the end product of it all?

I wondered if she had ever caught herself looking at me or thinking of me as a male; and if not, who was the poorer for it—perhaps both of us.

The sandwich tasted dry, though it was so fresh-looking and so prettily made up—the bread was so white, the lettuce leaves so green. From the taste of it, I wasn't sure whether the slab of covered-up meat was pork, beef or lamb, nor did I care. The coffee, though, was still wonderfully hot. But the clicking of the typewriter keys wouldn't leave me alone. Whenever Miss Collier stopped, I found myself waiting for the sound. And when it did start again, each key seemed to be tapping a nerve in me.

'Miss Collier.'

She stopped and turned around. I had called her on an impulse, to interrupt her typing. I was at a loss what to say next.

'What was your job before you started here?' I knew she had worked in a department store, but not much more. We were still on a last-name basis, as I was with everyone else at work.

'I was with Macy's. In the accounting department.' She looked at me, as if she had been expecting me to ask that question ever since I had hired her three months ago.

'I didn't know you had studied accounting,' I said, trying to make a compliment of it.

167

'I did. For a while.' And then, as if confessing to something from the past, she added, 'At college.'

'Then how did you ever land at Macy's with a college education?' I remembered my weeks at the Woolton Company, and couldn't hide my surprise.

Miss Collier took off her glasses and put them on her desk. Without them, her eyes were a childish blue, but a little restless, as if the effort to see were too hard. 'Just before Christmas during my second year at college, I ran across an ad. of Macy's. I applied and got the job.' She paused with a self-deprecating smile, as if the story were not worth the telling. 'That's all there is to it.'

I imagined her as a college girl and thought of the girls at Watson. Miss Collier might have been one of them. She could easily be part of the group on the campus, just the way she was, particularly in the mornings when she showed up bright, fresh, with that expectant look, as if the day held surprises for her. The years had neither added nor taken away anything from her pretty face. And like the girls at Watson, she somehow seemed no longer a girl and not yet a woman.

'And what did you do after college?'

'Oh, I never went back.' She seemed surprised that I had not known or guessed.

'But why didn't you?'

Again there was that self-deprecating smile. 'I thought I'd stay on and save up a little money and enrol again the next autumn. But, then, I stayed on . . . well, till this job turned up.'

When I asked her how long she had worked at Macy's and she told me four years, I couldn't help repeating, 'Four years!' Then, to cover up my exclamation, I asked if she liked it better here.

'Oh, much better,' she said. 'It's so much more interesting.'

'You shouldn't use the word "interesting" so lightly,' I said, but her seriousness discouraged me from making a joke of it. 'You should reserve that word for what you do outside the job,' I added lamely.

She peered at me, as if by looking harder and longer she might guess whether I was joking or in earnest, and what I really meant. Her serious expression was so expectant and so trusting that I suddenly felt I ought to tell her, warn her, make her understand that she was wasting herself—and the pity of it all. I ought to make her see the pointless tragedy of wearing out her youth and her good looks in a routine that could never give her any abiding returns, not even a memory except the memory of a single day, since all her days were alike and by overlapping cancelled out each other's traces. She should quit right now. Today. It was a Friday, a good day to quit. We had been paid that morning. Even going hungry, even becoming someone's kept girl friend, or a prostitute, would be better, more natural and human, for a girl like her, than living

168

surrounded by the grey office furniture and breasting the typewriter eight hours a day. I must make her realize how much was already wasted, how time was stealing upon her, upon her youth and vitality. I must drive her into taking a decision. Nothing could be worse than what she was doing now.

But as I was about to speak up, all the arguments I had meant for her turned against myself, and with a vengeance, as if finding their real target; as if what I had been doing for the past two years fell so much shorter of what I had expected of life than she could possibly have expected of hers.

The clerk and the other secretary came in. Miss Collier, after glancing at the door to greet them, continued to face me, as if still expecting me to speak up. I remained silent and she turned back to her desk.

The sound of her typewriter keys ran quick, even and impeccable —as smooth and perfect in their continuity as if being transcribed from one machine to another. The clicking sounds seemed so much more congenial than our words or silence had been, and Miss Collier so much more at her ease again. Soon she stopped and turned around. Before I had a chance to wonder what she might say, she reminded me of my appointment in the afternoon.

V   l was too restless to wait for the four o'clock appointment. I left the office early and walked all the way uptown to the wholesale district. I must have walked faster than I realized, for though I covered more than thirty blocks, I was half an hour early.

But the walk had done me good. If there were no complications in settling this hat order and the delivery date, I might get it over in ten or fifteen minutes. It was a $50,000 order, but with any luck it could be settled as easily as a $50 order—except for the delivery date. I had to make sure of that (it was what I had been sent for), or else we would lose the order.

Though I was early, a moment after I had given my name to the receptionist Mr. Satenstein, the manager, appeared down the corridor. He approached me with the calm, collected steps of a congenial host who happens to be free for the moment. His impersonal, cordial greeting bucked up my hope of winding up the hat order quickly and going home.

Mr. Satenstein motioned me to precede him down the hallway, and then opened a door for me. When I entered, I found myself in a spacious showroom with a set of deep leather chairs in one corner, a large oval table in the centre and glass-enclosed shelves along three walls displaying rows upon rows of straw hats.

Mr. Satenstein invited me to sit down, and then walked over to the far side of the table and, stepping up to the nearest shelf, pushed aside a panel and took out several hats.

The prospect of being shown all sorts of hats and of being initiated into the particulars of each model, made me speak up rather abruptly. 'Mr. Satenstein, about our order....' I didn't want to hurt his feelings, but I was anxious to settle the matter and leave. 'Our order, I hope, can stand according to the specifications we mentioned in our letter and over the phone. I just came here to confirm the delivery date.'

'Yes, I remember,' he said patiently, as if quite aware of the purpose of my visit. 'You asked for the Esquire model. Eight hundred and ninety dozen.' He pointed to another shelf, walked over and took out a hat.

'Yes, yes,' I agreed. 'But delivery must be within two weeks.'

'Delivery in two weeks,' he repeated thoughtfully. 'That'll crowd us a bit, but I think we can manage, though we might have wished for a little more time. It's the season right now for straws, but we always try to help when it comes to export orders.'

I was on my feet. 'Then, I can count on that as settled. You'll confirm it in writing.'

'We'll double check on that with the secretary on the way out,' he said. I waited, expecting him to lead me out, but he continued talking. 'I must tell you frankly,' he said, 'the model you picked out is really one of last year's. Mind you, not that I want to influence your choice, but I thought I'd let you know.'

I liked the casual way he said that, and if I hadn't been anxious to leave I might have shown more interest. 'I'm sorry we haven't made a better choice,' I said. 'But you know we place the customer's order and don't have much say-so ourselves. If it were up to me, of course, I would reconsider after what you've just told me.' I caught myself falling into that ingratiating way I had recognized so often in others when they tried to please me in a matter of business.

'Yes, I realize that,' Mr. Satenstein agreed. 'Still, we try to do our best by our customers abroad, and I'm glad to say they like to do business with us.'

'I'm sure they do,' I said, edging towards the door.

'Though you may have made up your mind on the kind of model you want, I'd like you to get the full benefit of your visit and show you....'

I should have told him then and there not to bother, that I really had no choice. The customer in Afghanistan had simply mailed us an ad. cut out from an American magazine. It was *that* model the customer wanted, and no other. And if the hats weren't shipped within two weeks, the letter of credit would expire and the deal would be off. The delivery date was all that mattered.

I nodded, though I realized that the longer I let him talk on, the

170

harder it would be to cut him off later. He evidently spoke for my benefit, and I felt cheap pretending interest, bent as I was on getting out. His voice was not unpleasant. He spoke in a quiet, unhurried, simple way—too confident to require emphasis or gesture.

He had begun to pick up various hats from among the pile on the table, holding them up for me to see. He did not promote any one model. Neither did he try to impress me. He stuck to the facts, explaining briefly and clearly each model, the composition of the fibre, the standards of grading and the special features of the design. The longer I listened to him the more I became aware of that quality of competence which distinguished businessmen like Mr. Satenstein from the common run. Such men seemed to know everything in their particular field. There was no sham about them or their wares. Their knowledge seemed to endow them with an integrity that was never compromised by the prospect of a sale.

Confronting such people as Satenstein, I wondered at times that they didn't see through me. A single question would unmask me. My very air of studied attention was a mask to hide my ignorance, my indifference and my distaste. Sometimes, I felt something akin to panic that they might call my bluff. The same sensation stalked me some mornings when I walked through the solid, marmoreal lobby of our office building; the dread that someone might tap me on the shoulder, and shake his head at my pretending to be one of the crowd briskly crossing the lobby to the elevators, confident of the day ahead and eager to reach their floors to start work.

Then, as if to make up for all the shortcomings of my job, I would meet someone like Mr. Satenstein, who would fire my ambition to become competent, to specialize in some field. There was nothing to prevent me. It was a matter of learning and experience. There was no limit to the choices open to me nor to the goal I could set myself. I could go to a university and resume my studies—it wasn't too late. Or I could start at the bottom in some business that interested me and work my way up. The mere prospect of working at anything with enthusiasm and energy was reward enough. I could see myself thriving on hard work, becoming a specialist in International Law or Economics or an expert in some special branch of business.

But my choice didn't seem to matter; every one suited me to perfection. I would try on guise after guise, until, imagining myself approaching the zenith of competence, I found that the pinpointing of all effort and ambition upon a single profession or a single aspect of business to the exclusion of all else, repelled me by its isolation, by its distorting limitations, which contracted life to a single vista and narrowed the angle of imagination to a single line.

Then, I would feel sorry for my betters, as I did now for Mr. Satenstein.

171

Mr. Satenstein pointed out a hat, its brim a bit wider than the average with a reversible band, checkered on one side and plain on the other, as the most attractive of this year's models.

'Very attractive. But it's a bit extreme, isn't it?' I said, when I realized he was expecting some remark from me. Mr. Satenstein continued to look at me, as if waiting for me to say all I wanted to say. I felt rude and hasty for having spoken up.

He took the hat off the shelf and turned it swiftly around. It came to rest on his palm, with the crown properly dented and the rim properly shaped, slanting forward, ready to be placed upon the head. He held up the hat a little, like a craftsman sure and proud of his product.

'If you will bear with me for a moment.' He spoke with that patience accorded to hasty critics. 'A hat,' he held it out at arm's length, 'can only be properly judged when it fulfils its function, when it rests on a head. Wouldn't you agree with that?' With his head a little sideways he looked at me like a kindly teacher clearing up a fundamental mistake in his student's reasoning.

'If you don't mind.' His arm extended towards me.

'Oh no,' I protested, drawing back. 'It would be unfair to try it on me. Unfortunately my head just doesn't fit any hat. No hat ever has fit me,' I added apologetically to soften my refusal.

'There isn't a head in the world we couldn't fit properly.' Mr. Satenstein chuckled. 'Many people think the way you do, and I tell you why . . .'

The chance of finding out why no hat ever fit me roused my curiosity.

'. . . and I tell you why. Because they never tried the right hat. It's as simple as that. There isn't a head in the world,' he repeated with conviction, 'we couldn't fit with one of our models right in this room.' He gestured to the shelves. 'The proper size, of course,' he added, as if not wanting to appear to claim too much.

Mr. Satenstein was so serious about his claim that I wondered what it might do to him should he ever run across a man no hat was really suited for. The challenge might prove too much for him, for his pride and métier, and might turn into an obsession.

He was still holding the hat he had taken from the shelf. At that moment, without warning, the accumulated fatigue of the whole week, of the long walk and the tension of the day—grown top-heavy by being loaded with yet one more business contact—snuffed out my last reserves. I sat down again, no longer caring to break off the meeting or to cut Mr. Satenstein short. I was content to sit in the soft leather chair and listen.

Satenstein's quiet voice matched the welcome tranquillity and privacy of the room. On the polished parquet floor the oval table, with the two hand mirrors and several hats reflected on its shiny surface, seemed the props of a private stage with Mr. Satenstein performing his inconsequential act.

'You don't seem to believe me,' I heard Satenstein say a shade more forcefully. I didn't know what made him say that. I may have smiled inadvertently to indicate attention, which Mr. Satenstein must have interpreted as an expression of doubt. 'But the fact is that a hat looks quite different when it rests on a head,' he persisted. He re-dented the crown and gave a twirl to the rim of the hat— again all in one gesture—and put the hat on, looking at me instead of at the narrow mirror on the wall. He stood there facing me, hat on head, without a trace of self-consciousness, as if that were the most natural stance in the world for him.

'Yes, you are right,' I made myself admit.

With the hat still on, Satenstein now turned slowly around. His tall, stooped figure had straightened up. Below the brim of the hat his face, which had struck me on meeting him as manly and of a certain distinction, now seemed to have lost its appeal.

I wasn't sure whether I had expressed sufficient agreement. 'It is really as you say,' I said, feeling some such words were expected of me.

I watched him take off the hat and put it down on the table. My attention must have lapsed for an instant, for next I saw him holding another hat in the same hand—the model he had shown me first and which we had ordered for our customer.

'It may not be quite my size,' he said. 'It's only a 57, but let me try it on anyhow.' He put it on. I could see nothing wrong with the fit. It seemed perfect for Satenstein. The next hat he picked up was, according to him, only a 56. It fitted him, too. Satenstein smiled when he looked inside the next one to check the size. It was a 60 and, he confessed, a mile too big for him. Again, with a deft gesture he formed it into shape, and when he put it on, it became him as well as the others!

As Mr. Satenstein went on trying hats for my benefit, remarking on most that they were either too big or too small for him, a touch of wonder got the better of me. All hats seemed to fit him. He encouraged this sense of wonder by proceeding to extremes.

There were hats with wide brims and narrow brims, high domes and low domes; the flat type, the dented type, the full crown, raised or slanting; rough palmito and finest panama; those with a band no wider than a shoestring and some with bands so wide they covered all but the very top. And the bands ran through all shades of the rainbow, from conservative greys and browns to such wild hues that I wondered who would ever wear them. Yet any hat placed atop Mr. Satenstein's head looked quite proper. There, colour matched shape, and extremes of colour, crown and rim acquired respectability. I couldn't take my eyes off Satenstein's head. Overtaken by a nervous alertness, I was unable to sit still. I rose from my chair, and then, not knowing what to do next, circled Satenstein's figure, pretending to view the hat on his head from all angles.

I tried to ward off the preposterous notion—the malicious fantasy —that Satenstein, in the process of trying on hats for years and years, had undergone some sort of transformation which made his head fit any hat, a malleable mould that serviced his product. When I encouraged him to try on another, I was banking on some law of averages that he would pick up one that wouldn't fit. And as he went on trying, the malicious desire to keep on watching got the better of me. I was even alarmed that an odd fit might break the spell and put an end to the spectacle. I teased him on with calculated comments. From the unwilling spectator, I had become the master of the show.

Any hat I wished could be transferred to his head. But try as I would, no hat looked ridiculous on him. There seemed more than physical rapport between the sizes and shapes of the hats and Satenstein's head and face, as if the moment a hat came to rest on his head, his personality became an adjunct to the hat, so that it might better parade fabric and form.

An excess of tension that rides and feeds on fatigue—a pointless agitation—was threatening to get the better of me. I coached myself over and over again that I must put a stop to all this and go. But I could not take my eyes off Satenstein. It was when I brushed against the table and a hat fell off, and I bent down to pick it up, that I said, 'I must go.' And looking at my watch, repeated, 'I must go.'

The table was heaped with hats. A strange disorder seemed to have come over the room. Most of the glass partitions were open and the shelves half empty. Mr. Satenstein followed me out of the room, and we stopped at the receptionist's desk where he checked through some files. He assured me the order would be delivered within ten days and that he would confirm it by letter.

We were shaking hands when Mr. Satenstein looked around as if looking for something.

'Where is your hat?' he asked.

'I'm sorry, I do not wear a hat,' I said, smiling apologetically.

'Never?' he questioned.

'Never.'

'But in business a gentleman . . .' he hesitated to phrase what he thought of a man without a hat, a matter far exceeding etiquette '. . . must have a hat.'

'I don't,' I said, suppressing a smile at his tone of righteousness.

He seemed genuinely at a loss what to say or do, while committed not to let this breach of an elemental rule go unrepaired.

174

'Just a moment,' he said decisively, laying his hand on my elbow, as if making sure I wouldn't bolt. 'Just a moment, please.'

He quickly stepped up to one of two display cases on either side of the waiting-room door. Before sliding back the glass partition, he looked at me sharply the way an expert surveyor might take in a distance or height, then took out a straw hat and stepped up to me.

'Please try this.'

Waving the hat aside, I tried to make light of it. 'It's very kind of you, but I am really used to going without a hat.'

'Please,' Mr. Satenstein repeated, stressing the word to urge me not to pass off the matter lightly.

'But I never wear a hat,' I persisted, not sure of my temper and the tone of my voice—nor whether Satenstein was really as serious about it as he appeared.

He didn't disguise his conviction that what I had said had no bearing on the issue. His hand was still extended towards me. When I made no move to comply, he added, '... as a personal favour.'

Instead of wording my refusal again, I shook my head gently and smiled.

'I'm asking you as a personal favour. Please take it.' There was no mistaking the issue. It was no longer a matter of rejecting the hat, but of rejecting a personal plea.

I thanked him and accepted the hat. I held it in my left hand, slightly away from my body. With the other hand, I pressed his as a token of appreciation for his entreaties, which I knew were for my benefit. He still looked at me as if expecting something more.

'Permit me. . . .'

Taking the hat out of my hand and swiftly giving it shape, he raised it with both hands as if to crown me. Instead of waving him aside, I bowed my head.

I was helpless to repel his gesture, though my submission was not to him but to something far greater—to the pressure I had resisted ever since I had refused to smile at college when I did not feel like it. Pride and self-respect had always somehow carried the day before. But now, even the will or wish to enlist them failed me, as if blunted by too many skirmishes and compromises—issues seldom involving an adversary or an outright challenge, but inconsequentials common to daily contact; no demand quite worth resisting, rejecting, but in their aggregate threatening to leave no margin for my proper self.

Mr. Satenstein told me to straighten up and I did as I was told. Then he led me to the full-length mirror and stepped aside. I didn't know what to do or say. I waited for a cue from Satenstein or from my own reflection. It made no move of recognition. The reflection resembled the anonymous faces topped by straw hats (brought out by the first rush of summer heat) I had passed on my walk that

175

afternoon. It was not that I really looked so much like them, only so much less like myself, what I imagined myself to be; so much less so that I no longer felt fit for or worthy of claiming any of those rights that set a man apart, each in his own fashion; as all men must set themselves apart who don't compromise their identities altogether under pressure of their times and their fellow men.

I caught sight of Satenstein in the mirror. He was standing behind me, a little to one side, looming tall and with a proprietorial air about him. There was an approving smile on his face, as if he were proud of the change he had wrought upon my appearance.

'Why, a hat is more becoming to you than to many a man I have seen,' he complimented me. I turned around. I tried to smile in agreement, but I felt my cheeks didn't move. 'Believe me, what I say is true,' he assured me. 'I really mean it.' It was when he repeated his assurances that some instinct belatedly reminded me to take off the hat and hold it out to him.

'Oh, please. It is yours, a present,' he exclaimed.

'I cannot accept it. I shall get one, but I cannot accept it.' The words that should have carried conviction trailed off.

'Oh, you must accept it from me, as a friend.' And he placed his hand on my elbow in a familiar gesture. I knew I should persist in my refusal, but I no longer cared. He followed me to the doorway and we shook hands again.

When I failed to put the hat on again, he made a joke of it. 'Now that you have a hat that fits you, you might as well put it on.'

I did as he prompted; and, then, dismissed by his nod of approval, turned and stepped out on the street.

I walked on towards my apartment west of Washington Square. I hunched up my shoulders and drew in my neck to help the hat stay on. A nasty breeze was whirling up dust and rags of paper around me. The brim of the hat snapped up. It felt turned up all the way around, like a saucer. It made me self-conscious, as if I were dressed in a costume. I hoped the next blast would carry it off, and straightened up a bit. The wind was getting stronger in relays—each lull overrun by stronger currents—but the hat stayed on. Torn pages of newspaper, half-lifted off the ground, raced in crazy cartwheels up to me, enveloped my legs, disentangled, and rustled on. And vicious gusts, lifting sprays of dust and grit, stung my face bitterly till, in the end, I had to brush, with my sleeve, the moisture from my eyes.

VI  Once across the threshold of my apartment, I was conscious of the blessing of having four walls, a kitchenette and a hot shower all to myself. At last, I was alone again.

I threw hat and coat on the chair and stretched out on the couch.

After a while, I called Miss Collier to check if anything had happened while I was gone. From the low table next to my couch, I dialled her number. Her voice, when she answered, had that tilt of pleasant surprise I knew so well from the office. I imagined her taking off her right earring as she did when taking a call. There was nothing new, she told me. A young lady had called, but didn't leave a message or her name. 'I believe she had called you before...' Miss Collier's voice trailed off to avoid saying more. I knew it was Joan. I had stalled her, as I did every week, hoping I might manage to get over the week-end without her.

I was about to say good-bye to Miss Collier, when she asked me if I had settled the hat order. I said I had, and then catching sight of the brim of the straw hat under my coat on the chair, I started telling her about the afternoon.

'The manager's name is Satenstein, an extraordinary man,' I told her. 'Every hat fits him.' The chuckle I started off with overlapped into laughter. I wondered how I could have missed the joke before. I found that I couldn't go on with the story without laughing; and I couldn't keep silent, either: as if silence or the absence of laughter might turn the joke against me. I had to make the story come off for the joke it was.

I started over again, but I couldn't get on with the story. Laughter got the better of me each time I started to say that every hat the man tried on really fitted him. 'I know it's unbelievable, but it's true,' I kept on assuring her. 'Every hat *did* fit him.'

Miss Collier's silence egged me on.

'I'm sure there were different hats,' I said. I mentioned some of the sizes I remembered. Why should the man want to fool me? Or go to the trouble of doing so, or have a whole showroom stocked with hats his size only? There must have been different sizes. He told me so himself. But they *did* fit him, one and all, I insisted.

I caught myself shouting. She didn't seem to catch on. 'Really, Satenstein beats them all,' I kept on repeating, 'I never heard of a case like this. It's extraordinary, fantastic...'

I waited for her to laugh, at least agree it was funny. Either I had botched up the story in the telling or it wasn't nearly as funny as I thought it was.

I started all over again, seriously this time. But the moment I stopped laughing, I no longer cared if the story ever got told or not. I was sure she wouldn't get the point, anyway. Nobody would. I wound up quickly, though insisting for the last time that it was funny.

'Funny and what?' she asked.

'Macabre,' I said, though the way she asked, she probably didn't know the word. 'You know, when something is so frightening you have to make a joke of it.'

177

She seemed to be expecting me to go on, or to explain some more, when I suddenly realized that what had happened to me that afternoon was beyond explaining—to her or to anyone else—least of all, my standing there at the end with bowed head to let Mr. Satenstein place the hat on me. Abruptly, I thanked her for the message and hung up.

When the 'phone rang, I thought it was Joan. I recognized Miss Collier's voice.

'I just called to see if you are all right,' she said. Her voice had an altogether different timbre now. It was spontaneous, yet bashful, with a note I had never detected before. She sounded concerned.

'Of course, I'm all right,' I said. 'What made you call to ask?'

She hesitated. 'Well, I was just wondering . . . you sounded sort of upset, if you know what I mean, and I thought . . . something had happened or you didn't feel right or something . . .' Her voice trailed off into silence, as if either hesitating to say what she thought, or not knowing how to say it.

I was all right, I assured her again, and it was nice of her to call. I thanked her and hung up, a bit puzzled about what had made her think I was not all right. She had sounded so nice, I was for a moment sorry I had hung up so quickly. If I had kept on talking, perhaps I might have managed to make her understand about the afternoon after all.

I tried to think of someone else I might call to tell about Satenstein. I dialled Joan's number. When there was no answer, I was relieved, as if luck had helped me avoid a needless risk. She wouldn't have understood, anyway, and I would have been caught; a moment's weakness, and I'd be in for another week-end, paying for the pleasure of spending Friday night with her, and being trapped into having her company Saturday through Sunday.

Off hand, I couldn't think of anyone to ring up. A few names and numbers passed through my mind, the names no more intimate than their corresponding numbers. My eyes were on the 'phone, as if by holding it in focus, they might make it ring. The Manhattan 'phone directory was on the lower shelf of my night table, on top of those of Brooklyn, the Bronx and the other boroughs. I took it up on my lap and leafed through the pages, as if some name were bound to catch my eye and give some meaning to those rows and rows of names. There must be millions of names, I thought. The multitude of columns, the sheer weight of the volume seemed to signify nothing but a perverse law—the more people, the fewer to talk to; the closer they lived together, the farther from each other's reach and the less they meant to each other. I could dial millions of people, without having anyone to talk to. Each of the parties in the book could dial any of the others within a matter of seconds, yet as human beings, they were farther from each other than peasants in the hills.

# PART VI

Pass us by and forgive us our happiness.
DOSTOEVSKY, *The Idiot*

I Each day after coming home from work I expected to snatch
a bit of rest to make up for the sleep missed the previous night.
By Friday, the sheer accumulation of the week's fatigue should
have helped sleep to get the better of me. Instead, it kept me
waiting.

Though stretched out motionless on the couch, I was perspiring.
My windows were open, but the shades blocked the air. If I raised
them any more, passers-by could peer into my basement apartment,
though to catch sight of me on the couch, they would have had to
bend down almost double.

I cursed myself for having postponed so long moving into a larger
apartment. I could well afford one now. But whenever I had roused
myself to check on larger and better places, I felt the change would
barely be worth the effort. At best, it would be a superficial improve-
ment; an elaborate pretence not towards others, but towards myself.
A fancier place would change nothing essentially, except my address
and the floor from which my window looked out.

Through my oblong, narrow windows (their lower halves below
the sidewalk level giving out on a cement pit) with their shades
drawn save for a few inches at the bottom, I had from my couch an
upslanting view of the sidewalk outside. I could follow passers-by
on my side of the street, pick up a pair of legs from the knees down,
follow them past the width of my three windows, then wait and
pick up another pair of legs coming in the opposite direction. The
stillness of the room caught every sound of footsteps on the cement
pavement, the particular rhythm and tread of every footfall. There
were the quick, lively steps of the young, especially of the young
girls with the clicking of their high heels, which seemed to sound
out a call, brief, alert, pert and proud; the even, almost monotonous
footfalls of the middle-aged, properly spaced, yet sometimes moving
faster as if ambitious to imitate those of their youngers and almost
succeeding, but not quite; and then, the sounds of elderly feet, less

179

distinct, slower by a fraction, and somehow weighed, as if planning each step ahead.

Gradually my sidewalk became empty and silent. Outside, it was getting dark.

Two people must have stopped on the sidewalk, not far from my windows. One of them was talking. He seemed hard pressed to control his temper. He had something to say and wanted to be heard out. He refused to be shaken off. He spoke so hurriedly I couldn't follow his words, but the scale and timbre of his voice came through clear. His voice had begun as an impatient murmur; then, rising in sound and temper, seemed to insist that his companion understand and accept what he was trying to say. Not sure whether he had convinced his listener, he started all over again without waiting for an answer, as if facing an obstreperous child or someone hard of hearing. His temper got the better of him, and he fell to cursing his companion with all the foul names unsteady lips, given free rein, can pour forth—uttering them so speedily and vehemently that his pent-up fury used the same curses over and over again. And not quite satisfied with his climax, he launched into a new volley. Then, in the midst of his outrage, he suddenly changed his tune, speaking again quietly, reasonably, sorry for his temper. From apology and retraction, he slipped into justification and complaint; then into whining and, then, into outright pleading, begging with such shameless insistence that even a real beggar could no longer have compromised and accepted rebuff. Throwing away all self-respect, his pleading became uncontrolled. It no longer claimed anything, not fairness nor justice. Stripped of all decorum, his was the elemental demand to which any creature in need is driven by instinct—the plea so naked that no fellow creature can deny it compassion or extort still more tribute before granting it; the cry that it was inhuman to keep him waiting for an answer any longer, to deny what a dog would have received from a fellow animal—some gesture of comfort, of understanding, any gesture but this indifference, this silence.

His voice broke. He was at the end of his tether with nothing more to say; and even if he had, no longer fit to say it.

I lay in the dark, waiting, as he was, for an answer, for a word, any word—at least for a sound to break the stillness, for a shout or for footsteps to walk off. But nothing happened. I got up and walked to the window and peered out under the shade. At first I could see no one. Then, by craning my neck, I just caught sight of him. From his posture, he was no longer young. With shoulders drawn up and chin down as if intently listening, he stood some yards off near a lamp post. I thought he was concentrating on the low voice of someone close by, for, after standing there immobile, he began to nod. Then he nodded again. His head shook up and down several times

180

in short, quick, successive jerks, like a puppet's, out of control. With the back of one hand he rubbed one cheek, then the other, then his eyes, his mouth.

I waited for his companion to speak up, and when he didn't, I pushed my head through the window, as far out as I could, to catch sight of his companion. There was no one else around, neither on my side of the street nor on the other. Just then, the lonely figure at the lamp-post gave himself a wild, impulsive turn, and turning his back on me, walked off, muttering to himself, his legs not quite steady, and undecided whether to cross to the other side or not. Then, I knew, it had only been a drunk talking to himself.

Something of the desperate tone, of the uneven cadence and the tremulous timbre of his voice lingered on with me in the room, and I wondered if he would have talked so truly and freely with a real companion. I was sure he would not, could not, as little as I had ever done. For the dialogues most true to myself I remembered always holding with myself alone.

My room was darker than the street outside. Rather than turn on my lights now, I knew I shouldn't stay alone any longer. I decided to leave, though I had nowhere particular to go.

II Outside, the air was muggy and stagnant, barely alive, as if the asphalt of the streets and the cement of the buildings were sucking in all the freshness and exuding their stored-up heat of the day. Part of the sky was loaded with clouds, their dark, molten hues matching the oppressive heat.

The heat made walking a chore, but I knew I must keep on walking to ward off one of those approaching climaxes that, some evenings, for no particular reason, threatened to bear down upon me with the accumulated wrath of moods and speculations checked and shied away from too long—like one of those imminent attacks of illness, of which it is said there is no specific cause or warning symptom, though the patient senses the impending fit.

After a few blocks I was sweating too much and slowed down. The short, irregular streets of the west side were badly lit, and I felt self-conscious about slowing to a halt in the semi-darkness. I stopped at the next corner where the electric light in the solitary show window of the cigar and candy store seemed to worsen the air within its radius. The square window took up the whole front of the store, except for the narrow entrance. Cardboard ads. and dummies crowded the window space, shutting the inside off from view, except for the ceiling where an old-fashioned fan with long blades made its unhurried rounds.

I stepped in, prompted as much by the prospect of standing for a few moments under the fan, as by one of the ads. that reminded

181

me I had forgotten my cigarettes. There was no one about, and the air inside was no better than on the street, but it had the peculiar texture and smell which some small, old shops have where there has been little turnover and much of the merchandise has been neglected. Magazine racks covered the wall space on either side of the entrance. The bulky counters, with the narrow gangways behind them, swallowed what little space there was. The single lamp suspended from the ceiling swayed in a slow circle above the old-fashioned glass compartments, which displayed without design or pattern candies, stationery, toys and do-dads—as if they were personal belongings accumulated over the years rather than business supplies. Only the counter nearest the door, with its neat stacks of newspapers and full niches of cigarettes on the wall behind, lived up to the mark of strict utility and business.

A woman came out from behind the curtain in the back corner, bringing with her the odour of foreign cooking. Though she saw me waiting, her heavy figure moved no faster up the short gangway behind the counters. Her large, dark eyes made no pretence of being on the alert. The lines of her face were neither premature nor set into any pat expression, but quite natural to her age and bearing— as was her grey hair, not uniformly grey but of dark and white streaks, the darkest strands still showing a certain lustre, and all brushed back into a knot that had come a bit loose at the end of the day. She was wiping her hands on her apron and seemed a little preoccupied, as if she had been called from the kitchen into the parlour by the arrival of a guest. It had been a long time since I had seen such a face or an expression so free of pretence.

I felt awkward disturbing her for the sake of a packet of cigarettes. I could see from her face how tired she was. When another customer came in for the evening paper, I stepped back. She repeated the name of the paper, as if his request were part of a conversation. Her eyes were on his face, but the customer was already scanning the headlines and, without ever looking at her, he pocketed his change and left.

I bought my cigarettes and, saying good-night, turned to leave. It was her 'Goota night, mister' which made me waver at the door. It was so different from those brisk greetings and partings that are tacked on to business as an additional service. Her voice had ended on that note which an incomplete phrase or an unfinished thought leaves behind, as if she might have wanted to add something, had she but known what; she seemed to be waiting, as I was waiting, for something more than a mere purchase to justify and round off our meeting. Her accent, and the tiredness in her voice, had given her words an emotional ring and message that showed off my words of parting for the rote they were, and along with them, all the words I had spoken that day.

182

Her 'goota night' made me feel as if someone had spoken to me for the first time after a long silence—the same sensation that sometimes used to come over me two years earlier while I was waiting for a job to show up. Like most people who assign their hopes to waiting, I had waited much longer for a job than I imagined I ever would; and nothing feeds loneliness more than waiting. I would seldom leave my apartment during business hours for fear of missing a call from one of the agencies, and gradually ceased going out altogether. Except for shopping for food and for borrowing books from the library, I had no reason to venture out at all. If I did, I didn't know what do with myself. The sight of so many people, the noise of the traffic and the fresh air made me feel like an invalid who was up too soon, and I would turn around, anxious to reach the safety of my apartment.

But some evenings, the accumulated silence of days would catch up with me. No longer able to contain myself, I would be driven to speak with someone, anyone. Rushing out of the apartment, I would seek refuge at the grocer's or have a few words with the librarian. The exchange of words rang sweet and auspicious, almost unique. My own voice seemed low, uncertain, as if not sure it could manage the words again after such long silence; while the syllables and phrases addressed to me had a sparkling, virginal sound. The dread of our conversation coming to an end by default would make me want to keep on talking. Yet nothing I could think of seemed momentous enough to be worthy of words, fit to be uttered or suitable to the occasion, except the words of taking leave. Still, the few words I had heard and spoken had their effect, as if reviving a neglected well-spring of energy and hope, leaving me if not gay, then at least content, as I made my way back to the apartment.

The large, tired eyes of the woman behind the counter were still on me. I tried to think of something to say, even thought of buying another packet of cigarettes. But it was too late. The doorknob was in my hand and the door half open. I hurriedly said good-night once more and stepped out. I had gone no more than half a block when there was a clap of thunder and heavy, large raindrops began to fall, without, it seemed, stirring or cooling the air.

III Trying to keep out of the rain by skirting the buildings, I kept on walking. I had gone several blocks when a bus drew up at the corner ahead of me. As I ran to board it, I heard the fast clicking of heels behind me. I didn't look around till I was aboard. A girl was running up to catch the bus. Her chubby figure checked her speed, making her short, hasty steps irregular and a

183

bit off balance. When she boarded the bus and stood up front paying her fare, I could see from where I was sitting that her calves were hefty and strong, rather than fat. So was the shape of her body beneath the transparent raincoat. The wet kerchief, tight around her head, set off the wide cheekbones and the simple, strong features. Her moist skin glistened, fresh and shiny, as did her eyes, as if enlivened by the adventure of being caught in the rain. She moved past the empty seat beside me towards the rear of the bus.

The rain was pelting against the window, and I decided to ride to the end of the line, wherever that might be. The long walk back would tire me out so I could sleep. But when the bus crossed Fifth Avenue, I knew I was on a cross-town route with no more than half a dozen stops ahead. The lighted marquee of a cinema glittering through the rain caught my eye. I hadn't been to a movie for so long that any show was bound to be new to me.

I got off at the next stop and ran back to the cinema. I had almost reached it when I recognized the same quick, awkward running steps I had heard behind me when boarding the bus. While buying my ticket, I glanced sideways to make sure. The girl was standing under the marquee, and a moment later I could hear her heavy breathing immediately behind me, waiting her turn.

Could I pick her up? To gain time, I asked the ticket seller about the show and when it would be over. If there was a chance it was now, before we stepped inside where the dark would make my approach doubly suspect. It was not the courage I lacked, but enough light-heartedness to make a joke of it should I be rebuffed, as probably I would be.

I moved slowly away from the box-office, and when I was sure she had finished buying her ticket, I suddenly turned around. We were standing face to face, and I was blocking her way.

'Are you by any chance following me?' I challenged her. The mockery didn't come off, but the bluff did. I sounded more dead-pan than I intended.

She was so taken off guard that it took her a moment longer than it should have to make her denial. 'Of course not,' she managed to say emphatically, taking my accusation at face value.

'But you did take the same bus I did, didn't you?'

She was caught in the dilemma of having to reject the implication without being able to deny the fact.

'And you did get off when I did, didn't you?' And before she could say anything, I added, 'And you followed me again when I came here and bought a ticket just after I did. Would you believe me, if I had followed you that way and then pretended it was all a coincidence?'

My smile gave me away. She was relieved to find I was joking. I stepped aside and she walked through the door ahead of me.

184

When the usher came up with his flashlight and asked me in a low voice if we were together, I nodded. She didn't protest, and he lighted our way past the crowded rows to two adjoining seats.

There was nothing I could say or do while the movie was on. I watched the screen. A horse was racing in a mad gallop, the rider bent low. Amidst the silent rocks, crags and gullies, the thud of the hooves was the only sound. The austere grandeur of the landscape dwarfed motion and rider. The technical perfection of the camera lent the mountains and the plain an authentic majesty they seldom have when seen in nature—the authenticity that such was precisely the setting and such the adventure of man pushing West. The setting alone would have made a hero of any man. Upon the naked immensity the solitary rider seemed too foolhardy and too brave to deserve any other destiny than to perish. He was limp over his horse's neck, close to exhaustion. He could barely keep astride, yet he urged his horse on to greater speed. Rider, horse and purpose were perfectly matched in the setting; the reality of it all was so compelling, the scene so attractive, that I was transported into identifying myself with the rider, sharing his hopes and fears, sharing his last ounce of fortitude, with barely enough strength to turn around for a glance at the smoke signals ominously rising from a hilltop where another horseman, an Indian, appeared.

The Indian summoned up, as his image on the screen always did, the glimpse I once had of his counterpart in the flesh, somewhere between Texas and California. A Negro had given me a ride in his old truck. It was so dilapidated that I wondered what we would do should the car break down, for we seemed to move across an endless plain of stone and brushwood, its only known limit the gas station we had left behind; there seemed no end to what was ahead and around us. At first I had paid no attention to what resembled a tall, straight cactus some distance ahead. No other plant could survive in this heat and desolation. Half dazed by the heat and dust that rose through the broken floorboards, I discounted as an illusion the elongated cactus shape apparently moving steadily towards us. It wasn't till we came quite close that I realized it was a human being, and then, it was by the mental detour of remembering a wooden cigar-store Indian that I recognized him for what he was.

The shiny, long hair was gathered tightly at the back of the head. I couldn't tell whether it was man or woman. The body was fully covered. A garment resembling a long skirt, tightly wound about the body, almost touched the ground. Over the upper part, he wore a brightly-coloured throw-over. His steps were short and stiff, his torso immobile. So was his face. His features registered no sensation as we passed. He was staring straight ahead. The skin of his face seemed not red, but the colour of long-settled dust that had not been wiped off or freshened by wind or rain. With his stiff, swathed

185

figure and motionless features, he seemed like a mummy, which the world had forgotten to bury.

I expected the Negro beside me to speak up. But his eyes remained on the road ahead. The tapping of his foot on the wooden floorboard kept impatient rhythm with the jazz from the truck radio, as if wanting it to go faster and louder. In the small driver's cabin, the music rioted senselessly and loud, as if temporarily out of control. A dreamy smile, so incongruous with the intent, listening expression of the rest of his face, hovered on his lips, though he was chewing gum. In relation to the mechanics of the motor and the radio, the Negro seemed as out of place as the Indian—more so when viewed against the landscape. Watching him, I wondered why the one race had perished and the other—though just as badly treated—had survived in a set-up equally alien and inimical to both.

On the screen the exhausted rider just managed to reach the primitive farm house when the enemy attacked. The Indians were coming. Rich in war paint and whooping their call of war, they came plunging up the crest of the nearest hill. There, they drew rein. The foremost riders were silhouetted against the horizon like equestrian statues, animal and rider one—even of the same colouring, their bows and arrows and shields and naked limbs blending with the land. Then they raced forward. The musket shots of the defenders echoed loud and heroic. Indians fell off their horses with showmanship, but dead nevertheless.

Something of the disappointment I had lived through when watching my first Western at college got the better of me. Perhaps my imagination was too exacting. It clung to a version so much more heroic and worthier of both sides; because both had had thrust upon them the greatness of an encounter which destined only one to survive. By depriving one side of quality and performance, by cheapening its manhood into savage lust and ugliness and evil, the victor was cheated out of greatness as much as the vanquished. And a true epic was reduced to a spectacle for the pastime of an audience which, perhaps, no longer had any yardsticks with which to measure a past so anachronistic to their present interests, a past which, though removed little more than two generations, seemed already to have receded farther in time than Thermopylae. Nor would they grant the former enemy qualities which they no longer claimed for themselves—a code of manhood too strict for compromise, one that required the race to perish rather than to survive tainted, its departure the only monument to its greatness.

Soon after the first volley from the besieged shack, the girl appeared, catering with a pail of water and a towel to the exhausted rider who had dropped to the ground, head slumped to one side.

186

She broke the spell. No camera, no costume, no make-up could make her appear authentic, instil depth into her eyes, character into her presence. Except for her costume, she might be almost any girl I had met at college, in California or New York—though her figure and picture-pretty face perhaps came closer to the standards of beauty prescribed by ads. But she seemed as much coached into her rôle as other girls seemed in theirs, as college girls, secretaries, wives and mothers.

I didn't want to spoil the picture for myself, now that I still had to sit through it. But with the appearance of the heroine, there was little left for guessing. The lanky fellow with the clean-cut smooth features was the good guy who'd get the girl. The one with the moustache was the bad guy who'd try and fail and get his come-uppance. That they were clad in buckskin shirts and chaps and high-heeled boots was incidental; they might have been dressed in business suits or dinner jackets and the story would still be the same. It wasn't that this or any other movie was so infantile, but that they all seemed to run on a formula which nobody ever tried to change, beyond adding every now and then a gimmick. This time there was the Negro, standing in the background, rolling his funny eyes in terror, his full, beautiful voice rising in prayer—fun and symbol mixed in one. If I had been alone this would be about the right time for leaving. But the girl on the seat next to me was absorbed in the picture.

IV  When the show was over, I waited till we reached the exit before I addressed her again.

'You see, I'm not as forward as all that. I was as quiet as a school-boy, wasn't I, though we were in the dark? If you were the teacher, wouldn't you give me good marks for behaviour?'

She nodded.

'And won't you reward me by having a bite or a cup of coffee with me? I know you might not think it proper. We weren't introduced and all that. You don't even know my name, do you?'

She had to shake her head again.

I told her my name and used the pushy phrase, 'What is yours?'

'Margaret Bardet.'

Going one better on the native custom of flattery, I asked her how she spelled it.

'Now that we're properly introduced,' I said, 'you'll accept, won't you? You probably guessed that I'm a foreigner, and they won't let in nasty foreigners. Only nice ones like me. And you must let me apologize for accusing you of following me. I couldn't think of anything else to say. At least, give me credit for not being too corny.'

'That I do,' she said and laughed.

We found a restaurant that was still open. All during dinner I felt strangely light-hearted. To keep up the mood, I kept on talking, to amuse her and myself. It wasn't till we were at dessert and coffee that the imminent prospect of being alone again rushed in on me. I was too keyed up by too much talking and by gulping the red wine too quickly to face it calmly. I wasn't sure whether I was more alarmed at having no plans to press my luck with the girl once dinner was over, or at the thought of being left alone again. This ambiguity as to what I really wanted should have disturbed me.

Our second cup of coffee was almost empty. So was the restaurant, except for a solitary man at a window seat. Through a slit in the curtains, which he held apart, he was watching the street. His head jerked around each time someone entered the restaurant, though he must have seen the approaching newcomer through the window. Each time he turned his head, his expectancy lent a note of alarm to his movement. Set off by a shirt collar too big and an ill-fitting coat, his scrawny neck and haggard face had the sickly aspect of a man suffering loss of weight or of one who fails to gain it back after an illness. Each time he turned, I was struck anew by his ugliness, a pointless ugliness for which no single feature could be blamed. The sight of him, so anxiously waiting, jerking his head again and again, provoked the eye. The more I looked at him, the uglier he seemed.

The girl noticed him, too. 'He is ugly, isn't he?' she said with a little grimace, but without malice.

'I wonder what makes him so ugly, though,' I said.

'Nothing. He just is.' And she laughed as if responding to a joke.

'Somebody must not think so,' I said. 'Because he is waiting for someone.'

He was looking at his watch again. His neck seemed drawn out longer still, and his face was caught in one unvarying expression— that of waiting, a waiting that had used up his calm and all variations of legitimate hope, had made all excuses for delay, had widened all margins and leeways, accounted for all contingencies, except for the ultimate one; that whoever he was waiting for might not show up. The overriding quality about him was no longer his ugliness, but the anxiety and hope of his waiting.

'How can you be so sure he's waiting for someone?' the girl said.

'There must be somebody,' I said. 'Besides, God created us in pairs. That's probably why *we* met.'

'Are you teasing again? I'm sure you've met prettier girls than I am.'

'Almost every girl I've met has said that,' I said lightly. She

188

showed how slighted she felt. 'Only *they* were right. But you are wrong,' I added quickly.

The compliment was overdone, had got out of hand. She wasn't accepting it at face value. How could she? Her face, like her body, had that chubbiness that makes some girls look younger than their twenty or twenty-five years, and later, much older in their thirties. And there was nothing in her manner nor her features that might have teased me into searching for shadings and subtleties. But she was pleasant and forthright, without finesse or pretensions, showing her reactions simply and unconsciously. When the waiter had approached with the first course, her eyes had followed his arm as he put the plate in front of her; she had looked at the antipasto, as if not sure which heap she should try first, but sure that each would taste good. And after each bite, she had looked up at me, as if prompting me to back up her choice. She hadn't disguised her appetite. Nor did she disguise her reaction now at my exaggerated compliment. I felt uncomfortable; I would rather be caught in a lie by a woman than fail to bring off an exaggeration or a bluff.

'How pretty a girl is, really depends on when you meet her, how you meet her and what you see in her,' I said.

'What do you see in me?' she took up.

She had spoken too quickly, though. And hers wasn't the idle question of a beautiful woman nor the bantering of a clever one, which can lead a man on to make an ass of himself. She was in earnest. I might have fed her a string of flatteries, letting her credulity be my cue. But I was too taken up with speculating what her reaction would be were I to tell her the truth—that on an evening like this it mattered but little whom one met, if only one met someone.

Looking at her across the table, I wondered what she would say if I told her truthfully that it really didn't matter whether she was pretty or not. I could also have told her how strangely calm and contented I had felt sharing dinner with her, as if her presence had averted or dispelled some ominous portent that had been gathering in upon me. Without her, I would probably be walking the streets, sustained by those brief diversions that traffic, motor, man and show windows grant a man who is out accumulating fatigue as prepayment for a few hours sleep. Instead, I had found in her company something of that rest and repose convalescents must know after a crisis.

I must have waited too long before answering. 'You don't want to tell me, do you?' she said. 'It might hurt my feelings.'

'A man doesn't hurt a woman he has just met,' I said, a bit sharply. 'All that comes later when they get to know each other.' I was annoyed with myself for flaring up. 'If you really want to know, I

189

am just a bit grateful to you and whatever gods there are that I don't have to sit here alone like that poor fellow over there.'

The waiter, like a laggard apparition, had appeared from somewhere near the cash register in the far corner, and was now standing a few paces off. He hovered there, like someone who has wandered in and then forgotten why. Like so many waiters in small foreign restaurants, he had the resigned air of a craftsman whose job no longer requires his skill but only the motions of it. I felt sorry for him and his like; yet glad that his kind of profession, along with that of servants, was dying out in America. The waiters and waitresses in modern restaurants were a new breed, like mechanics, and as efficient in their motions; but as ignorant as their customers of what good food or good service really was. The food they served was as hygienic as their uniforms and as functional. Nowhere else in the world were the tomatoes cut up so prettily or so red, the spinach so green and the potatoes so uniform in roundness and size; and nowhere else could the food be so void of savour, so innocent of spice or condiment or art. Whenever I dined in an expensive restaurant boasting good food and a foreign cuisine, I often wondered how the diners around me (who had worked their way up to afford such prices) could pretend to indulge taste-buds they had never had time to develop, and to enjoy flavours and textures that could only be odd to them.

I paid the waiter, and just as I was handing Margaret her raincoat, my glance fell upon the man waiting at the window table. With both palms pressed down against the table, he bent stiffly forward; his torso seemed to lift, though he actually hadn't risen. The flesh of his eager face was drawn tight like rubber. I followed his stare and saw a girl coming in through the door. She was tall and thin; even with a shorter neck, her head would have been too small.

The affinity of her ugliness with his was striking; she, too, was ugly without any one feature particularly at fault, except, perhaps, for the sharp nose and the forehead made so much lower by hair cut in a straight fringe above the eyebrows. Before giving way to relief, her features still bore traces of the fears and self-reproaches that must have been hers till she opened the door—fear of being too late to find anyone still waiting for her, and of that melancholy guilt and resignation the handicapped are so prone to when in danger of forfeiting a chance, common to others, but so rare for them—and because of no greater reason than a silly oversight, of miscalculating the hour or getting caught in the traffic.

Her long legs sped her towards the man before he had managed to get well on his feet. His face answered hers—the fears and forebodings of the past half hour feeding his felicity now. The ugliness I had seen in him when he had been alone was no longer there.

Like hers, it had given way to such a glow of gladness that anyone catching sight of him now would notice only his expression of release and happiness.

I touched Margaret's arm and nodded towards the window table. The man and woman were looking into each other's eyes, their hands entwined over the table top.

'Was I right?' I said. She nodded. 'Sometimes it does work out.' I didn't know why I felt so cheerful saying it.

Outside, I suggested we go to a bar. I couldn't sound very enthusiastic about it, but where else was there to go? The only two outdoor cafés I knew of closed by ten.

'I better go home, it's late,' she said.

'It would be late on any other day, but it is Friday night.' I knew I must go on talking. 'I don't blame you for not wanting to go to a bar,' I conceded, 'I don't like those places myself. But it isn't too late to walk a bit, is it?'

'Where?'

'Oh, anywhere, just for air.'

I took her arm and we began to walk. The air seemed deceptively light and fresh after the rain. But we had gone no more than half a block when I began to feel uncomfortable dragging my feet in the heat.

'I feel a bit silly having nothing better to offer than walking in this heat,' I said. 'But look,' I was trying to sound casual, 'why don't you let me invite you to our club? It's a very simple, small place. You might like it.'

'What sort of a place is it?' Though she tried not to show it, her curiosity was defeating any doubts or suspicions she might have had.

'Oh, you mustn't expect much. It's for the kind of people who don't like to go to bars and such places. Anybody comes and goes as he pleases. And thank God, it's never crowded. It's very quiet. It may even be too quiet for you.'

'Oh no. I don't like crowds myself.'

'Then chances are you may like it. Why not give it a try? It's not far from here.'

She thought for a moment. 'All right, but I can't stay long.'

'You can leave any time you want to,' I assured her.

When we reached my apartment, I rang my own bell and then pretended surprise that there was no answer. Either everyone had gone home already, or none of the club members had come yet. But it didn't matter, I assured her. It was such a small club that each member had his own key.

I opened the door with my latch-key. Whatever Margaret was about to say when she caught sight of the apartment within was cut short by the sound of footsteps descending from the floor above.

191

'You can get mad at me later,' I whispered urgently. 'Only don't let's give the impression we are coming out of the apartment. I wouldn't want anybody to think . . .'

She gave in to the pressure of my arm and we quickly stepped inside. I closed the door and we waited till the sound of steps reached the ground floor, passed the door, and was cut off by the click of the entrance door of the apartment house.

Then I opened my apartment door wide and stood aside. 'Of course, you may go,' I said. 'Only I wish you wouldn't. Look, it isn't such a chamber of horrors, is it?'

She glanced dubiously, but curiously, around the room.

'And you needn't get mad. It was just a joke, or call it a trick, we sometimes played on girls in Vienna.'

She made no move to step out, though her hand was on the door knob.

I quickly added, 'And now that you are here, why don't you let me make you a cup of coffee before you go?'

She wavered for a moment more, and then let me take her raincoat.

I went into the kitchenette to make the coffee, as Margaret took a chair. 'In Persia, if people drink coffee together they are supposed to have nothing but good-will for each other,' I said, making up the story as I went along. I told her she must not break the tradition.

'I thought you were European—Austrian or something,' she said.

'In a way I am. How can I help it? I grew up there. But I am really Persian,' I told her. 'It doesn't make much difference here, though. America doesn't leave much room for anything but its own ways.'

'Why do you say that?' There was a sharpening of attention in her voice, as if I had said something personal.

'I don't know. I've just felt that way about it.'

'But tell me,' she persisted. 'Why did you say that?'

'Say what?'

'Oh, what you just said about America.'

'What did I say?'

'Well, that we don't like other people's ways and all that.'

'Why should you?' I knew it was no good trying to explain or even talk about it. Any answer that wasn't tuned to praise of America was suspect, and was invariably taken as a personal affront. It didn't matter what the question was or who asked it. 'Why should you?' I repeated. 'Aren't your ways the best, any-how?'

She took my veiled question as a statement of support, and her face, which had looked sulky and stupid when she was concentrating, now relaxed. Everything was all right.

I poured the coffee and handed her a cup. I took my own to the couch and pushed aside the books on the side table to make room for it.

'You must do a lot of reading, don't you?' she said, as if she had guessed something odd about me.

'It just looks like that. Half of them are from the library and I'm too lazy to take them back.' I was making light of the books, belittling them, now that I didn't need them. Now that I was not alone, they seemed a poor substitute for company, their characters accomplices to my weaknesses. I held off thinking of those evenings when, after reading for a while, I felt more at one with their world than with the one I passed through during the day.

'The good thing is that the books stay with me after you go,' I said. 'Though I'd rather it was the other way around. Or don't you believe me?'

She didn't seem to take this as much of a compliment. 'Oh, I don't know,' she said, glancing around the room.

'Now, what else do you want to know about me?' I said, to start her talking.

'Well, I really don't know anything about you. You haven't even told me what you do for a living.'

Her question put me on the defensive for fear she might identify me with my job. This seemed to be the great mark of identity; tell me what you do for a living, and I will know what sort of a man you are. Unfortunately, I could no longer claim, as I used to, that my job was a makeshift. I must have sounded a bit apologetic when I said I was in the import-export business.

'You don't sound very enthusiastic about it.'

'Why should I?'

'Then why don't you get a job you like?' she said.

'I suppose I should,' I said lamely. 'I only hope you like yours better.' She had told me she was working in a mid-town flower shop.

'Yes, I do,' she said.

'So did I,' I said, 'when I worked for a flower wholesaler in Los Angeles. For all I know, I might still be there if the fellow hadn't been such an ass and insisted that I wear one of those confounded buttons.'

'What's wrong with wearing a tag? It's part of the job.' There was a challenge in her voice, as if by belittling Mr. Wright, I had cast disparagement on a national custom. There was a lack of smoothness about her and her gestures—a coarseness which sometimes confident and contented creatures have, to whom life is a set of well-manageable issues and the only complications the result of mismanagement and unreasonable prejudice.

'Nothing's wrong with it, I suppose,' I said.

193

'Well, looking around here one would never guess you had anything to do with flowers. I bet you never had a flower in this room,' she said.

'No, I haven't had,' I admitted. 'But I will. I promise, next time you come.'

'You shouldn't do it for my sake. You should have them around for what they are.'

'I'll try to learn. You seem doubtful about that.'

'Well, frankly, it doesn't look very hopeful. I suppose you're too much taken up with your books and that sort of thing.'

'What sort of thing?' I asked.

'Oh, all that. . . . ,' She made a vague gesture to indicate the room. 'Your books and your writing, I suppose.'

'What writing?' I asked, astonished.

'That,' and she nodded towards the typewriter. 'You do write, don't you?' she added, no longer sure of her first impression.

'Well, no. What gave you the idea?'

'It looks as if you did, anyway.'

The old typewriter on the table—pushed up against the phoney fireplace—would never have been there if the sound of typing hadn't caught my ear one summer evening, a year earlier, from the first floor window of a house I happened to pass. Whenever I passed that house, I heard the typewriter going. I began to envy the solitary, unknown creature for the company he had in the responsive chatter of the machine. And when I bought myself a typewriter, it was better company than I had imagined. Writing letters became, after a while, no longer the solitary pastime of communicating in a silence which seemed only to heighten my sense of isolation. The sound of the machine, once I got started, was no mechanical noise set off by my pressing down the keys, but was attuned, as it were, to my mood, to what I was thinking and feeling. The machine made no demands upon me; it seemed always waiting, always ready to serve and respond to my moods, never recalcitrant or ahead of me, but just in step. When I wrote fast, its hurried echoes, as smooth and flowing as what I wanted to say, confirmed and encouraged my speculations and hopes. It was abrupt and impatient when my temper was short. Then, the keys stumbled and seemed confused, as melancholy and aimless as I was when I no longer knew what to say yet didn't want to stop writing. My letters became longer and longer. I rarely finished them at one sitting. And when I did finish one, it fell so far short of what I wanted to say that I didn't mail it off. Hundreds of pages were now stacked up near the machine like an unfinished manuscript.

I almost started to tell her about the typewriter. But the truth struck me as too far-fetched to bear telling. The typewriter would seem a mere fad, and as irrelevant as the other objects in the room that were my own—the three tea-pots (for two, four and six cups), the rows of tea cans from which I mixed my own brew for the pleasure of it; the little Persian rug that I had bought in a rush of sentimentality; the large tin box of Persian rice I had had so much trouble finding in New York, in order to cook myself some food once in a while that didn't insult my appetite and would yield some savour. All these seemed petty parts of a make-believe now, artifices and props to sooth a pride and temper worn raw in a different climate.

I told her the pages next to the typewriter were just left-over copies of business reports I had typed at home. She seemed to see nothing odd in that.

It irritated me to find myself groping for something to say next. With her, it couldn't matter what I said. She had neither the looks, the intelligence nor the sophistication of other girls who had sat in that chair on other evenings. I couldn't help wondering what Joan would have said could she see us now. Compared to Joan, this girl wasn't even worth looking at. Finding me in such company would be incomprehensible to her, just as it would be incomprehensible to me were I to see another man, given the choice between this girl and Joan, choose this one. I had no answer either. Except for the attraction which any new affair incites, Margaret had little to offer.

And yet, looking at her across the room, I did find a stimulation which none of the others, though so much prettier, had roused in me. It seemed as if what mattered were no longer the good looks and clever tongues the others had so much in common, but what set this girl apart—even if it were only her shortcomings; as if difference, for sheer difference's sake, had become more attractive by its very rarity than the grace and prettiness shared by so many others. After the trim, slender, well-shaped (yet shaped so much alike) figures of Joan and the others, the hefty outlines of Margaret's body attracted me more than I could explain.

None of the girls who had preceded her in that chair would have sat there, as she did, making no effort to appear at her best. She seemed unaware that she looked coarse, except in profile; her wide cheekbones added too much roundness to her face when facing me full. Neither did she seem to realize that glancing so straight at me all the time emphasized the close setting of her eyes, and gave her look something of a stare. Having a foot drawn up under her made her hips look too wide, and instead of leaning a bit forward to underplay her large breasts, her posture was adjusted entirely for comfort.

She let me refill her coffee cup, but refused the cognac. It was then that she asked me about the samovar in the corner. She had never seen one. I told her I had bought it in a fit of house-keeping, in order to have hot tea always at the ready, but then found out I could boil water much quicker on the gas stove. 'But it is company of a sort when I'm alone. It is always there, and if you look at it long enough it will sometimes take on all sorts of shapes. Just keep on looking at it.'

She looked at the samovar and shook her head. 'I can't see anything more than when I looked at it first.'

'It isn't as easy as all that,' I said. Her bland expression reflected no more than idle curiosity. I would have sounded an utter fool were I to confess how, sometimes, when I lay awake, the samovar assumed odd shapes—strange landscapes I had never seen, figures and faces no less strange, which promised, but always withheld any significance or meaning. Any object in the room which remained under my stare too long was liable to yield to that process. The telephone or the typewriter would dissolve into a misty, fluid panel, then slowly consolidate into some undecipherable distortion—yet so overwhelmingly real that I was hypnotized into waiting for its ultimate shape and message. But always short of coherence or recognition, the image would weaken in outline, melt and relapse into its normal shape. Except for a vague sensation of having missed something akin to a revelation, these night visions left no memory until, one day, when I was passing some paintings exhibited in a show window, the lines and blots making up the seemingly haphazard composition struck me with a shock of recognition. The artist had caught and given expression, if not to one of my experiences, then to one of his own affinitive to mine, in which the senses conjure up a totally different reality.

'Try to think of nothing,' I said to Margaret. 'And keep on staring. It won't work if you think of anything.'

'It still won't work with me,' she said.

'Try once more. And relax.'

'But I am relaxed.'

'Now wait . . .' I said, getting up. I stepped over behind her and, taking her head between my hands, shifted it to a new angle, telling her to close her eyes for as long as she could. Standing behind her, I wondered whether she was too innocent to sense what I was about to do, or whether she was so sure of it that she was just waiting for it. I bent over and kissed her on the lips.

Though she withdrew her lips, I felt she had lingered a moment too long.

'You shouldn't have done that,' she said, getting up. 'Now I must go.'

She collected her coat and bag and we left the apartment without exchanging a word. Walking alongside her, I felt her arm resting on mine with a directness and immediacy as naked as our hands. But this sensation was numbed by the apprehension that the next block, the next building might be hers and bring about our parting.

And when she pointed across the street and said that was where she lived, my self-reproach for kissing her and cutting short my companionship, gave way to a wild, irrepressible alarm at being left alone again. Had she stayed an hour, even half an hour longer, the remainder of the night could have been got through somehow. But now, I was worse off than when I had left the apartment hours earlier.

I cursed the moment I had left my place, and the rain that had made me jump on the bus. And the carefree mood I had felt during dinner mocked me now with a vengeance—as if any evening could ever pass without extracting its due of self-control. There was always a price. For even had Margaret stayed overnight, I knew how utterly I would wish her gone by morning, when each word and move of hers would grate upon my temper and upon my need to be alone again. I would curse my weakness of the night; though a day, a week, a month later I would court another night with her. It was as if some fatality always exposed me anew to temptation; and after each surrender I sensed myself more immune to and yet more afraid of the next climax. It was as if each crisis of loneliness bequeathed some intangible burden and danger to the next, merely withholding its full impact upon me till, eventually, some day or night, caught off guard, I would knuckle under and confess, even if to no one but myself, how wretchedly dependent I was on others— though I knew such a confession would, like some flaunted taboo or a supreme interdiction broken, sicken my marrows.

We were at Margaret's door. My mind was already ahead of the words I was going to say about seeing her again, of her tentative reply and my setting a definite date. I was searching wildly for some way to postpone—if only for a few minutes—our parting. Even after we had exchanged good-nights and set a date for the next evening, I still didn't abandon a last hope of stalling her from entering the door she had already half opened.

'Don't go yet. Please.' The plea escaped me, and along with it another particle of my self-respect. But the words that had seemed like muffled, drawn-out shouts within me sounded on my lips calm and common—words anyone might say who didn't want to part with a girl on her doorstep. For a moment I was afraid she would laugh or put me off with a word or two. Instead, she slowly shook her head.

'At least, let's walk around the block,' I said.

'It's really too late for that.'

'But it isn't too late to ask me in for a cup of coffee. You can be that generous, can't you? I'll go any time you want me to. That isn't asking too much, is it?'

'Well, all right,' and I followed her in.

V A car almost ran me over when I rushed across the street. The driver shouted curses after me, but I didn't turn around, bent as I was on getting far away from Margaret's apartment and all that had happened after we stepped in and she switched øn the light. . . .

The ceiling light had flickered, gone out, lit up again and gone dead. Waiting in the dark for the light to come on again, I felt as if I had been in this place before. Only the girl was different. But the extra pillows I had glimpsed crowding the day-bed, the large lampshade in the shape of a sun-bonnet and the giant glass ashtrays were interchangeable details, common to all the small apartments I had even been in—details meant to justify the pathetic claim to a home more permanent, cosier and less impersonal than a hotel room.

'Oh, damn it,' she exclaimed in the dark. 'They promised to have it fixed this morning.'

'Never damn the dark . . .'

She made for the floor lamp across the room, and lightly bumped into me. I hardly moved when I kissed her. She didn't stir, and when I kissed her again I felt her lips drawing more substance from mine than mine from hers. Against her thick, insolent lips my own felt thin, dry, almost chaste. Belatedly I put my arms around her. Yet when I nestled my face in the hollow of her shoulder amidst the strands of hair fallen loose from her bun which had come undone, I was submerged in such utter contentment that I postponed lifting my head to return my lips to hers. The same contentment suffused me again, only more excruciatingly so, when, a while later, our bodies touched. But her naked body, impatient with my stillness, began to importune mine with such urgings that I felt she was about to possess me, rather than my body hers. It was by an act of will that I roused myself into responding to her, only to find that will was not enough.

Matched against the blaze of her healthy, demanding body, my own was deficient, sick and taut with effort, unfit—sullied and punished for having sought too often in embraces a refuge from loneliness rather than a true consummation; for having made my body serve needs other than its own; for seeking in the irreducible closeness of a woman's body another sort of intimacy which was not her body's to give.

Ahead of me the avenue stretched far; I couldn't see the end of it. Its straight line relieved me of all decision, save that of walking on and on. Only by keeping on the move could I ward off becoming the target of my own thoughts or squaring accounts with myself. Even at side streets, where the hot air seemed a bit thinner, I didn't linger. The avenue was silent and deserted, as if some blight had struck the city. The few cars passing by seemed belated stragglers

198

trying to catch up with those who had already fled for the week-end. Without crowds and traffic to give them purpose, the skyscrapers now seemed merely the grandeur of pomp and caprice. Amidst them a church was tucked away like a quaint landmark, its spire's reach for the heavens pathetically short compared to the adjacent towers. The only reminders that all this silence and desertion was temporary and would give way to the busy cycle of Monday, were the few undarkened show windows.

Each was a focus, drawing my eye as any light will in the dark. Behind the polished plate glass, the wares and fashions vaunted the glamour of the female, embellishing and proclaiming the attractions of that sex. Slim hands raised in coquettish gestures heralded the chic of gloves; legs, slender yet full, thrusting out of thighs muffled in waves of tulle, exhibited stockings so sheer as to give skin, form and flesh a perfection nature unaided could never achieve. Large eyes, made larger by extra eyelashes and more luminous by mascara, stared a hypnotic message; necks, almost too fragile for the weight of the necklace they displayed; corsets and brassieres imprisoned such firmness of hips and breasts as to make their substance impatient of covering.

Though I had ceased paying attention to such exhibits long ago, tonight they seemed to hold my eyes, as they had done during my first days in New York, when everything around me seemed calculated to rouse and tease my instincts. It had started in the mornings when Alex turned on the radio and I heard the husky, bitter-sweet songs of love. Something of women, love or sex labelled the bread and coffee and cigarettes we had for breakfast. And when I stepped out on the street, there was no sight, no ad., no store front, that didn't hint, whisper or shout in some way or other about hips, breasts, legs—about happiness, smiles and love. It wasn't till later, after college, that it struck me that this spreading of sex all over to promote wares was worse than pornography. And the resulting unawareness was worse, in the long run, and more wearing than any debauch; and the casual glance worse than the outright leer.

I walked slowly on, and with each display window I passed, I felt less sure whether the female models had been fashioned to imitate the living, or the living the models. All artificiality, if pursued persistently enough, acquires eventually something of the authenticity of the real until it ends by serving as a model to the real. Those exaggerated gestures, those over-perfected limbs and fashions in the windows seemed less artificial than they should have. So much of women, I sensed, had become but imitation of their betters in the show windows. At times I felt that I had met the same girl over and over again, just as I felt now that I was seeing the same mannequin in every window: all of them so slender, so neat and clean, so well-dressed and cheerful; and always a touch more attractive when

199

beheld from a few steps off than when seen close. And all lacking something of that savour which sets one woman apart from another.

A vague animosity stirred in me as I passed each window, the reaction of a man who had thought himself immune to the blights that had struck others, and who suddenly finds himself an invalid like the rest—just another of those colourless males who lives up to his rôle only in business, and shows up in statistics as another of those millions who are prematurely impotent.

My anger was spilling over into the anarchy of rage. I felt I had been marked a victim from the moment of meeting my first date at college, of holding the first girlish hand and exchanging the first kiss. Those creatures, so lovely to behold behind the plate glass, were twins and sisters to all the girls and women I had met. There wasn't one who didn't belong to that smiling sorority, their fresh, bright faces and trim figures mocking all that I had expected and thirsted for in them. I damned them all—the pretty, pert, budding creatures at college; then those a few years older, but no less lovely, I had met in California—some of them already married, but all of them, though no longer girls, not yet women either, as if their boy friends and husbands had failed to make women of them. I thought of their laughter, their talk, their holding of hands and giving of themselves to me in parked cars—in cars parked alongside dozens of other cars —their fumbling with me like adolescents or as casually as if I were their husband.

But their ages didn't really matter. Neither in California nor in New York would they relinquish their claim to that eternal youth promised them by money, make-up and fashion. At forty and fifty they behaved and appeared deceptively like women of thirty and even younger, more like sisters to their daughters than the mothers they were. They never seemed to age, nor want to mature. Even Doris, the buyer I had met on the train, seemed hardly older by a day when I ran into her in New York years later. Only the tell-tale wrinkles, which would not have been unattractive if she hadn't tried to hide them, broke through their coat of powder after a few drinks and belied the youthful gaiety of her bright, darting eyes. Her slim body, never at rest, fascinated and repelled me at the same time. In five years she had aged not a whit, and when dressing in the morning or undressing at night, she seemed an eerie, artificial combination of age and girlish youth, desperately dedicated to bringing alive some feminine quality stunted or suppressed in her youth.

Ahead of me at the corner was yet another window alight. It seemed alive with movement as I approached. I was sure I had seen figures moving within. But when I came up to it, it was still. On the floor were narrow mats, two stools and some dresses heaped up in the corner. I had the swift sensation of recognizing Joan standing naked in the centre. The illusion passed when the dummy remained immobile. But her similarity with Joan would not be shaken off. I looked again, not at the naked body, but at the face; then, again at the figure. Joan and the dummy could have been twins. Both their faces had the same adolescent cast, the same straight, slightly lifted nose and full mouth, their hair bobbed and brushed back to one side in the latest fashion. And the dummy's eyes held the same semi-vacant stare, as if harbouring an unspelled question—optimistic, wide-eyed and half-expecting to meet up with a pleasant surprise which an uncomplicated world held in store for them. And as identical as their faces were their bodies—classic in their proportion, but with a litheness which made them more beautiful than statues of old. And both, more conscious of their sex when dressed up than when naked.

The first time I saw Joan in the nude, her flawless body made me search for some imperfection, as if to make sure that desire and imagination were not playing tricks on me. She was one of those rare women who looked much better in the nude than when dressed. Yet she seemed more conscious of her body when clothed.

The splendour of her figure was a bright promise of passion, just as the splendour of my surroundings at college and later had been of other facets of life. It never occurred to me that a woman's body, blessed as hers was, might serve as no more than an outward show; that like so much else around me here, the outward spectacle had come to be an end in itself. I could not shake off the aftertaste— which I had come to recognize so well—of having done something with her which should have yielded more pleasure than the minimum nature insists upon. And later, when I tried to make her yield herself truly and receive fuller pleasure, her patience left me with a dash of self-reproach, almost self-disgust. She made me feel as if my initiative had been something perverse or brutish, bent on distorting something essentially simple and quick—'fun', she once called it.

Still, Joan's casualness, her matter-of-fact attitude, lent at first a certain charm to our intimacy; that initial charm which comes from indulging in pleasures that promise no entanglements and no consequences. I expected such freedom to add to, not detract from, our intimacy. The deadly corollary of such freedom—indifference of the senses and of the emotions—was still unconceived by me.

I felt no more intimate with Joan at breakfast than I had at dinner the night before. Nothing in her voice, eyes or gestures ever seemed to harbour that additional flavour or hint which follows, or should follow, the union of two bodies. At times, when I glanced at her and then about my small room, her bits of underclothing somehow seemed to convey a greater intimacy than her figure did. Just as

201

now, the bits of dummy's clothing lying on the show-window floor seemed more provocative than the naked wax figure.

VI  Large drops of rain—few, irregular and slow, like pebbles falling back to earth—fell upon the asphalt, wetting spots larger than their size. The air seemed darker than the sky, and with a peculiar drag, too sluggish ever to be stirred by a breeze. The avenue was no longer familiar to me. I must have walked farther than on any other night. I would have hailed a taxi had there been one in sight, not to escape the rain, but because of my fatigue which had suddenly caught up with me. Ahead, a neon sign spelled 'Bar'. Though it was less than a block away, covering the distance took such an effort that when I reached the entrance, I rested for a moment with my hand on the door-knob before pushing in the door.

Inside, I remained for a moment standing where I was. The cool, conditioned air enveloped me with ineffable tenderness, soothing and benevolent, as if dispelling a pall and granting a benediction. My pulse relaxed and the perspiration began to dry from my forehead. The air tasted so refreshing that I wanted to inhale it in big gulps, and so light that my body felt disengaged of its weight and myself freed from the task of holding it upright. Unsure of my balance, I hesitated to move in this new atmosphere which, like a drug, seemed to unyoke me of all tension. Free of harassment, my senses seemed shy and at a loss how to apply themselves. It wasn't until several heads turned my way that I ventured forward and took the corner seat at the bar.

The white figure behind the counter, which had seemed part of the decorative arrangement along with the coloured bottles and glittering glasses (all doubled by the large mirror), moved forward, listened to my order, retreated, and after placing my glass of beer in front of me, resumed its place in the shiny, intricate setting.

My impulse was to drink the beer down at one gulp. But the tall, slender, frosty glass with its foam and its even film of moisture so close in front of me had the ineffable beauty of a chalice which my touch would spoil. I couldn't remember when I had last had a sensation of accidental beauty—not of the arranged beauty of museums, theatres or books, but of the casual beauty of a sight or sound, accidental, unexpected, perhaps not great but sweet and breathtaking in its passing.

The moisture on the glass was already dissolving into drops and rills. I touched it, and with the frosty touch still on my palms, sipped the drink slowly, lapsing into one of those rare contentments which contain no wish other than that the moment last on. Pleasant music reached me from no particular direction. The melody seemed to rise and recede, attuned to my pleasure and whim.

What a blessing such places existed, I thought. And how pleasant it all was. It had been childish of me to avoid bars all these years, as if sitting alongside others in such places were in itself a confession of loneliness, an unmanly huddling-up for the sake of company. It was certainly more pleasant to sit here than to be alone in my apartment. And the bar had the inimitable advantage that one could always leave, with some place to go to, one's own place; a process that somehow couldn't be reversed without getting spoiled. And there was always just the right pinch of distraction about—not enough to impinge on one's independence or privacy, but sufficient to help the solitary guest maintain the outward aspect he liked best to present to the world. He could be a quiet, self-contained spirit calmly nursing a drink to help him solve a problem too personal to be shared and too intricate to be unravelled lightly.

The tinkle of a glass, pure and delightful as a chime, rose over the diffused background of incidental noises and murmurs. Its minute vibrations were thinning swiftly, like delicate, quivering threads in the fabric of rougher noises, when an abrupt burst of laughter nearby made me look up. It broke off as it had started, sudden and disconnected, as if lacking source from within or stimulus from without; it was merely stating itself. There was no response nor second burst of laughter.

From the faces alongside the bar counter, I couldn't guess who had laughed. I wondered how laughter could so abruptly pass from a human face without leaving a trace.

The music, so soothing when I had come in, soon seemed loud and intrusive in its sheer mechanical persistence. I tried not to listen, but there was no holding off the tune nor the volume of voices rising above it. Everybody seemed to be talking, and everybody seemed to be lecturing, their conversation mere interrupted monologues set on proving something or other, each insisting that he be heard out. Even the outbursts of merriment had a boasting, hostile quality, as if the merrymaker weren't sure whether he had laughed to call attention to himself, or just to assure himself he was having a good time. And when occasionally someone called out for another round of drinks, it was as if he were renewing a persistent claim to being a good fellow.

Covertly, I glanced along the row of faces lining the bar to my right, and then at their reflections in the mirror opposite. How drab and colourless Americans seemed when they weren't busy or on the move. And they were ugliest when trying to relax and enjoy themselves. Then, some vital spark went out of them and left them drab and weary copies of each other. It wasn't their flesh and bone that

203

was so colourless, but their expressions, or lack of any. Twenty persons of any other nationality lined up like this, side by side, however shrunken and wretched, would, man for man, show more mobility, their faces reflecting a far greater variety of human frailty and strength than this well-fed, prosperous breed, who seemed, individually, as incomplete as men without shadows.

Even the face of the president whose smiling portrait hung over the mirror could well be interchanged with any along the bar and no one be better or worse for it. So could the face of the jolly, fleshy, smiling bishop whose picture I remembered from the morning paper. Both had those shrewd eyes that disclaimed any quality not common to everyone else, as if they were no better nor worse than the next man and had only happened to follow different callings. And like all the portraits I had ever seen in this country, both were smiling. Everybody was always smiling except when alone. Smiling seemed such a permanent fixture on every face that other expressions had no chance. And when some dropped their smiles at unguarded moments, their faces seemed naked and lost.

Among the people around me, only the bartender seemed a healthy specimen of the race. And he was on the move. I watched his brisk, efficient movements. Each move was confident, swift and serving the next. From picking up a glass, filling it with ice and fluid, and slipping it smoothly across the counter, the whole process seemed to be one continuous motion. And how gracefully he moved, with that touch of beauty allied to competence, which no other nationality seemed quite up to. His alert features, his white, crisp jacket and his easy, sure gestures, which never seemed to come quite to a standstill, reminded me of the times when waiting for a ride, I had watched gas station attendants converge upon a car that drove in. There, too, was that co-ordinated movement, the task effortlessly performed, each attendant knowing precisely his cue and purpose. Against the backdrop of the clean, efficient gas station, their figures and motions had, from a distance, a grace and harmony that made me forget they were at work—so spontaneous and free was their performance. I had sensed some of that same quality even in people alongside me on my jobs; in the flower shop sorting flowers, in the liquor store, stacking bottles. Even on the street, the swift, lanky gait so particular to Americans gave each man an élan, a saving grace, which no other people could claim or imitate.

But what happened when they stopped working and tried to relax? When they indulged in their brand of a good time—the reward for all their work and ambition? That work and ambition had given them more and richer tools for enjoying life and leisure than any other people had. Yet the faces along the bar and those looking out from the mirror were neither relaxed, contented nor glad. Pretentious, self-conscious and awkward, all of them seemed

204

constrained to work up a gaiety which took more out of them than the hardest job could have done.

I searched the mirror for an exception. As my eyes passed and re-passed the row of faces, I suddenly realized I had been surveying my own reflection along with the others in the line-up. There I was, now that I couldn't ignore myself, less animated perhaps than the others, but on the whole merging as one with the rest. Almost, not quite. There was something a bit odd about my image—nothing conspicuous or flattering, though, since all distinguishing expressions seemed to have worn off the original cast. It was merely a collection of features. My nose seemed too big, my chin with its cleft too massive, my temples too wide apart, and my head, with the black hair combed straight back, seemed too big and bulky though it was hunched between my shoulders. And the eyes beneath those eyebrows that seemed too wide and too thick, were withdrawn, as if resigned to responding only on cue (if respond they must), and no longer wanting to challenge or provoke. I seemed always on the verge of looking away, as if my eyes wanted neither to account for what they beheld, nor to be held responsible for what others might read in them. They were eyes altogether taken up with avoiding contact and just bearing up, indifferent to seeing. Staring, though at nothing within focus, seemed their habitual expression. Yet they seemed never free of a certain apprehension that, nevertheless, something unpleasant might intrude into view.

I lowered my eyes, and was looking at my glass of beer when a voice beside me said, 'You are Mohamed, aren't you?'

VII It was the same man I had noticed eyeing me from the other end of the bar. Now, he was standing at my side with a half-empty glass in his hand.

'Yes, I am Mohamed,' I said. My suspicion that he might be drunk was contradicted by the fact that he had known my name and by his slow, gentle voice—confident, yet ready to withdraw should he be mistaken.

'You don't remember me, do you?' His horn-rimmed glasses and crew-cut struck me as if it were a uniform that had become fashionable lately. He was well groomed and his coat sat well on his shoulders. I searched his face for a clue. It was a pleasant face which could bear scrutiny without being the worse for it. His disarming, almost bashful smile made no claim on me while assuring me that he remembered me. And he returned my glance with a bemused expression, as if turning over an amusing, but self-deprecatory, anecdote in his mind.

'I'm Andrew F. Archer. Remember now?'

His quoting the middle initial sounded add and out of place. I had never ceased to wonder why Americans insisted on inserting it between their names, unless as a kind of distinguishing rubric to fortify their personalities. But how quickly they dropped it, even insisted on being called by their first names after an introduction, as if even the use of the surname might set its bearer too much apart from the Jacks, Charlies, Eds and Daves. This informality, which had attracted me in my early days, was beginning to wear on me. It was too obligatory to be pleasant; more obligatory, I felt, than the formalities and etiquettes of Europe which had seemed so awkward and archaic compared to the easy informality here. But the local kind of informality was actually stricter; it resented any and all reserves, the rights of withdrawal or preference. It aspired to a sort of quick intimacy which could not but be meaningless. Only behind the protection of etiquette and formality did man seem capable of retaining his inner freedom to evaluate and cherish the experience of meeting another human being.

Andrew F. Archer was looking at me. I recognized him not by his name, but by the glass in his hand; by the way he held it. I remembered him from my first week in New York. I had been lunching with Alex. We caught sight of Andy standing at the bar, very much as he stood before me now—neat, relaxed and with a boyish look about him. Even now, in spite of the threads of grey at his temples and the lines around his eyes, he reminded me of some of the students at college, just as they had reminded me of him. Alex had invited him over to our table, but Andy wouldn't accept unless he could stand us a round of drinks first. I had liked him instantly. He didn't ask how I liked America, as everyone else had done. Though a while later, I insisted on telling him without being asked what a fantastic, marvellous place it was. He had heard me out, eyeing me now and then as if not sure whether I was pulling his leg or really meant it all. When I told Alex that night how Andy had struck me as a bit melancholy and sad, Alex guffawed and told me that Andy, making $20,000 a year as the youngest senior salesman in their outfit, could afford to look that way. But Alex couldn't. 'If I were making his kind of money, I wouldn't mind looking melancholy. It's his way of relaxing while his mind works ahead to the next deal.'

Andy didn't budge that day when Alex rushed off to work after lunch. It was Friday, he kept on saying, and he had done more than a week's work. He insisted I stay and tell him some more about America. I don't know why, for his lively eyes became dull for stretches at a time, lighting up only when he asked the waiter for another drink and me another question. And I kept on wondering why such a nice man should want to spent the afternoon in a windowless bar unless he was unhappy or so lonely that he preferred my company to his own. And later, when he was a bit drunk and I

206

helped him to a taxi, he looked so helpless and forlorn that I felt I was abandoning him as the taxi drove off.

'I remember,' I assured him now, inviting him to join me. 'And I remember even the advice you gave me when you drove off.'

Andy looked a bit puzzled, as if giving advice were the last thing he would do, much less expecting anyone to remember it. He finished his drink and ordered another. 'What was the advice I gave you?' he said. As he looked at me, he was smiling, but it was a different smile—impersonal, loose and indiscriminate, as if trying to adjust in advance to whatever I was about to say.

Suddenly, I was no longer sure I should tell him; a kind of censorship had started to operate in me recently whenever I was about to express an opinion or preference that wasn't the general one. It wasn't a question of lack of courage; it just wasn't worth while. Americans were always disappointed, then hurt, if not instantly praised. And they didn't seem to realize how much more insulting it was *not* to apply stricter standards to their country than one would to any banana or oil republic.

But remembering my afternoon with Andy, I dropped my guard with him. 'You told me over and over again: "Mohamed, promise me, never become a salesman. Stay out of this rat race." '

'Did I really?' he chuckled. 'Well, did it do you any good?'

His question was so casual and playful that it almost seemed to retract the advice he had given me. I should have answered in kind, and I did start lightly enough. 'I wish I could give you all the credit, but I couldn't have become a salesman if I'd wanted to. If I'd starved, as I almost did. And not by choice, either.' I told him about the Genuine Silk Company in Los Angeles and how I'd run away and what I thought of Schroeder's credo. I slipped into bragging, instead of making a joke of the story. But now that I had, I waited for Andy to back me up, perhaps even to praise me.

Instead he seemed surprised, as if my reminiscence had been indiscreet or in bad taste. Possibly he was taken aback by my high-strung, almost vindictive outburst against salesmen and the way they set the tone of American life.

'Well, tell me,' Andy said, passing over what I had said, 'what have you been doing with yourself all these years? It must be five years or so . . .'

'Almost six.'

'Well, it's been a long time,' he went on, as if I had taken his calculations too literally. I sometimes wondered what had happened to you—whether you had stayed on in the U.S. or gone back home.'

His query sounded too sociable to be really personal, at least not personal enough for the occasion. Briefly, I told him about college, about hitch-hiking to California and then landing back in New York. Once I got started, I could not slow down, because no incident was worth the telling unless it was tied up with others. For the point was often not in what had actually happened, but in my reaction to it. And the reaction wasn't necessarily at the time the incident occurred. As often as not, the impact of some experience was brought out by other, later, experiences which would then set off, like a fuse, a delayed reaction no less violent or real for having been delayed.

I was still talking on when Andy raised his eyes from his glass and looked past me. The bartender was standing close by. 'It's closing time, I suppose,' Andy said to the bartender.

We were the last customers, and Andy remarked on that, too. He seemed more at ease talking to the bartender than listening or talking to me.

We were both silent while I waited for the bartender to ring up my change. Nothing about the bar hinted that people had come, sat together, sipped drinks, talked and gone. The plastic top of the counter and of the tables around shone as brightly as if they had never been used. Order prevailed; no chair seemed out of place, no ashtray smudged. Even the floor seemed impervious to scuffing and refuse, as if the modern layout denied anyone the right to linger long enough to leave a trace; as if it were more immune to human marks than rock and stone.

It was when we stepped outside that I asked Andy about Alex. I felt a bit guilty for not having done so sooner, and for talking about myself. I told Andy how I'd tried to look up Alex after returning to New York. His office would only tell me he was no longer with them, and then I got stuck at his last forwarding address where he didn't seem to be known at all. 'It was on upper Fifth Avenue. That's the kind of address Alex always wanted, didn't he?' I said, remembering how Alex wrote off the rest of New York as an aberration.

'I thought you knew. Alex is dead.'

I waited for Andy to go on. 'What did he die of?'

'He killed himself,' Andy said, pressing his lips together and watching me, as if waiting for me to match his solemnity.

'But how?' I was impatient for Andy to come out with the whole story instead of waiting for me to pry the details out of him.

'He shot himself.'

For a moment, I imagined Alex waving a pistol around his head in a phoney game of Russian Roulette to bluff a girl into giving in, and then howling with laughter, his hands up in the air.

'Did he die?' I asked stupidly, as if with Alex, even the bullet might play a trick and turn it all into a joke in the end. 'Was he dead instantly, I mean?'

Even before Andy began his slow nodding, I realized that his

208

answer didn't matter. Nor Alex's way of dying. I felt no sorrow for Alex, though his laughter rose up in my mind, reminding me that he had been the only one I had laughed with in this country. I felt no sorrow for Alex, for I was too much taken up with envy; an envy that rose up too quickly to be hedged, and which bared my admission—so long evaded and suppressed—that I no longer cared to carry on, and could not carry on if I wanted to. No promise of the future could match for me Alex's reward—being set free from the monotonous chore of facing another day. The bitter pity of it all was that what I envied Alex for had been so often near my reach and I had let the chances slip by. There had been so many chances —when taking a fast curve in the hills around Los Angeles in the delivery truck; when walking blindly up the New York streets at night, taking crossings in spite of approaching cars, yet always jumping out of the way at the last moment; or when looking down from my office window, but always turning away in the end.

'Why did he do it?' I asked, though the why and when didn't matter very much, for I knew the answer much better than Andy or anyone else could know it.

Andy shrugged.

'Did money have anything to do with it?' I said, though of all the reasons there might have been, this was the one I would have suspected least. Yet it was precisely the reason everyone would have suspected of *me* had I done what Alex had. I had so often been given to understand that money was at the bottom of most troubles that I was parroting a notion I had been taught all these years.

'No, it wasn't money.' Andy shook his head. 'No, it definitely couldn't have been money,' he repeated, as if absolving Alex on that count. 'He was spending a lot, but he was making a lot, too. At the rate he was going ahead, they'd have tapped him for a junior executive's post in another year or so. He was making good money. Twenty-five thousand plus. So it couldn't have been money, could it?'

'How did he ever get that far ahead?' In spite of myself, a touch of awe had crept into my voice. I knew enough about salaries to know it wasn't easy to reach that bracket in so short a time.

'Why, selling ...,' Andy said, as if it were the most natural thing in the world. 'Remember how he joked about the company, our rules and quotas? He liked to make fun of things. But you should have seen how serious he was when he hit his stride and got into action. I trained him, you know.' Andy spoke of Alex as if he had been a soldier advancing into battle. 'I was really proud of him. He was doing a first-rate job. And one evening, he takes a walk in Central Park and shoots himself and his two little boys. Just like that.' Andy snapped his fingers.

'Then, why did he get married?'

'Most people do, don't they?'

'But that's no reason for Alex...,' I meant to say 'for Alex to get married', but Andy interrupted me.

'... And the company likes its young and upcoming men to settle down, start a family and all that. It gives them stability, purpose, you know what I mean.'

Damn the company. I knew Alex wouldn't have got married for those reasons. Perhaps he had hoped that marriage might put an end to his isolation and his dilemma, not realizing that his wife might neither comprehend nor even notice needs particular to him —needs that had their roots in a way of life other than her own. And I knew too well that nothing tunes loneliness to a higher pitch than the relentless presence of someone whose company is shared out of weakness, someone whose good-will and indiscriminate cheer are pegged to her own key, so that they only heighten the tensions of which they know nothing.

But why did he take it out on his children? Why have children in the first place, unless he hoped to find in them something which he couldn't find in his wife or in anyone else? Suddenly, I remembered the Slovak family I once roomed with on my way to California. I no longer remembered the town, but I did remember the family's name. It was Voydic. Though I had taken room and breakfast only, they wouldn't hear of my eating dinner out. There was always an extra plate set for me, though I made a point of not showing up till dinner was over. But I couldn't always resist the temptation. Those meals recalled savours no food in America had ever had for me. And for the sake of that pleasure, I didn't even mind the food smells that wafted in and about the small house long after Mrs. Voydic had cleared the dishes—smells that would have told any passer-by that this was a foreigner's house.

I was sitting with Mr. Voydic after our Sunday lunch in the small, stuffy drawing-room when Voydic's son opened the screen door leading in from the front porch. A step or two behind him were two other youngsters. Mr. Voydic was just lighting his pipe, drawing quick puffs. He seemed to be waiting for the youngster to speak up.

The kid just stood there, saying nothing.

After he was sure of the pipe, Mr. Voydic, perhaps because he was embarrassed in front of me by the youngster's silence, spoke up:

'Vell, vhat haf you been doing vith yourself?' In the small room his thick accent boomed all over. One of the faces behind the screen door widened into a grin.

He would never have worded that question that way in his own language. Neither would he have volunteered it in that fashion, if he could have heard himself. But, like most foreigners he used such a pat phrase because, hearing it come off so easily on the natives' lips, he thought it would come off as easily on his own. His failure

210

to bring it off absurdly distorted his words, giving them a false note, as if he were showing off or eager to please.

The boy stood there looking down, his slim body taut with wishing he were somewhere else. Then, without looking at his father, he said, 'Pop, can I have a quarter?' Though his accent was pure, his tone of voice was a sham. So was his low, reasonable way of speaking, and so was his pretence at playing the supplicant, the son.

'Vhat foar?' asked Mr. Voydic, still trying to sound jovial.

The kid seemed to resent the question less than he did having the situation drawn out. I was beginning to feel uncomfortable, too. Without me around, Mr. Voydic might not have asked the boy what he had been doing, and would have given or refused the twenty-five cents without further ado. Now, both father and son were self-conscious of their respective rôles, and I felt sorry for both of them. For the sake of the kid, I wished Mr. Voydic would say yes or no and get it done with. And with the father, I resented the sloppy way the child stood there, as if he no longer cared. His ill-mannered sulk spoiled his good looks. I could imagine him six or eight years later on a campus like Watson's, perhaps better-looking than most, but otherwise indistinguishable from the other students—tall, slender, clean-cut and cheerful.

How American the boy looked already; and how foreign still, the father. Either of them, taken separately, fitted well his rôle. But seen together, face to face, they had less in common than strangers would. Their physical resemblance—the wide cheek-bones, the thick head of hair, blue eyes set in deep sockets—only heightened the intangible contrast between them. Each seemed tuned to a rhythm, set on a course that went against the other's grain—a flaw of affinity that could not but goad any contact between them, even if it were cushioned by good-will, into a clash. It was as if an instinctive disapproval of the other's disparity egged each one on, for lack of a specific target, to continual resentment, an animosity that spilled over and infected whatever the other might say or do next; and how it was said or done. It was an animosity, singular in its composition, more pervading and irresistible (and for less outward cause) than could exist or spring up between father and son, man and man, or even between enemies, anywhere else in the world. I recognized it as the same brand of animosity that sometimes welled up at odd moments in me, and for no particular reason—sometimes against foreigners and sometimes against Americans, though both were innocent of cause. Its virulence was charged with such malevolent temper that afterwards I felt ugly by the excess of it. Then, depending upon my mood, one or the other—foreigner or American—seemed to me an anachronism or an obscenity of man.

'Foar the movies!' Mr. Voydic exclaimed, repeating what the boy had just said. In contrast to his son's matter-of-fact request, Voydic's exclamation sounded strangely theatrical. 'You vent to the kiddie show this morning. That's enough. Vhat next!' And he turned to me for solidarity. He sat there, pipe in hand, his big shoulders hunched, his features still saddled with the expression he had assumed to match his exclamation.

Glancing from the father to the boy, I was carried away by the speculation of how hilarious precisely the same scene would strike the boy were he to see it in a movie. And how noxious and oppressive the son would strike the father could he but watch other actors play out such a scene, if he could but see what I imagined I saw on the kid's face now, though it was almost expressionless except for a touch of a sneer at the mouth. Quickly, the boy turned his head to check how much his pals behind him had seen and heard.

'I tell you vhat. If . . . ,' Voydic started saying.

'Skip it,' the boy interrupted and, followed by his two companions, walked off.

Watching the boy go up the short path, I felt that no strangers could be more alien to each other than the man at my side and the boy, now passing out of sight, who, because of the accident of having been born in America, had disinherited his father—and himself of two thousand years.

Some such nightmare as this must have caught up with Alex; or was it just one more day of living that drove him insane?


**VIII** 'It must be getting late,' Andy said, raising his wristwatch to his eyes. He peered at it closely. Then, unable to make out the time, he leaned forward and almost stumbled. 'Well, what are your plans?' he said, straightening up. His voice had a forced liveliness; he had trouble getting the words out clearly. His drinks were beginning to affect him.

I told him where I worked, and about my hopes of being sent abroad.

'So, you'd rather go home?' His words were oddly spaced, and he emphasized *home*, as if it were an odd destination.

I felt I might hurt his feelings if I said outright, 'Yes'. 'Well, it isn't quite a matter of choice,' I hedged. 'It just happens that . . .'

'Look,' he said, impulsively, laying his hand on my arm, 'if it's just a matter of a better job, maybe I could help you get in with our company.'

I assured him my salary was all right. With commissions and expense account, it was nearly $10,000. But when I started to thank him, I had trouble keeping my voice steady. Perhaps, not needing help, I was giving free rein to my emotions, churned up by the memory that most of my jobs in America had come to me in just

212

such a way, with the help of someone I barely knew and with a generosity almost impersonal in its sweep. Help was always extended so casually and in such a matter-of-fact way here, as if helping a stranger to find work or a better job were too much of a common rule to be accounted a virtue—a custom rather than a personal impulse—as if my material dilemma amidst the rich pattern of living were a knot or flaw that ought to be set right. Who and what I was seemed almost incidental. For, the same man who would go to no end of trouble helping me land a job, who would invite me to drinks and dinner, would freeze up if asked for a small loan involving, perhaps, no more than what he had spent on taking me out, as if the loan were a personal matter and helping me land a job was not.

'I really mean it. I'd be glad to . . . ,' Andy said.

'You really do?' I was paraphrasing him, not questioning him. And it was almost by way of apology that I told him it wasn't always easy to get my visa extended. 'It's getting harder and harder to make them renew my permit.'

'Aren't you a citizen yet?' He seemed truly surprised.

'No.'

'But you have your first papers, don't you?'

'Well, no . . .'

'But don't you want to become an American citizen?'

'Frankly, I never thought of it, I mean, changing my citizenship.'

'But if you want to stay on in this country . . .'

'I don't see that that's got so much to do with it,' I interrupted. 'I lived for nine years in Austria, and nobody expected me to change my citizenship. And there's a Persian in Paris—he's been there for thirty years and has stayed a Persian. I don't think the French would think better of him if he changed his country.'

'But don't you think it's a bit different over here. I mean, if a fellow wants to settle down for good and . . .'

'Well, I'm not quite sure I would want to.'

'You can't really mean what you say,' Andy said, as if giving me a last chance.

'Yes, I mean it.'

He sized me up, as if he had at last caught on to what I really was. His body stiffened, and his slack jaws masticated a bit, as if out of control.

When he spoke, his voice was no longer that of one man talking to another, or of a man speaking for himself alone. It was charged with that excess of righteousness which rings out when a man feels himself the mouthpiece of his people, and of truth, voicing a collective conviction—a conviction he cannot proclaim without at the same time passing judgement; the mandatory sentence, anathema, on whoever is not at one with him, the judge. And the verdict permits no defence, for it presupposes evil intent and guilt; the culprit has forfeited all rights by abusing his freedom and choosing not the right.

'If you don't like it here,' said Andy, 'then why the hell don't you go back where you came from?'

I should have walked off, as I had done when such words had been thrown at me before. I should have shrugged them off as a rudeness, and the man uttering them as an exception. Though, each time I heard that phrase again, it left me with the eerie notion that these words and the way they were said—so identically voiced and worded—signified something more than rudeness, and that those who indulged in them were not such exceptions as the next one, to whom I would tell the story as a joke, would assure me they were. Perhaps, those who uttered the phrase were exceptions for speaking up, but not for thinking it. Their imprecation involved more than mere manners. It sprang from a source deeper than opinion, from motives more compelling than personal antagonism. It lurked and stirred behind and beneath any comparison between America and the rest of the world. Neither personal nor national pride need be touched. The mere expression of doubt that not everything here was of the best or for the best, was enough to light the fuse. Why should my saying that *lulé-kebab* tasted so much better than an American hamburger draw such wrath? Or that I preferred an original waltz to its jazzed-up version? Or that some skyscrapers were designed by European architects?

Andy wasn't the first to hold my not taking out first papers against me. But facing him now on the long deserted avenue in the sullen heat of the night, I felt his words reviving all previous voices, which added their charge and challenge to his and forced me to take a stand. His taunt held me fast. Silence was no longer enough. Unless I accepted and obeyed the injunction to answer him, or rejected it with something greater than silence, it would follow me on and on whichever way I turned. The longer I stood there with Andy glaring at me—his posture encouraged by my silence into a sort of belligerent pose—the more urgently his abuse pressed for an answer.

For an instant, I wished some rage would well up in me and make me hit out at Andy, or that Andy would hit out at me instead of just standing there waiting for me to speak up or shut up.

We both noticed that a light was switched off nearby. A man stepped out of the bar and locked the door behind him. When he turned, I recognized the bartender. He no longer looked so trim and different as he had when standing behind the bar. Now, in dress, looks and posture, he could have been any one of the guests who had left before him. He took a last drag from his cigarette and then flipped it away before unlocking the door of the nearest parked

214

car and stepping in. I watched the glow of his discarded cigarette, incongruously aware that he was smoking the same sort of cigarette Andy and I were smoking; if not the same brand, then of the same quality and price. Though in other countries, a man in his position would smoke a cheaper brand, and would think twice before discarding a half-smoked cigarette.

The glow in the gutter held my eyes, and for a moment I was sure that if I could but talk and talk long enough about it to Andy— about how the bartender had looked to me in the bar and how he looked when coming out, and about the way he smoked his cigarette and the way he drove off, that Andy would withdraw his question. Instead, it was Andy who spoke up.

'Yes, why the hell don't you get out of here?'

The change of phrasing struck me, as if I had been asked a brand new question—no longer arbitrary, but one I should have asked myself long ago. 'Why didn't I quit America? Why the hell didn't I . . . ?'

A host of answers crowded to the fore, all clamouring for a hearing, each wanting to be first. No words or images seemed fitting or sufficient to contain them all. It seemed as if some faculty in me had magnified all my reactions and experiences in this country out of proportion, as if I had been a guinea pig which, through some quirk of nature, had responded to everything in terms too extreme for measure or expression.

I felt trapped with answers that could not be worded, only felt and imagined. How could I convey reactions that cancelled each other out? Or explain my being so inordinately attracted to this country one day and repelled by it another—sometimes the same sight or sound provoking opposite reactions on different days? Each experience seemed to bequeath its residue of wonder and resentment within me, leaving me to balance myself on a scale whose cups were never steady, but jerking constantly up and down, weighted or lifted by sensations and moods I could not control.

Andy was still staring belligerently at me, as if I had been trying to avoid his eyes. His stance was that of a challenger who had waited long enough. So was the smirk around his mouth. He turned to walk off.

'Wait!'

He stopped and turned back. I stepped forward.

'You asked me a question,' I said. 'You must want an answer.'

'Well . . . ?'

I started out calmly enough. 'I don't know why I don't get out,' I said. 'It's not a question of my not liking it here. I just can't carry on any more. There is too much of everything for me. There are too many cars, too many buildings, too many people, and though there are millions of them, they all look alike. Too much food and

215

it all tastes alike. All sights and sounds are stamped the same. And so are all your people, their faces, their voices. Yours and those in the bar and those I meet and pass every day. What you all say and what you think is for ever tuned to the same note. There is nothing and no one that is not the like of the others, as if all men and things were of the same mould, repeated and multiplied by the millions and millions. Don't you understand how the monotony of repetition can make poverty of plenty and a prison of life? And of man a marionette? And no one cares—or no one dares to go against the grain.'

Andy started to say something. His lips moved, as if he were at a loss for words to match his indignation. I went on talking before he could interrupt.

'Sometimes, I have the feeling that from the day I arrived in this country I have heard over and over again the same words and notions, as if you no longer bother to choose your own words and your own thoughts, but speak in quick, handy phrases and think in quick, handy thoughts, ready-made for all, that short-cut your vocabulary and what you say to a sort of primitive lingo which makes you talk and listen by rote.

'Do you know what I do, where I sometimes go, when I want to see a new face again? I wander down to the piers. Sometimes I am lucky and catch sight of some immigrants. Watching them is like witnessing something I had half forgotten still existed—how varied human beings can be. At the sight of them, I feel more in the presence of the human—and God knows, those newcomers look awkward, old-fashioned and pathetic enough—more in the presence of the human than amongst the crowded faces on Times Square or any other square in America. I want to warn them, though I don't know against what, for I know it's best for them to come to this country. And I know, too, that those arriving are the lucky ones and that there are millions waiting their turn. And I envy them their hopes and their sense of wonder, that wonder I felt when I arrived. And with them, I bless this country for giving them a new chance in life.

'But when, on my way back from the docks, I pass your well-dressed, well-fed people again—those set, self-same faces that are nowhere but in America—then I almost curse you for letting them come, and I curse them for coming. For some day soon, they, and if not they, then surely their children, will look identical to those of the crowd, indistinguishable from each other and from you. Re-moulded to your likeness, they will add their presence and pressure to the monotony there already is—the monotony so busy and aglitter with numbers and plenty. What all the unspeakable chicanery and oppression of their pasts could not rub out of their souls, their faces and their voices, will be rubbed out here.'

Andy spoke up. 'Then why the hell don't you tell them to turn right around and go back where they came from, and you can go right with them. We'd sure appreciate it if . . .'

'I'm not talking about them,' I broke in. 'I am talking about myself. You tell me to get out of here. But, tell me, where to? To Europe? To my own country? But they are all trying to become just like you. The whole world wants to live like you. They may sneer and laugh at you behind your back, but there is an American hidden in all of them, and that's coming to the fore. And where will it all end up? They'll all end up as second- or third-rate imitations of America—or worse, for they're imitating the worst of you. The good they can't even grasp, much less copy. And they think they can remain what they are, while jazzing it all up with your glamour. Just as you think, in a different sort of way, that you can hang on to a bit of their tradition and worldliness by building more and more museums and getting up more orchestras, or by having a bottle of wine on your table, lit up by a candle or two alongside a phoney fireplace, and pretend to make it an old-world occasion.'

Though Andy had been looking at me, he gave a start, as if waking up.

'Bullshit,' he said contemptuously.

The word caught me off guard, and like a dead end, blocked me for a moment from going on.

'You always come up with that in the end,' I said. 'And there's no answer to it. No words can stand up to it. It sort of sums up your attitude to everything that doesn't fit in with you. With that word you have debunked a lot of things, a lot of old beliefs and super-stitions. Debunked them more effectively than any logic could. And the funny thing is that much of the time you are right. But you have gone too far. You not only have knocked everything off the pedestal, but knocked down the pedestal, too, by doing away with the idea that anything is worth looking up to. In your heart of hearts you don't look up really to anything or anybody. And why should you? That's what made you what you are and your country what it is today—the greatest country on earth, as you call it. If you hadn't gone your own way debunking all the old things, you'd amount to no more today than a raw, backward version of Europe.

'But you are not great enough to come out in the open with it, to stick up for what you yourself are. You haven't the courage. You hide behind the torn banners you once pulled down, and that's what makes your protestations of allegiance to them so ridiculous. Almost obscene. You protest too much the old virtues which need no protesting, if they are there. Whoever heard of swearing alle-giance every morning to the flag, as your children are made to do? Of advertising virtue and promoting honesty as the best policy, as if this were open to doubt? It's no longer enough to be born an

217

American; you have to be a good American. No longer enough to be a citizen; you must be a good citizen. And you try teaching the "good" the way you'd teach efficiency to mechanics and secretaries. This preaching and teaching of the Good, the True and the Beautiful has become a national mania, a new sort of voodooism. Anything and everything, if only boosted long enough, is supposed to come real.

'But you are much greater than you make yourselves out to be. You don't need all that chest-beating. You don't need all the haloes. It was you who showed up haloes for what they are—how the colours fade and run, how phoney they are. My God, just be yourselves. Every man on his own. You made up your own rules and values as you went along and didn't give a damn what the rest of the world thought of you. Once upon a time, you held a horse thief lower than a murderer, because that was right and true for you. You didn't moralize about it or try to justify it. It was just that way. And the only good Indian was a dead Indian. But now you've got women's clubs prettying up the reservation and bragging about the rising birth rate of the Navahoes.

'It was you who showed what man can do when free from the shackles he was born with; shackles that made it immoral for him to try to break them or to ask from life more than a crust of bread, if that. It was you who put a stop to that and to all the infernal bowing and scraping; you, who taught man to stand up and use his fists instead of saying "Thank you, sir" when another man called him names and forgot to smile. You told anybody you didn't like to go to hell. Not to get out of here, but to go to hell, which is man's talk.

'Now, you even smile before you know who the other fellow is and before you hear what he says. And you've all got to be joiners, or be shunned and called odd. The backbone you straightened up once is now massaged into a curve again. If you come down to it, that's worse in a way. It's more degrading in the long run to bow to the pressures nobody admits than to the knout, which is real. A man knows whose hand wields the whip and where and how it hurts. But how is a man to defend his self-respect against indignities coated with smiles and goodies, which brand him as immoral if he wants none of them?

'It's one hundred and eighty million ganging up on one. Each of you comes up against the rest, if he wants to draw a free breath. There's no end to the pressure to conform. Nowhere on earth do you find so many groups who try to do good to you, so many fraternities, brotherhoods, associations and clubs. So many get-togethers and communal rites. So much talk about good fellowship and getting together and being neighbourly. But all that promoting somehow turns sour and has a false note and never works out quite

218

the way it should. It leaves you stranded in the end, as isolated, as unloved and unloving as you started out. It comes as a relief to hear a fellow stand up and say, "Hurray for me! To hell with everybody else!"

'And let anyone take your pretensions to virtue seriously, and he's in trouble. You'll give a million to charity and foundations, but a fishy eye to any fellow who wants to borrow a dollar. You build more and fancier schools, but anyone who has anything else on his mind except getting ahead you call an egg-head. And if he doesn't make as much money as you do, a failure. That's what the father thinks of his son and the son of the old man who hasn't done better than his neighbour. You make such a to-do about your schools and churches, but you'll fire the padre or the teacher who doesn't jazz up the service and lasso you into his congregation or class like a barker does suckers at the circus. For a good "spiel," even your churches aren't big enough. You crowd into a sports arena to be saved.

'You go to Europe on a sort of bargain pilgrimage, but all you notice is what a contractor or plumber would remember after surveying a run-down piece of real estate. What I can't understand is why go to all that elaborate pretence that you still play the game by the old rules? That you aren't so different from other people, after all, just a little better, maybe, and more advanced. But you *are* different, more different than you realize and more different than the rest of the world can ever imagine.'

'Bullshit,' Andy said again, slurring the word and tossing his head in a swivel movement, as if addressing somebody else. He tried to narrow his eyes in contempt and irony, yet his glance became no sharper, nor more direct. His eyelids were heavy, and he blinked as if trying to keep his eyes open. Without their alert, smiling approach, his features seemed so much older than when we had met. He took a last deep drag from his cigarette and flipped it away. With the same hand out, he seemed to be making way for himself. When he started to step past me, I blocked his way.

'Now that you asked me, you must hear me out.' It was as much a plea as a demand. I didn't want to stop talking—for my sake, not his. Nothing of what I had said tonight had ever come to me quite that way before; and never together, but in bits and pieces, at odd moments and in odd moods, never quite worth the saying.

Andy must have taken my move as a threat. He pulled himself up, as if demanding to know whether he was challenged or not, as if daring me. His stance looked odd. What he took as a threat to his stiff balance came not from me but from the drinks he had had. He shrugged, and leaned against the wall. 'Okay, I'm listening,' he said, nodding his head.

'Make no mistake about it, the two don't mix,' I went on. 'The

219

rest of the world and America. On the surface, they may not seem to differ much from you. Some may even still be called your kin. But let them face too many of you and for too long and they'll balk. They sense what the Indians must have sensed—no, don't laugh, it's terribly true. The Indians, primitive as they were, did have a way of life of their own, a code of honour and self-respect. They must have sensed in their blood what others do now—that your lives and theirs don't mix, can't mix. That they cannot drink from the same cup as you and not perish. You are much stronger than you, or they, realize. And your weapons more deadly than guns. You come with gifts. And you come not to conquer but to help, to help others live "a better and richer life" as you call it—the American way of life. But they don't know that by aping you, they become less of what they are without really becoming more like you, ending up as caricatures of their former selves and of you.

'They don't know any of that. They only see you from afar and in the movies, and your country as a giant department store where everyone browses, buys and indulges his fancy. They don't know—how can they?—that amid this plenty something is missing; something human that you took for granted while you were forging ahead. And now that you have everything, the question haunts all of you, though few will confess it: why am I not content and at peace? Why don't I love life better, for all I need I have, and all I want is mine?

'And there is no answer. For you have made a promise come true at last. You have made a land of plenty on this earth, not in the next; you have banished hunger, cold and poverty from your part of the world. You'll tell me there are poor men in America, too. Yes, but an American might be poor for a day; poverty with him is not a state of mind the way it is with other people.

'You have made a dream come true. You don't know it. It takes a foreigner to tell you that, and also that you are cursed for it, whether you deserve it or not. Man has always been cursed when he made a dream come true and didn't put another in its place. And that is what snatches all joy from your grasp and gives your laughter a false note. You can flaunt the omen when you are at work and busy, but it haunts you when work is done. No peasant finds so little reward when the sun goes down as you do at the end of the day. And you are at your worst on Sundays. Walk through New York or any American city on Sunday and tell me if there's a sadder sight in the world or a lonelier creature on God's earth than the idle American.

'And that's what I cannot forgive you, and why I cannot live amongst you; that, having everything, you are so unhappy. Yes, unhappy. And yours is a new kind of unhappiness, unlike any the world has ever known. It's not the old kind that's been wedded to

220

man from the beginning, the unhappiness of cold, hunger, and want. Nor that inflicted on man by man. Nor that which he brings down on his own head by his loves, hates and jealousies. Yours is new and nameless. And in spite of all your pastimes, your tricks to stave off facing it, that unhappiness seeps through to the heart of each of you. It's there in spite of all your shoutings that you are the most prosperous people on earth and that your country is God's country.

'Yes, I shall get out of here. Not because I really want to, but because I must. I must go, though I know that, after America, there's no going back to anywhere. But I must go, if only for a little rest. And I know there will be times when I shall yearn to come back. I know that. Yet I can't help it. Perhaps I shall love you better from afar. Perhaps I had set you on a pedestal and believed more than you did that your country was "the last best hope" of man. Now, let me go in peace. And you go with God, as we Persians say, though you are so sure of yourselves that I feel a bit foolish saying it.'

Andy, chin down, nodded. I waited for him to say or do something—call me names, push his way past me, hit out at me: or, on a sudden impulse, perhaps, to stretch out his hand to show that he had sensed, if not understood, what I had been trying to say, though I had left so terribly much unsaid. But he didn't move; he didn't even look up. His back was resting against the wall. His head was tilted slightly forward, as if still listening for me to go on. Then, amid the silence about us my ears caught the long sounds of his breathing. Though not quite even, his breathing had the unconscious rhythm of sleep.

Perhaps it was just as well. I turned and walked off down the street.